THE MODERN SHOTGUN

BOOKS BY THE SAME AUTHOR

IN THE GUNROOM

NOTES ON SPORTING RIFLES

BIG GAME HUNTING IN THE HIMALAYAS AND TIBET

THE IDENTIFICATION OF FIREARMS AND FORENSIC BALLISTICS

FLY TYING: PRINCIPLES AND PRACTICE

NOVELS

THE TIGER OF TIBET

THE MYSTERY OF THE MEKONG

THE SHEET IRON TARGET MOUNTED ON A MOTOR CAR WHICH WAS USED BY MR. C. E. ALLAN AND THE AUTHOR IN THEIR INVESTIGATION OF THE STRINGING OF SHOT

On the left is Mr. Alec Mackay who drove the car throughout the experiments

THE MODERN SHOTGUN

VOLUME III.
THE GUN AND THE CARTRIDGE

by

MAJOR SIR GERALD BURRARD
BT., D.S.O., R.F.A. (RETIRED)

LONDON: HERBERT JENKINS

First Published by
Herbert Jenkins Ltd.,
3 Duke of York Street,
London, S.W.1,
1932

Second Edition	*1948*
Third Edition (Revised)	*1950*
Fourth Edition	*1952*
Fifth Edition (Revised)	*1960*

Printed in Great Britain by Butler & Tanner Ltd., Frome and London

WORKS CONSULTED

The Modern Sportsman's Gun and Rifle (Vol. I), by J. H. Walsh (1882).

Memorial des Poudres et Saltpêtres (1890).

Tir des Fusils de Chasse, by General Journée. 2nd Edition (1902) and 3rd Edition (1920).

The Gun and its Development, by W. W. Greener. 9th Edition (1910).

High Pheasants in Theory and Practice, by Sir R. Payne-Gallwey (1914).

Sporting Guns and Gunpowders, Part I (1897) and Part II (1900).

PREFACE TO SECOND EDITION

IT is now nearly seventeen years since the First Edition of this Volume was completed and during that time two great advances have been made. The first was the introduction and ever widening use of slow-burning powders of the Neoflak type, which made heavier shot charges possible without any increase in pressure. The second was the employment of the fully crimped turnover following on the discovery of the cause of Cartwheel Patterns. These last can now be eliminated and the consequent benefit to shooters is remarkable.

Further in the past ten years great advances have been made in the detection of flaws in steel. I have tried to touch briefly on these advances and in this connection I have received unstinted help from the Research Departments of G.E.C., Ltd., Metropolitan Vickers, Ltd., and Rylands Bros., Ltd. I cannot express adequately my gratitude to the Metallurgists and Physicists concerned.

Other alterations and additions have been made as the result of very many helpful letters from readers in all parts of the world, and I would like now to thank them again for their kind suggestions.

And once more must I thank my many friends in both the Gun and Ammunition Trades for their ever generous co-operation.

It is this friendly, kindly and constructive criticism which I have received on all sides which encourages me to hope that this New Edition will be given the same sympathetic welcome which was extended to its predecessor.

GERALD BURRARD.

WILLOW LODGE,
HUNGERFORD,
BERKS.

December, 1947.

CONTENTS

A*

CONTENTS

LIST OF TABLES

LIST OF ILLUSTRATIONS

PLATES

LINE DRAWINGS

INTRODUCTION

THE problems which arise in connection with the actual use of the Gun and the Cartridge together are considerably more varied and more complex than those which belong either to the Gun alone or to the Cartridge alone. Further, I believe that many of them are even less generally understood by the shooting public than questions relating to gun construction and to ballistics, with which I tried to deal in Volume II. I have, therefore, done my best to consider the whole problem of the inter-relation between the Gun and the Cartridge in its many phases, from patterns to bursts. I must confess to being appalled by the length of this survey of the subject ; but as I worked I found that so many points kept on arising that it was impossible to deal with it both adequately and briefly. So I trust that if parts of certain chapters appear to some readers to be redundant they will bear in mind that I have done my best to prune rather than to expand, and that I have raised no point which I have not known to be of interest to at least some section of practical shooting men.

It may seem that I have given undue prominence to the subject of burst guns, and that the photographs of various types of bursts are so numerous as to be out of proportion with the other illustrations.

I would explain, however, that all these photographs are essential for a proper understanding of a subject which is exceedingly intricate. It is a subject which I hope will never arise in the experiences of the great majority of my readers. Nevertheless, it is also one which, to the best of my belief, has not been dealt with in detail before. I hope, therefore, that the chapters on bursts, together with the plates, may help both sportsmen and gunmakers should any accident occur.

I included the final chapter with extreme diffidence: partly because I realise my own lack of competence to expound; partly because it seemed somewhat beyond the scope of the book; and partly because it was only adding a long chapter to what may seem to many to be an unduly long volume. I showed the draft, however, to my friends Mr. Eric Parker and Mr. Ingo Simon; and both were so encouraging that I determined to risk it.

I could never have written the chapters on patterns without constant reference to the work of the late Mr. R. W. S. Griffith, who can be regarded not only as the father of shotgun ballistics, but as the chief pioneer in scientific research into the complicated and difficult subject of patterns. My regret is that I never had the privilege of meeting Mr. Griffith personally; but I would like to place on record my gratitude for the instruction and inspiration which I have derived from a study of his work.

Parts of some of the chapters on Patterns, Loads and Odds and Ends have appeared in articles in the *Field* and *Game and Gun* during the past few years. And although all such parts have been rearranged and largely rewritten, I am sincerely grateful to the proprietors of these papers for their permission to republish what had already appeared in their pages.

As before, I have to thank my friends Lieutenant-Colonel Philip Neame, V.C., D.S.O., R.E., and Mr. F. W. Jones, O.B.E., for their kindness in reading and re-reading the various drafts of all the chapters in this Volume and for their helpful and constructive criticism.

And again, I would like to thank Mr. H. R. Marchant for the trouble and patience which he always showed in taking the photographs of the burst guns. The results, I think, speak for themselves.

It only remains for me to say that no one can be more aware of the shortcomings of this Volume than myself; that I will always welcome criticism; and that I hope my critics will not forget the difficulties which the writing of a work of this nature entails.

GERALD BURRARD.

WILLOW LODGE,
HUNGERFORD,
BERKS,
October, 1931.

THE MODERN SHOTGUN

THE MODERN SHOTGUN

CHAPTER I

BORING AND PATTERN

WE have now reached a stage in the study of our subject when the numerous details of gun and cartridge design become merged into the attainment of a single object, the effective delivery of the shot charge. Ideal results can only be obtained by a perfect combination of gun and cartridge, and so we must examine the means by which the best possible degree of co-operation is obtained. But before doing so it may be as well to consider very briefly the factors which together constitute ideal results.

A shotgun differs from a rifle in that the projectile consists of a large number of small pellets instead of a single bullet. In the case of a rifle the flight of the single bullet has to be controlled to the exclusion of other matters ; but in that of a shotgun the problem presented is that of controlling the flight of anything from 200 to 300 different pellets in such a way that as few pellets as possible are wasted. Consequently the shotgun really presents a more complex problem than the rifle, and it is for this reason that there is so much diversity of opinion among gunmakers and shooters as to the exact extent of control which should be utilised.

There can be no doubt, however, that an ideal result of a discharge from a sporting gun is obtained when the pellets comprising the charge have spread out evenly so as to cover a sufficient area to enable the shooter to strike the target. The greater the area over which the charge spreads, the more easy it is to hit the target, but if the pellets are spread out and separated too much it may happen that they will fly all round the target without hitting it. Consequently the degree of spread must not be so great that the density of the charge is merely dissipated in the air.

So it will be realised that the actual problem with which we are faced is to determine a combination of gun and cartridge which will propel a charge of shot so that:

(1) It will spread out evenly and regularly;

(2) The spread will not be so excessive that the pellets become so separated from each other that there is a possibility of them flying round the target without striking it;

(3) The pellets of the charge will have sufficient striking velocity to enable them to penetrate the target when they strike it.

The spread of the shot charge is universally known as the "Pattern," and the three points just enunciated together comprise what is an ideal pattern.

It will, however, be obvious that other factors enter the problem, such as the range at which the shot is taken, and the size of the target. These are really the complications which prevent universal agreement as to what constitutes a perfect pattern, and they will be considered in due course. The three fundamental essentials, however, are recognised by all; so I will first deal with the means adopted for controlling the pattern, and we will then be free to consider to what extent the degree of control should be exercised.

BORING

The work of shaping and finishing the inside of the barrel, or bore, is known as boring; and the boring of the barrel of a shotgun is just as important as that of a rifle. The latter is bored with several spiral grooves, as is well known; but the bore of a shotgun is left perfectly smooth. The shape of the bore, however, is of paramount importance in controlling the pattern. This has been realised from the very early days of game shooting, although it seems probable that Colonel Peter Hawker was one of the first to study the matter seriously, and it is also probable that the famous Joe Manton owed much of his success to Hawker's staunch advocacy of his weapons. For Joe Manton took just as great pains in the boring of his barrels as he did in the perfection of his flint locks.

Although any cross-section of the bore of a shotgun should always be perfectly circular, the bore itself is seldom, if ever, a true cylinder from end to end. In the days of the flint lock the breech end of the bore was usually made "tight behind," that is, the bore was tapered slightly with the largest diameter farthest from the breech. The opposite to this was "open behind" when the taper ran in the reverse direction, the diameter at the breech end being the greatest.

A barrel which was bored "open behind" certainly gave better ballistics, but the "tight behind" principle was usual so as to facilitate rapid loading from the muzzle.

The centre part of the barrel was almost always a true cylinder, and the front third was usually "relieved," that is tapered with the diameter increasing as the muzzle was approached.

The extent and degree of the "relief" was generally believed to have a pronounced influence on the pattern, but with the universal adoption of the breech-loader, guns became to be bored as true cylinders from end to end, although this method was modified to one in which the front portion was of a slightly greater diameter than the rear part. This system of boring was not the same as the old relief because the front part which was of larger diameter was parallel and not tapered, the only taper being that which connected the two cylindrical parts of the bore. This widening of the bore was introduced because it was found to tend to greater regularity of pattern, and it is still commonly adopted in a modified manner by nearly all gunmakers. The diameter of that part of the bore nearest the chamber cannot be increased because certain legal limits for the dimensions of the different sizes are laid down in the Proof Rules, and gunmakers are bound to work within these limits.

CHOKE

But about the year 1873 the invention of Choke revolutionised the boring of shotguns. There still seems to be a certain amount of doubt as to who was the real inventor of choke, and the history of the invention has been discussed so fully both by J. H. Walsh in *The Modern Sportsman's Gun and Rifle*, and by W. W. Greener in *The Gun and its Development*, that there is no need to enter into the question here. It is, however, a fact that in 1875 a sportsman wrote to the *Field* offering a prize of ten guineas to whoever should be adjudged the inventor. A committee was formed which heard all the available evidence and in due course awarded the prize to Mr. W. R. Pape, of Newcastle, on the strength of a patent he had taken out in 1866. Be that as it may, it is only fair to state that the development of the choke system of boring undoubtedly owes much to the late Mr. W. W. Greener.

Choke in a barrel is really a constriction of the bore at the muzzle. In other words, the barrel is so bored near the muzzle end that the diameter is decreased. The actual manner in which this is carried out depends to a certain extent on the amount of constriction to be made, but the usual plan is to start tapering the bore at a point *about* 1 to 1¼ inches from the muzzle. The tapered part lasts for about ½ of an inch when the maximum reduction in diameter is reached, and the final ½ or ¾ of an inch of the barrel is bored parallel, this last parallel portion being of the same diameter as the smallest end of the taper.

The diagram in Fig. 1 shows the longitudinal section of a choke. In this diagram the amount of constriction has been purposely exaggerated in order to make it clearly visible, and it is only intended to indicate the principle of a choke boring.

It will be seen that there are really two parts which together constitute the choke; namely, the tapered portion or "Cone," and the "Parallel."

There is no definite ruling as to the best relative

lengths for these two portions, and every gunmaker and every barrel-regulator has his own views on the subject. Further, it is a fact that two barrels bored in an exactly similar manner will not give similar results, and so it frequently happens that the final decision is made by the barrel-regulator who shapes the cone so as to obtain the best patterns. This can only be done by a prolonged series of actual tests for pattern, and such tests occupy a considerable amount of time as well as entailing the expenditure of an appreciable number of cartridges. All this adds to the cost of manufacture, and it is for this reason that cheap guns cannot be relied upon to give such regular patterns as best-grade guns. The former

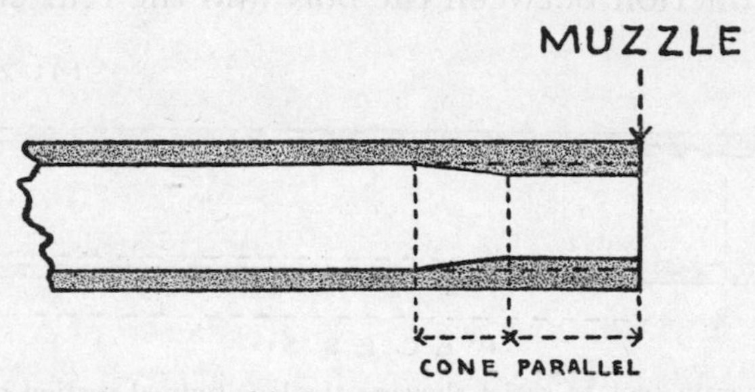

FIG. 1.—Diagram (not to scale) showing the longitudinal section of a choke-bored barrel at the muzzle end.

have not been submitted to the actual pattern trials which are regarded as an essential part of the finishing of the latter, and the result is that the barrels of the cheap gun are left as they have come off the machines, while those of the high-grade gun have been carefully touched up by hand.

This final regulating is of paramount importance and adds one more of the innumerable points of superiority which a high-grade gun possesses over a cheap one.

The total amount of constriction in a choke, that is the amount by which the diameter of the Parallel is smaller than the diameter of the bore, may be anything from 3 to 40 thousandths of an inch. And as a general rule it may be assumed that the greater the constriction, the longer both the Parallel and the Cone.

The maximum length for the Parallel appears to be about $1\frac{1}{4}$ inches, and this is generally only used in conjunction with the maximum constriction of 40 thousandths of an inch. With smaller constrictions the Parallel is shorter, until the smallest practical constriction of 3 thousandths is reached, when there is no Parallel at all, the front end of the Cone coinciding with the muzzle.

The length of the Cone varies from about $\frac{1}{4}$ of an inch to $\frac{7}{8}$ of an inch, or even 1 inch; the longer cones being naturally used for greater degrees of constriction.

So it will be seen that as a general rule a long Cone and long Parallel go together, and are only found in conjunction with a large degree of constriction.

The junction between the bore and the rear end of the

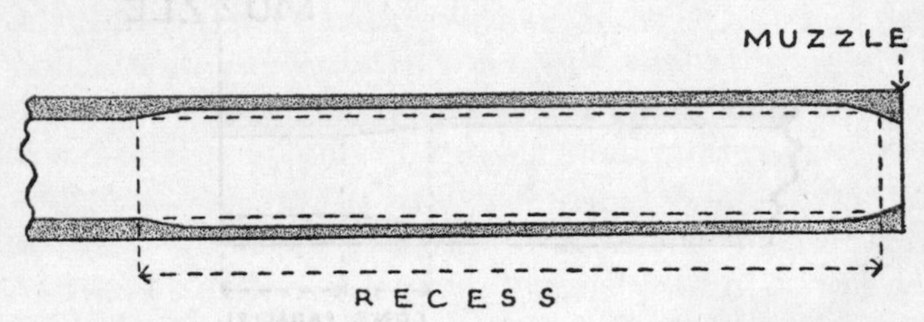

FIG. 2.—Diagram (not to scale) showing the longitudinal section of a recessed barrel.

cone is usually smoothed off in a curve, but some barrel-regulators will at times make this junction in the form of a distinct angle.

The actual angle, or pitch, of the cone naturally depends on its length and the total amount of constriction in the choke. For any given degree of choke the pitch of the cone is usually sharper when the cone is short than when it is long, and generally speaking a sharp pitch tends to increase the density of the pattern. But if the pitch is too sharp the pattern becomes irregular, and there is no hard and fast rule as to the best pitch to adopt in conjunction with any particular degree of choke.

The diagram in Fig. 2 shows a type of boring which is frequently adopted with very slight chokes of but 3 to 5 thousandths of an inch, especially when these occur at the very muzzle and the Parallel is entirely omitted. This system of boring is merely an enlargement of the bore immediately in rear of the Cone, this enlargement being termed a "Recess." The length of the Recess is generally about 6 inches, and the diameter of the recessed portion is from 3 to 5 thousandths of an inch greater than that of the bore. The result is that the length of the actual Cone is increased, and this helps to concentrate the pattern.

A Recess is by no means universal even in guns bored with very slight chokes, and it is usually inserted during the final shooting and regulating for pattern. And it thus becomes a regulating device to give the pattern desired, for it frequently happens that the regularity and density of a pattern are both improved by the addition of a Recess, although there is no hard and fast rule.

These facts all show the great variations in procedure adopted by gunmakers in boring chokes. These variations do not arise so much from differences in views as from the fact that no two barrels will behave quite alike when bored in an identical manner. For this reason it is impossible to state whether any particular combination of Cone and Parallel, or Recess and Cone, is the best. I am, however, inclined to believe that very short Parallels are not quite so good as longer ones, except in the case of the very slight chokes adopted in improved cylinders. I only put forward this idea with extreme diffidence, but it has certainly been my experience that barrels with fairly long Parallels have seemed to give more regular results with all sorts of cartridges than those with very short Parallels, or none at all. I will readily admit that I have not tested a sufficient number of guns to come to any definite conclusion—one would have to test several hundred different barrels with various loads—and it may be that the results which I have noticed have been accidental.

Nevertheless it does not seem altogether unreasonable to think that the Parallel should be sufficiently long to take the whole of the shot charge at the same time, and thus impart a steadying influence after the upset it must receive on being constricted by its passage up the Cone.

But, on the other hand, the combination of a moderate constriction of, say, 10 thousandths of an inch and a Parallel of nearly an inch will result in a less concentrated pattern than a similar constriction and a shorter Parallel. It will, accordingly, be seen how impossible it is to lay down any definite ruling.

CLASSIFICATION OF CHOKE

Theoretically a choke is any constriction at the muzzle of a gun, but in actual practice a smaller constriction than 3 thousandths of an inch is seldom, if ever, adopted. So it will be realised that any gun is "choked" which has its barrels bored with constrictions at the muzzle which may vary from 3 to 40 thousandths of an inch. In technical parlance 1 thousandth of an inch is always known as a "point," so the smallest constriction which gives any appreciable effect is one of 3 "points."

An "Improved Cylinder" boring is one in which the constriction is from 3 to 5 "points," from which it will be seen that "improved cylinders" are really nothing more than very slight chokes.

At the other end of the scale we have the "Full Choke" which is a constriction of 40 "points," and mid-way there is the "Half Choke" with its 20 "points" of constriction.

In between the Improved Cylinder and Half Choke there is the "Quarter" or "Modified" Choke, but the latter term is very vague in its meaning, and some gun-makers actually mean a choke of between Half and Full when they use the term "Modified."

Similarly, although Improved Cylinders are usually bored with from 3 to 5 "points" of choke, some gun-makers call barrels bored with quite 8 "points" "Improved Cylinders." It is, naturally, very misleading to compare the results given by these different "Improved Cylinders" or "Modified Chokes," and so I cannot help feeling that it would be altogether better to describe the boring of a barrel by naming the actual degree of constriction. If this were done barrels would always be described as having 5, 8, 10, 15, 25, 30, etc., " points of choke," and ambiguity would be decreased.

A disadvantage of this system would be that barrels bored with the same number of points of choke would not necessarily give similar results, and when a shooter buys a gun and is told that the choke is the same as that in some other gun, he naturally expects both guns to behave alike when it comes to testing them for pattern.

But the variations of individual barrels from the normal are seldom so great as to render such a system of classification abortive: and in any case the classification suggested would be considerably less ambiguous than the vague terms in common usage. It is, however, to say the very least, doubtful whether sportsmen as a class would take to such descriptions and so the terms " Full " and " Half " choke will remain. If to these were added " Quarter " and " Three-Quarter " to the complete exclusion of the indefinite " Modified " the range of classification would be fairly comprehensive.

The best way of all, however, to describe the boring of any barrel is by its behaviour. And since the whole object of boring is to obtain the best possible control of the shot charge, or in other words, to obtain the best possible patterns, we must next consider the question of pattern.

PATTERN

When a shot charge leaves the muzzle of a gun the pellets cluster together and do not separate to any appreciable extent until they are from 3 to 4 feet from the muzzle, when they begin to spread outwards and so cover an ever increasing area as the range becomes greater. The degree of spread is approximately proportional to the range, but not exactly so. This is because the outside pellets do not travel in perfectly straight lines, but move with a slight " curl," something after the manner of a " sliced " golf ball which is given a spin about a vertical axis and so tends to move laterally to that side on which air resistance is lessened by the presence of the spin.

Shot pellets are not necessarily given a spin, but the outer ones are deformed by their passage up the bore and past the choke so that they are no longer round, and therefore do not fly in absolutely straight lines ; but this deviation from the straight line is, of course, normally very small.

Since the amount of deformation of the outside pellets must vary from round to round, the exact degree of " curl " with which they travel will be different in the case of every shot. And it is on this account that the diameter of the total spread is not absolutely proportional to the range. Nevertheless it is roughly so ; and the diameter of the spread at 40 yards, for example, is very nearly double that of the spread at 20 yards, while at 10 yards the spread is approximately one-third of that at 30 yards.

MEASURING PATTERN.—The spread of the shot charge is, as has been explained, termed the Pattern, and since it is essential that we should be able to make comparisons between the patterns given by different guns and cartridges, some form of measuring pattern must be adopted.

When anything is measured certain units must be employed which are usually accepted for the sake of their convenience. What the exact unit is in any particular case is immaterial ; the only point that matters is that all who take the measurements should use the same unit. In measuring patterns the unit is the number of pellets of what may be termed the standard size of the standard charge of shot when propelled with standard velocity which lie in a circle of 30 inches in diameter when fired at a range of 40 yards.

In the case of an ordinary 12-bore the standard shot charge is $1\frac{1}{16}$ ounce. A charge of 33 grains of Smokeless Diamond should develop standard ballistics with this shot charge, and consequently this combination is most generally used because Smokeless Diamond is the powder in most common use in this country. But there is no reason why any other powder should not be used provided the pressures and velocities lie within the normal limits. But if no special mention of the powder is made it is assumed that the load consisted of 33 grains of Smokeless Diamond and $1\frac{1}{16}$ ounce of No. 6 shot. No. 6 is used simply because it is the most popular size in Great Britain. So the reasons for the selection for this combination in the case of an ordinary 12-bore are obvious.

In the case of other sizes the load and size of shot should always be specified when patterns are quoted.

The 30-inch circle is taken for the unit of area simply as a matter of convenience. The custom was adopted in the days when gunmakers first began to bother about the patterns of their guns, and it has become so thoroughly established that any change would be as mistaken as it would be purposeless. Some area must be taken: to give a true comparison it must be circular; the size of the circle is really immaterial; and now it has become established, why change?

But the distance of 40 yards is another matter. I have often heard men say, "Why 40 yards? Why not 25 or 30 yards, the ranges at which most game is shot?"

This seems a very reasonable question, especially in view of the fact that the spread of the shot charge at any distance is roughly proportional to the range.

It must, however, be remembered that the most essential quality in any individual pattern is that the pellets in the circle should be spread evenly all over that circle. There should be no clusters in one part, or open spaces in another in which a bird might escape without receiving a single pellet: the distribution of the pellets must be even.

Further, a gun should throw regular patterns. That is, there should be approximately the same number of pellets in the circle every time.

Even and regular patterns are to a gun what close and regular grouping is to a rifle. The parallel is exact.

Now it is perfectly possible for a pattern to be patchy

and irregular at 20 yards and yet appear quite satisfactory. This is because at that close range the patches would not be so large that a bird could escape in them without being hit. When looking at patterns one instinctively thinks of the possibility of a bird escaping in any open space there may be, and at 20 yards these open spaces are so comparatively small that they are very deceiving. But at 40 yards the diameters of these open patches will be just about twice as big, which means that the areas of the patches will be about four times as great as they were at 20 yards ; and so it happens that a pattern which looked quite satisfactory at 20 yards would be condemned immediately at twice that range.

So it will be seen that pattern testing at 40 yards puts a considerably more severe test on the gun than would be the case were the patterns taken at some shorter range.

In view of this fact it may be wondered why 50, or even 60, yards is not adopted as the pattern range instead of 40, as at these distances the test would be still more severe. The reason is that it would be too severe. Even at 50 yards the pattern given by the great majority of guns is so open, that is the shot charge has spread out to such an extent, that there are comparatively few pellets in the 30-inch circle and so it is most difficult to see whether the distribution is even, except in cases where the pattern has been concentrated to an exceptional extent by a very heavy choke. And at 60 yards this difficulty is present with the very fullest choke.

If a gun threw a pattern at 50 yards which was sufficiently dense to judge properly, it would concentrate its charge too much at close ranges for practical purposes of sport. The distance of 40 yards is the longest at which it is possible to combine sufficient density of pattern for judging an even spread and a boring of the gun which will not concentrate the charge too much at short ranges. And it is this fact which makes 40 yards the most suitable range at which to assess a pattern, and therefore the range to be adopted as the unit of distance for measuring patterns. However, when one inspects a pattern at 40 yards it is a mistake to be too exacting; for it must be remembered that the test is purposely being made at a greater distance than the usual sporting ranges so as to exaggerate irregularities.

Testing for Pattern. Having seen what units are used in making the measurements of pattern, the reader who has had no personal experience of the work may be interested to learn how the actual testing for pattern is conducted.

The essential apparatus consists of a sheet-iron target which should be at least 6 feet square. This is placed in a vertical position and the gun to be tested is used for shooting at this target from a range of 40 yards. The target is whitewashed before every shot. Contrary to a very general belief amongst sportsmen, the 30-inch circle is not drawn until after the shot has been fired. This plan is adopted because the object of the trial is to test the combination of gun and cartridge and not the shooter's accuracy of aim. All that the shooter has to do is to try to centre the charge as far as possible in the middle of the target. The centre of the densest part of the pattern is then selected by eye and the circle is described with a wooden compass of 15 inches radius. By this means the human element is eliminated as far as is possible.

After the circle has been drawn the number of pellet-marks inside it are counted and the general regularity of spread is noted. The target is than whitewashed over again, when all is ready for the next shot.

Any gunmaker who has much work to do has several targets, six or ten, in a row touching each other so that the whole " butt " is a wall of sheet iron 6 feet high and 36 to 60 feet long. It is thus possible to fire a number of rounds in succession, and not only is time saved but there is the further advantage of being able to view a number of patterns from a barrel side by side, which helps the regulator to form an opinion as to the regularity of the patterns.

He can then touch up the choke or make a slight

recess in order to increase or reduce the density of the pattern if necessary, or else to improve the regularity. And it is really wonderful how an expert regulator can make the barrels of a gun give the desired pattern within a few pellets. Incidentally, this is where time and money is expended, for which the purchaser of a high-grade gun should not object to pay.

It should be noted that the 40 yards is actually measured from the target to the spot where the shooter stands, and not to the muzzle of the gun.

Home testing of patterns is a most interesting and instructive pastime, as it teaches one better than anything else which load will suit a gun best. It also makes a very valuable check on the behaviour of any fresh lot of cartridges.

But to be of any use the work must be conducted properly, and in the manner described. A single target 6 feet square is ample for home work, and a 4-foot target will do, although it is not easy to centre the charge every time on such a small target. The target can be set up in any convenient spot where it does not interfere with the beauty of the garden or landscape, and once in position it can become a permanency.

Whitewash is not a very convenient or pleasant medium to use for painting the target, and Mr. E. P. Bernard has pointed out the great superiority of a non-drying white paint such as is used for air-rifle targets and sold by Messrs. Parker-Hale, Ltd., Bisley Works, Whittall Street, Birmingham. This paint is not very costly as one coat will normally last a month, and all that one need do after every shot is to smooth the surface of the target down with a flat brush.

For those who do not mind a little trouble I can recommend Mr. Bernard's instructions for making up a non-drying paint. This paint consists of zinc oxide mixed into a cream with the rectified petroleum that chemists sell for medicinal purposes. As it is difficult to mix these two ingredients direct because of the syrupy nature of the oil, Mr. Bernard first mixes the zinc oxide into a paste with a little paraffin, afterwards stirring in the petroleum little by little until the desired consistency is obtained. But long and patient stirring is necessary in order to make a good emulsion and to prevent the separation of the ingredients.

I am also much indebted to Mr. Bernard for the following note on making a suitable compass for inscribing the circle.

Mr. Bernard writes:

"A piece of wood 16¼ inches long by 1 inch wide by ¾ inch deep is pierced by a perpendicular 2-inch wire nail about ½ inch from one end, which projects about ⅜ inch underneath. Fifteen inches away, at the other end of the piece of wood, a 2-inch length of brass gas tubing of ¼-inch bore passes through the wood similarly to, and parallel with, the nail. In the underneath end of the tube a little cylinder of cork taken from a cork borer is stuck, projecting about ⅛ inch. This tube is the 'pencil' of the compass. The wood is made to grip it vice-wise by slitting it for about 3 inches with a saw and passing a screw through close behind the tube to tighten."

The best way of counting the pellet marks is to take a fired cartridge-case and wipe out the marks with this, one by one. It is a curious fact that few people can count much more than ten accurately, and fewer still more than twenty. For this reason the safest course is to make a stroke on the target above the circle directly ten pellet marks have been erased, and then to start counting again. If this is done the number of strokes can be counted when all the pellet marks have been obliterated and the odd number of the count left over can be added on.

There is nothing in the least difficult about testing for pattern, but to be of any value the test must be conducted properly and with suitable appliances. If these are not available it is far better to have the test carried out by a gunmaker. Tests made by shooting at a newspaper, such as are sometimes made by sportsmen, can be very misleading, because no newspaper is sufficiently large to permit even the best of shots placing his pattern correctly every time. Unless this is done a circle may be drawn round the edge of the pattern when an entirely false count will be obtained. Sportsmen should remember that a pattern test is of little value unless all chances of human error are eliminated, and consequently it is essential to use a target at least 4 feet square, and better still 6 feet square, when the placing of the whole charge on the target should be a certainty.

THE EFFECT OF CHOKE ON PATTERN

All shooters know that a choke gives a "closer," or more concentrated, pattern than a cylinder barrel ; but not many realise the proportions of the whole shot charge which the different types of boring in common use place in the 30-inch circle at 40 yards. And since this relation is one of the fundamentals of a proper consideration of boring and pattern, I will give it in tabular form.

TABLE I

PATTERNS GIVEN BY DIFFERENT BORINGS

Type of Boring.	"Points" of Choke.	Percentage of the Original Number of Pellets in the Shot Charge which are placed in the 30-inch Circle at 40 Yards.
Full Choke	40	70
Three-quarter Choke . . .	30	65
Half Choke	20	60
Quarter Choke	10	55
Improved Cylinder . . .	3 to 5	50
True Cylinder	Nil	40

These percentages are *approximately* true for all sizes of guns and all sizes of shot within reasonable limits. It may happen, for example, that one particular gun puts 63 per cent. of No. 6 in the circle and only 58 per cent. of No. 5. But such variations are minor exceptions and nothing more. The general rule is universal.

To the best of my belief Mr. Max Baker was the first

PLATE II

THE BACK VIEW OF THE MOVING TARGET USED BY MR. C. E. ALLAN AND THE AUTHOR

Showing the method of attaching the plate to the motor car

to realise these classifications; and in any case he deserves the greatest credit, as well as the thanks of all gunmakers and sportsmen, for the clarity with which he tabulated them in the original editions of the *Shooters' Year Book*. There can be no doubt that these tables first established order out of chaos.

If we return to our original unit for measuring pattern in the case of an ordinary 12-bore, it will be seen that a charge of $1\frac{1}{16}$ ounce of No. 6 shot was taken as the standard. There are 287 pellets in this charge and so it will be realised that the different borings give the following patterns:

Full Choke (40 points) . . .	200
Three-quarter Choke (30 points) .	187
Half Choke (20 points) . . .	175
Quarter Choke (10 points) . .	160
Improved Cylinder (3 to 5 points) .	145
True Cylinder	114

These figures represent the patterns quoted by gunmakers when describing the shooting of any particular gun, and from them it is possible to obtain an idea as to the boring adopted. For instance, if the right barrel of a gun is quoted as giving a pattern of 140, and the left 170, we would know that the right barrel was bored "improved cylinder" and the left very nearly half choke. It will accordingly be appreciated how important the measurement of pattern can be, especially when the results are considered in conjuction with the percentages given in Table I, as with these data one can make a very fair inference as to the pattern likely to be obtained when using a different size of shot or a different weight of shot charge.

For example, from the patterns quoted by the gunmaker we decide that the barrels of a gun are bored improved cylinder and half choke. Then we will know that they should give 50 and 60 per cent. patterns. So with a charge of $1\frac{1}{8}$ ounce of No. 4 the patterns will be about 95 and 115; and with 1 ounce of No. 7 about 170 and 200.

As a matter of interest and convenience the following tables are given which show the percentages in the 30-inch circle at 40 yards for the different borings of all the weights of shot charges of the different sizes of shot which are likely to be encountered in any size of gun. So if the pattern is quoted for any gun when using a certain weight of any size of shot, the boring of that gun can be obtained from the tables.

Although these tables are of unquestionable value the percentages which they give should not be regarded as infallible. The idiosyncrasy of every gun, indeed of every barrel, must be remembered, especially when the loading varies from the normal or from the load with which the gun was originally regulated. I have known, for instance, a pair of full choke guns all four barrels of which actually gave as dense, or even denser, patterns when using an ounce of No. 5 as they gave with an ounce of No. 6. I have also known a barrel which gave a regular 60 per cent. pattern with an ounce of shot and a good 70 per cent. pattern with $1\frac{1}{16}$ ounce. But such extreme departures from the normal are exceptional, and as a rule a gun will throw a comparatively constant percentage in the 30-inch circle with all ordinary shot sizes and loads, provided the ballistics are normal.

For the ballistics developed by a cartridge can have the greatest influence on pattern, and it is for this reason that the use of the standard load is such an important point in the measuring of pattern.

But there are other factors besides ballistics which can affect pattern, and all these factors will be considered in the next chapter.

There is, however, one factor which would appear to have a comparatively constant effect on pattern which should be mentioned now. This is the fully Crimped Turnover closure to the front of the cartridge which does away with the necessity for an over-shot wad. Crimped cartridges came into use a comparatively few years before the outbreak of the late war and as yet they are not as generally known as they deserve to be, while the war years prevented the accumulation of data sufficient to justify any hard and fast law. There is, however, not the slightest doubt that the crimp sealing of the case gives an appreciably closer pattern than that given by a similarly loaded cartridge with the ordinary over-shot wad and turnover.

I have examined about 300 patterns made with different guns and crimped cartridges and it would seem that in all types of boring there is an increase in pattern density of just about 5 per cent.

This means that when crimped cartridges are used each type of boring "goes up one place," the improved cylinder giving the 55 per cent. pattern of the quarter choke; the quarter choke the 60 per cent. pattern of the half choke; and so on until the full choke gives approximately a 75 per cent. pattern.

I have, therefore, included an extra table for full choke giving 75 per cent. patterns, but it should be understood clearly that it is intended only to suggest the patterns which may be expected when using crimped cartridges. All the other table headings are those suitable for ordinary cartridges with over-shot wads, and if the corresponding pattern for crimped cartridges are required the table giving the next closer type of boring should be used.

TABLE II

TRUE CYLINDER (40 PER CENT.) PATTERNS

Size of Shot.	Pellets in 30-inch Circle at 40 Yards from different Weights of Shot Charge in Ounces.																
	1½	1 7/16	1⅜	1 5/16	1¼	1 3/16	1⅛	1 1/16	One	15/16	⅞	13/16	¾	11/16	⅝	9/16	½
BB	42	40	38	37	35	33	32	30	28	26	24	23	21	19	18	16	14
B	48	46	44	42	40	38	36	34	32	30	28	26	24	22	20	18	16
1	60	58	55	52	50	48	45	42	40	38	35	32	30	28	25	22	20
2	72	69	66	63	60	57	54	51	48	45	42	39	36	33	30	27	24
3	84	80	77	74	70	66	63	60	56	52	49	46	42	38	35	32	28
4	104	98	94	89	85	81	76	72	68	64	60	55	51	47	42	38	34
4½	120	115	110	105	100	95	90	85	80	75	70	65	60	55	50	45	40
5	132	126	121	115	110	104	99	94	88	82	77	72	66	60	55	50	44
5½	144	138	132	126	120	114	108	102	96	90	84	78	72	66	60	54	48
6	162	156	148	141	135	128	122	115	108	101	94	88	81	74	68	61	54
6½	180	172	165	158	150	142	135	127	120	112	105	98	90	82	75	68	60
7	204	196	187	179	170	162	153	144	136	128	119	110	102	94	85	76	68
8	270	259	247	236	225	213	202	191	180	169	158	146	135	123	112	101	90
9	348	334	319	305	290	276	261	246	232	217	203	189	174	160	145	130	116

TABLE III

Improved Cylinder (50 per cent.) Patterns

Size of Shot.	Pellets in 30-inch Circle at 40 Yards from different Weights of Shot Charge in Ounces.																
	$1\frac{1}{2}$	$1\frac{7}{16}$	$1\frac{3}{8}$	$1\frac{5}{16}$	$1\frac{1}{4}$	$1\frac{3}{16}$	$1\frac{1}{8}$	$1\frac{1}{16}$	One	$\frac{15}{16}$	$\frac{7}{8}$	$\frac{13}{16}$	$\frac{3}{4}$	$\frac{11}{16}$	$\frac{5}{8}$	$\frac{9}{16}$	$\frac{1}{2}$
BB	53	50	48	46	44	42	39	37	35	33	30	28	26	24	22	19	17
B	60	58	55	53	50	47	45	43	40	37	35	33	30	27	25	23	20
1	75	72	69	65	63	59	57	53	50	47	44	40	37	34	31	28	25
2	90	86	82	78	75	71	67	63	60	56	52	49	45	41	37	33	30
3	105	100	96	92	87	83	79	74	70	65	61	57	52	48	44	39	35
4	128	122	117	111	106	101	95	90	85	79	74	69	64	58	53	48	42
$4\frac{1}{2}$	150	143	137	131	125	118	112	106	100	94	87	81	75	69	62	56	50
5	165	158	151	144	137	130	124	117	110	103	96	89	82	75	69	62	55
$5\frac{1}{2}$	180	172	165	157	150	142	135	127	120	112	105	97	90	82	75	67	60
6	202	194	185	177	169	160	152	143	135	126	118	109	101	93	84	76	67
$6\frac{1}{2}$	225	215	206	197	187	178	169	159	150	140	131	122	112	103	93	84	75
7	255	244	234	223	212	202	191	180	170	159	149	138	127	117	106	95	85
8	337	323	309	295	281	267	253	239	225	211	197	183	169	154	140	126	112
9	435	417	399	381	362	344	326	308	290	272	254	235	217	199	181	163	145

TABLE IV

Quarter Choke (55 per cent.) Patterns

Size of Shot.	Pellets in 30-inch Circle at 40 Yards from different Weights of Shot Charge in Ounces.															
	1 1/2	1 7/16	1 3/8	1 5/16	1 1/4	1 3/16	1 1/8	1 1/16	One	15/16	7/8	13/16	3/4	11/16	5/8	9/16	1/2
BB	57	55	52	50	48	45	43	40	38	35	33	31	29	26	24	21	19
B	66	63	60	57	55	52	49	46	44	41	38	35	33	30	27	25	22
1	82	79	76	72	69	65	62	58	55	52	48	44	41	38	35	31	27
2	99	95	91	86	82	79	74	70	66	62	58	53	49	46	41	38	33
3	115	110	106	100	96	91	87	82	77	72	68	63	58	53	48	43	38
4	140	134	128	122	117	111	105	100	94	88	82	76	70	64	58	53	47
4 1/2	165	158	151	144	137	130	124	116	110	103	96	90	82	76	69	62	55
5	181	174	166	159	151	143	136	129	121	113	106	98	90	83	76	68	60
5 1/2	198	190	181	173	165	157	148	140	132	124	115	107	99	91	82	74	66
6	222	213	204	195	186	176	167	158	148	139	130	120	111	102	93	84	74
6 1/2	248	238	228	217	206	196	186	175	165	154	144	134	124	113	103	93	82
7	280	268	257	245	234	222	210	198	187	175	164	152	140	129	116	105	94
8	371	356	340	325	310	293	278	263	247	232	217	201	186	170	154	139	124
9	488	458	438	419	398	378	359	339	319	299	279	259	239	219	200	179	159

TABLE V

Half Choke (60 per cent.) Patterns

Size of Shot.	Pellets in 30-inch Circle at 40 Yards from different Weights of Shot Charge in Ounces.																
	1 1/2	1 7/16	1 3/8	1 5/16	1 1/4	1 3/16	1 1/8	1 1/16	One	15/16	7/8	13/16	3/4	11/16	5/8	9/16	1/2
BB	63	60	57	55	53	50	47	44	42	39	37	34	32	29	26	23	21
B	72	69	66	63	60	57	54	51	48	45	42	39	36	33	30	27	24
1	90	86	83	79	75	71	68	64	60	56	53	49	45	41	38	34	30
2	108	104	99	94	90	86	81	76	72	68	63	59	54	50	45	40	36
3	126	121	116	110	105	99	95	89	84	79	74	68	63	58	53	47	42
4	153	146	140	134	128	121	115	109	102	95	89	83	77	70	64	58	51
4 1/2	180	172	165	157	150	142	135	127	120	113	105	98	90	83	75	68	60
5	198	190	182	173	164	157	149	140	132	123	116	107	99	90	83	74	66
5 1/2	216	207	198	189	180	171	162	153	144	135	126	117	108	99	90	81	72
6	243	233	222	212	203	193	182	172	162	152	142	131	121	112	101	91	81
6 1/2	270	258	248	236	225	214	202	191	180	168	158	146	135	123	112	101	90
7	306	293	280	268	253	242	229	216	204	191	179	165	153	140	127	114	102
8	405	388	370	355	337	320	304	286	270	253	236	219	203	185	168	152	135
9	522	500	478	457	435	413	392	369	348	326	304	282	261	239	218	195	174

TABLE VI

Three-Quarter Choke (65 per cent.) Patterns

Size of Shot.	Pellets in 30-inch Circle at 40 Yards from different Weights of Shot Charge in Ounces.																
	1½	1 7/16	1⅜	1 5/16	1¼	1 3/16	1⅛	1 1/16	One	15/16	⅞	13/16	¾	11/16	⅝	9/16	½
BB	68	65	62	60	57	54	51	48	45	42	40	37	34	31	28	25	23
B	78	75	71	68	65	62	58	55	52	49	45	42	39	36	32	29	26
1	97	93	89	85	81	77	73	69	65	61	57	53	49	45	41	36	32
2	117	112	107	102	97	93	87	82	78	73	68	64	58	54	49	43	39
3	136	131	125	120	114	108	103	97	91	85	80	74	68	62	57	51	45
4	166	159	152	145	138	131	124	117	110	103	97	90	83	76	69	62	55
4½	195	187	179	170	162	154	146	138	130	122	114	106	97	89	81	73	65
5	214	205	197	188	179	170	161	152	143	134	125	116	107	98	89	80	71
5½	234	224	214	204	195	185	175	166	156	146	136	126	117	107	97	88	78
6	263	252	241	230	219	208	197	186	175	164	153	142	131	121	110	99	88
6½	292	280	268	256	244	231	219	207	195	183	171	159	146	134	122	110	97
7	331	318	304	290	276	263	249	235	221	207	194	179	166	152	138	124	111
8	438	420	402	384	366	347	329	311	293	274	256	238	220	201	183	164	146
9	566	542	518	495	471	448	425	401	377	354	330	306	283	260	236	212	188

TABLE VII

Full Choke (70 per cent.) Patterns

Size of Shot.	Pellets in 30-inch Circle at 40 Yards from different Weights of Shot Charge in Ounces.															
	$1\frac{1}{2}$	$1\frac{7}{16}$	$1\frac{3}{8}$	$1\frac{5}{16}$	$1\frac{1}{4}$	$1\frac{3}{16}$	$1\frac{1}{8}$	$1\frac{1}{16}$	One	$\frac{15}{16}$	$\frac{7}{8}$	$\frac{13}{16}$	$\frac{3}{4}$	$\frac{11}{16}$	$\frac{5}{8}$	$\frac{9}{16}$	$\frac{1}{2}$
BB	73	70	67	64	61	58	55	52	49	46	43	40	37	34	31	27	24
B	84	81	77	74	70	67	63	60	56	53	49	46	42	39	35	32	28
1	105	101	97	92	88	83	79	74	70	66	62	57	52	48	44	39	35
2	126	121	115	110	105	100	95	89	84	79	74	69	63	58	53	47	42
3	147	141	135	129	122	116	110	104	98	92	86	80	74	67	62	55	49
4	178	171	164	156	149	141	134	127	119	111	104	97	90	82	74	67	60
$4\frac{1}{2}$	210	201	192	183	175	166	157	148	140	132	122	114	105	97	88	79	70
5	231	221	212	202	192	183	173	164	154	144	135	125	115	105	97	87	77
$5\frac{1}{2}$	252	242	231	220	210	199	189	178	168	157	147	136	126	115	105	95	84
6	283	270	260	248	236	225	213	201	189	177	165	153	141	130	118	106	95
$6\frac{1}{2}$	315	302	289	276	262	249	237	223	210	197	184	171	157	144	131	118	105
7	357	342	328	312	298	283	268	253	238	223	208	193	178	164	148	134	119
8	472	453	433	414	394	374	354	335	315	295	276	256	237	216	196	177	157
9	608	583	558	533	508	482	457	431	406	380	356	330	305	279	254	228	203

TABLE VII (A)

FULL CHOKE (75 PER CENT.) PATTERNS

Size of Shot.	Pellets in 30-inch Circle at 40 Yards from different Weights of Shot Charge in Ounces.															
	1½	1 7/16	1⅜	1 5/16	1¼	1 3/16	1⅛	1 1/16	One	15/16	⅞	13/16	¾	11/16	⅝	9/16	½
BB	80	75	72	69	66	63	60	56	52	49	45	42	39	36	33	29	26
B	90	87	83	80	75	71	67	64	60	56	52	49	45	42	38	34	30
1	112	108	104	99	94	89	85	80	75	70	66	60	56	51	47	42	37
2	135	129	123	117	112	106	101	95	90	84	78	73	67	61	55	50	45
3	158	150	144	138	131	123	117	111	105	98	91	84	78	72	66	59	53
4	192	183	175	167	159	151	143	135	128	119	111	104	96	87	79	72	64
4½	225	214	205	196	187	177	168	159	150	141	132	122	113	103	93	84	75
5	247	237	227	216	206	196	186	175	165	155	145	135	124	113	103	93	83
5½	270	258	247	236	225	214	203	191	180	169	157	146	135	124	112	101	90
6	303	291	278	265	253	241	228	215	202	189	177	164	151	139	127	114	101
6½	338	324	310	295	281	267	254	239	225	211	197	182	169	154	140	127	113
7	383	367	351	334	319	303	287	271	255	239	223	207	191	175	159	143	128
8	506	485	464	443	422	401	380	359	338	317	296	275	254	232	211	190	168
9	652	625	598	571	543	515	489	462	435	407	380	363	336	299	272	244	217

CHAPTER II

FACTORS AFFECTING PATTERN

IT was explained in Volume II that there are four ballistic elements of a shotgun and cartridge, namely Pressure, Velocity, Pattern and Recoil; and that all four were interdependent. I have already dealt fully with the elements of Pressure, Velocity and Recoil, but we have now come to a stage in our consideration of the ballistic element of Pattern when we must study the effects of its interdependence with Pressure and Velocity. Recoil, as has been seen in Volume II, is really a function of Velocity, and so does not in itself have any direct effect on Pattern.

However, before we begin to consider the effects of ballistics and other factors on pattern it will be as well to bear in mind that an ideal pattern should be spread perfectly evenly over the effective area, while the density—that is the number of pellets in the 30-inch circle—should be as nearly as possible constant when the same weight of shot charge made up of any particular size of shot is fired from the same barrel. These are two of the essential attributes of a good pattern, and any factor which tends to make a gun give uneven or irregular patterns is detrimental to good results in the actual shooting field.

Let us now take these factors in turn.

PRESSURE. The ballistic element of Pressure is the most important of all the factors which affect pattern. The standard pressure at one inch is about 2·75 tons for the ordinary $2\frac{1}{2}$-inch 12-bore cartridge, and if this is exceeded to any appreciable extent the pattern suffers considerably, high pressures tending to what are termed " blown " or " scattered " patterns. Such are obtained when the total spread of the shot charge is greater than normal, as the density of the pattern must then obviously be decreased, while the distribution is never even and regular.

The higher the pressure the more pronounced is the scattering effect on the pattern, and ordinary 2½-inch 12-bore cartridges which develop pressures of 3·25 tons and over will never give such good patterns as those yielded by cartridges in which the pressure is a ton lower. And if the pressures exceed this last figure by any appreciable amount the patterns will be so blown and scattered in an ordinary gun as to be of little practical use.

The expression "ordinary gun" has purposely been used as British game guns are not usually bored with very heavy chokes, and it is a fact that the greater the degree of choke the more the scattering effect caused by pressure is overcome. A full choke, for example, will give fairly evenly distributed and regular patterns with high pressure cartridges; yet those same cartridges would prove useless in an improved cylinder gun on account of the blown patterns. But even in the case of the full choke the density of the pattern would suffer, and the actual count of the number of pellets in the 30-inch circle at 40 yards would be appreciably less than that given by a combination of the same gun and cartridges developing a lower pressure.

It will, therefore, be realised that a high pressure spoils both the even distribution and the density of the pattern, although these evils can be counteracted to a certain degree by choke, and the heavier the choke the better the results. And in this connection it should be understood that a high pressure does not necessarily mean a dangerous pressure, or one which is likely to strain the action in any way. When considering pattern a pressure should be regarded as high which exceeds the standard by more than 0·4 of a ton in the case of a 2½-inch 12-bore cartridge, or by a proportional amount in the case of those cartridges in which the standard pressure is appreciably higher than that developed in an ordinary 12-bore.

Low pressures have an exactly opposite tendency to high pressures and help to increase the density and regularity of spread of a pattern. This fact can be so marked as to result in a badly bored gun giving quite decent patterns with very low-pressure cartridges when it would give but poor and irregular, or "patchy," patterns with cartridges which develop standard ballistics.

But the pressures must not be too low, or the quality of the pattern may fall off altogether.

In an ordinary 12-bore the pressure should never be less than 2 tons, and it is always better to regard this as the lowest working minimum.

Since this figure is 0·7 of a ton lower than the normal British standard, and since these "soft" pressures help the pattern the reader will probably wonder why cartridges are not loaded to develop these lower pressures. This point has really been dealt with in Volume II, but it may be as well to point out again that it is never advisable to work to a minimum limit. If the average pressure developed by any batch of cartridges is only slightly over 2 tons, a number of cartridges in that batch will be giving pressures which are considerably lower, and the velocities developed by these cartridges will be too low for sporting purposes. For it is no use to concentrate on obtaining the very best possible patterns unless the striking velocities of the pellets are sufficiently high to ensure penetration at sporting ranges. And it is for this reason that the standard of round about 2·75 tons has been adopted.

It should also be remembered that without raising the pressure to a certain extent it is impossible to meet the growing demand amongst a wide section of the shooting public for cartridges which develop a higher velocity than the standard. If guns were always regulated for pattern with cartridges which developed pressures of but 2·25 tons, the changes in pattern would be far greater when using 3-ton cartridges than if the guns had been regulated for 2·75-ton pressures.[1]

[1] I have quoted the actual values for pressures which occur in a 2½-inch 12-bore cartridge because it is much the most common. But the principles apply equally to all sizes and lengths of cases, the variations from the standard pressures being proportional to those which I have given as examples. A complete Table of standard, maximum and minimum pressures for every size of British cartridge is given in Volume II.

So it is really to the advantage both of the cartridge manufacturer and the gunmaker to have the standard pressure on the high side rather than the low: the cartridge manufacturer because he will be less likely to suffer from complaints of lack of penetration; and the gunmaker because his guns will hold better patterns with lively cartridges.

The reason for this influence of pressure on pattern is probably to be found in the deformation of the shot pellets which compose the charge; although some authorities lay a proportion of the blame on the muzzle blast.

But the question of pellet deformation is undoubtedly of primary importance, as it has a most potent effect on the whole spread of the shot charge during flight, both laterally and longitudinally. It was touched on in the last chapter and considered in Volume II, and detailed repetition is unnecessary. So I will only state here that the whole shot charge receives a sudden blow on the ignition of the powder and possibly a check when it passes the chamber cone and enters the bore, and another check when it passes the choke. Both this blow and these checks must make the pellets bang up against each other, while the outside pellets must suffer considerably from their contact with the cones at the head of the chamber and the beginning of the choke. Further, during the actual passage of the shot charge along the bore the outside pellets must be abraded by friction, while the whole charge must be pressed together with such force that the inner pellets will tend to become misshapen.

The result is that a certain amount of deformation of a proportion of the pellets in the shot charge is inevitable; and the greater the deformation, both in the variation from the spherical and the number of pellets so misshapen, the greater must be the number of pellets which cannot be relied upon to travel in approximately true trajectories during their flight through the air.

Now the greater the gas pressure the more violent

must be the banging and jostling which the pellets receive, especially on the initial impulse and during their passage of the first part of the bore. And so it is not difficult to realise that the pattern suffers in consequence.

So the evil influences of high pressures will be readily understood, the whole tendency being to scatter the shot charge to an excessive degree. It is also not difficult to appreciate why a heavy choke helps to overcome this tendency since the action of the choke is to concentrate the shot charge.

Very low pressures give bad patterns simply because the very fact that they occur shows that the combustion of the powder is not normal. In such circumstances the pressure and velocity will be extremely irregular, and so it is easy to realise that the patterns will be erratic.

Velocity. The element of Velocity tends to have a similar effect on Pattern as has Pressure, that is, a high velocity helps to make the patterns scattered and irregular while a low velocity helps towards an even distribution and an increase in density. These effects can no doubt be explained in part by the fact that as a rule high pressures and high velocities go together as do low pressures and low velocities. But even when every allowance has been made for the effects of pressure it would seem that there still remain further effects which can only be attributed to velocity. For example, it frequently happens that the pressures developed by two batches of cartridges are almost identical, although the velocities of one batch are considerably higher than those of the other. In such cases the patterns given by the cartridges with the lower velocities are almost invariably better than those obtained with the other batch, even when both lots are fired in the same barrel. This might seem conclusive evidence, yet even so I am not at all sure that the high velocity deserves all the blame. For by the use of special powders it is possible to obtain high velocities in conjunction with good patterns, and this would seem to absolve velocity. Such powders are not always suitable for use in 12-bore cartridge-cases shorter than 2¾ inches, but cartridges of this length need heavier guns than can be used with effect and comfort by the average man under modern shooting conditions in Great Britain.

In order to obtain increases in velocity in the ordinary 2½-inch cartridge, heavier powder charges are usually necessary, and although such charges may not seem to increase the pressure unduly, the extra bulk of powder is not completely converted into gas so quickly as the normal charge. This tends to somewhat higher pressures near the muzzle ; and any increase in pressure at this end of the barrel must cause a corresponding increase in muzzle blast, which might easily have a most disturbing effect on the shot charge, and therefore on the pattern.

With ordinary cartridges comparatively slight increases in observed velocity—that is up to 1,100 f.s., or thereabouts—do not in themselves have much effect. But when an observed velocity of about 1,150 f.s. is passed the patterns begin to suffer.

The remedy is the same as that for high pressures, namely plenty of choke. And if good patterns at long ranges are desired when cartridges are being used which develop an observed velocity of 1,150 f.s. and over, a half-choke gun is essential, while a full choke is better still. And even when these heavily choked guns are used the patterns will not be so close as they should be for the borings : that is, a full choke will no longer give a 70 per cent. pattern, nor a half choke one of 60 per cent. In fact 65 and 55 per cent. would probably be as much as could reasonably be expected from the two types of boring respectively. And when the observed velocity is round about 1,200 f.s., even a full choke will seldom give a denser pattern than 55 per cent.

On the whole, I think it is correct to assume that high velocities do tend to scatter the pattern to a certain extent. But I think this tendency is frequently exaggerated and that other causes, such as muzzle blast, enter the arena.

The reason for this detrimental effect on pattern can be attributed almost with certainty to the greater deformation of the pellets which must accompany any increase in velocity. The higher the velocity with which the shot charge travels down the bore the greater must be the effects of abrasion on the pellets ; the deformation caused by the jostling together which the pellets receive, and the sudden check in velocity due to the choke. And in this connection it must be remembered that any increase in observed velocity represents, in round figures, double that amount of increase in muzzle velocity, which means that the acceleration of the shot charge during its journey down the bore must be correspondingly greater.

And this suggested explanation is supported by the fact that the effect of velocity on pattern differs in one important respect from that of pressure in that the pattern never seems to suffer from abnormally low velocities provided the pressures are satisfactory. Such a ballistic combination occurs when light powder charges are used in conjunction with extra heavy charges of large sized shot, and when cartridges are loaded on this principle the patterns are usually very good.

In view of the fact that one of the causes of pellet deformation helped by a high velocity is the sudden check resulting from the choke, it might reasonably be thought that a true cylinder would be less susceptible in the matter of patterns to high velocities than other types of boring. As a matter of fact the reverse is the case, and true cylinders are so unreliable when used with cartridges which develop an appreciably higher velocity than the standard that they can be regarded as almost useless. The explanation probably is that whatever reduction there may be in pellet deformation resulting from the absence of choke is more than counterbalanced by the steadying control which the choke exercises, especially if there is undue muzzle blast.

TURNOVER. In the case of cartridges sealed with over-shot wads and a turnover, the turnover can influence pattern to a tremendous extent, but this influence is indirect rather than direct. I have already dealt at great length with the effects of turnover on both pressure and velocity, and so will not repeat myself here. But in view of the intimate connection between turnover and pressure and velocity, the effect of turnover on pattern is not difficult to understand. In fact so great is this effect that an experienced and skilful loader can, by varying the turnover, load up cartridges to give almost any desired pattern, within reasonable limits, in any particular gun. By making the turnover very heavy he will raise the pressure and get more open patterns in a gun bored with plenty of choke ; a light turnover will reduce the pressure and so help an open shooting gun to give a denser pattern ; and similarly, a light turnover will reduce the tendency of an indifferently bored gun to throw uneven, irregular and patchy patterns.

From this it might be argued that a light turnover is all to the good. But it must be remembered that a light turnover lowers the ballistics, and the velocity is then frequently insufficient to ensure adequate penetration at long, or even moderate, ranges. Further, a light turnover will not stand up to ordinary usage in transit and the shooting field. The shaking which cartridges must inevitably receive when being carried about will, in time, tend to loosen the turnover ; and the lighter the turnover the more rapidly does this loosening set in. And when this occurs the ballistics can be lowered to such an extent that the cartridges give mere " squib " effects and are, of course, quite useless against game.

So it will be seen that too light a turnover is fatal.

But too heavy a turnover is almost as bad owing to its detrimental effect on pattern. For although a close shooting gun can be made, by this means, to give more open patterns, such cannot be relied upon for regularity either in distribution or density.

The ideal turnover is unquestionably one which pulls out at 40 to 45 lb. when tested as described in Volume II.

There is frequently a considerable difference in turnover strength between cartridges loaded at a factory and by a gunmaker. As a general rule, factory loaded cartridges have a tendency to be loaded very tightly with heavy turnovers, while the gunmaker's cartridges are rather "soft" and have light turnovers. The explanation lies in the fact that the turnovers of all factory loaded cartridges are made in machines, while those loaded by the gunmaker are usually turned over by hand; and the machine can naturally bring a higher pressure to bear. It is for this reason that factory loaded cartridges do not usually give such close patterns as those loaded by the gunmaker, and it is also for this reason that I must confess to a personal preference for cartridges loaded by a gunmaker. But they must be well loaded, and some gunmakers are very bad offenders in the matter of too weak a turnover, so this is a point to which particular attention should be paid.

And here I may mention that the fact that a particular gunmaker's name is printed on the case, and even on the over-shot wad, is no proof that he loaded the cartridges on his own premises, although he may have done so. Cartridges are commonly loaded in the factory for individual firms of gunmakers in all parts of the world, and cartridges which bear the printed legend, both on case and wad, of a gunmaker's or cartridge-dealer's name and address are just as likely to have been loaded at Birmingham as at Dusteypur or Greenhornfontein.

I would like to make it quite clear that I am casting no aspersion on factory loaded cartridges. They are excellent; and I would always prefer to use them to those which had been loaded by some gunmaker whose work in this respect was an unknown quantity. My preference for cartridges loaded by gunmakers is rigidly confined to those loaded by certain firms who have made a special study of this work.

One point, however, is of paramount importance and needs special emphasis.

When any gunmaker, or shooter, is testing a gun for pattern it is absolutely essential that the tests are made with similarly loaded cartridges to those which will be used in the actual shooting field.

For a gun may give quite respectable patterns with the possibly weak cartridges used by the barrel regulator, which he has probably loaded up himself; but this same gun may give very different and altogether inferior patterns with the more lively cartridges which the shooter uses in the field.

And in this connection gunmakers should be very careful in the selection of the cartridges used by the barrel regulators when finishing off the barrels and testing them for pattern. If the barrel regulator loads these up himself it is more than probable that they will be on the soft side. After all, the regulator wants to get the best possible pattern, and it is only human nature to help this end by loading.

So the gunmaker should be sure that all his guns are regulated with exactly the same cartridges as those which he sells to his customers for use against game.

The importance of this point is undoubtedly realised by many gunmakers, but it certainly is not by all.

This applies especially to guns in which crimped cartridges will mostly be used.

WADDING. I am inclined to think that after pressure the wadding is the most important of all the factors which affect pattern.

And the most important part of the wadding is the felt wad; and in the term "felt" I include any substitutes for felt which may be used.

The object of the felt wad is to seal the bore completely behind the shot charge and so ensure (1) that the full force of the expanding powder gases is utilised to the maximum advantage; and (2) that no gas can escape past the felt wad itself and so disturb the shot charge in the bore.

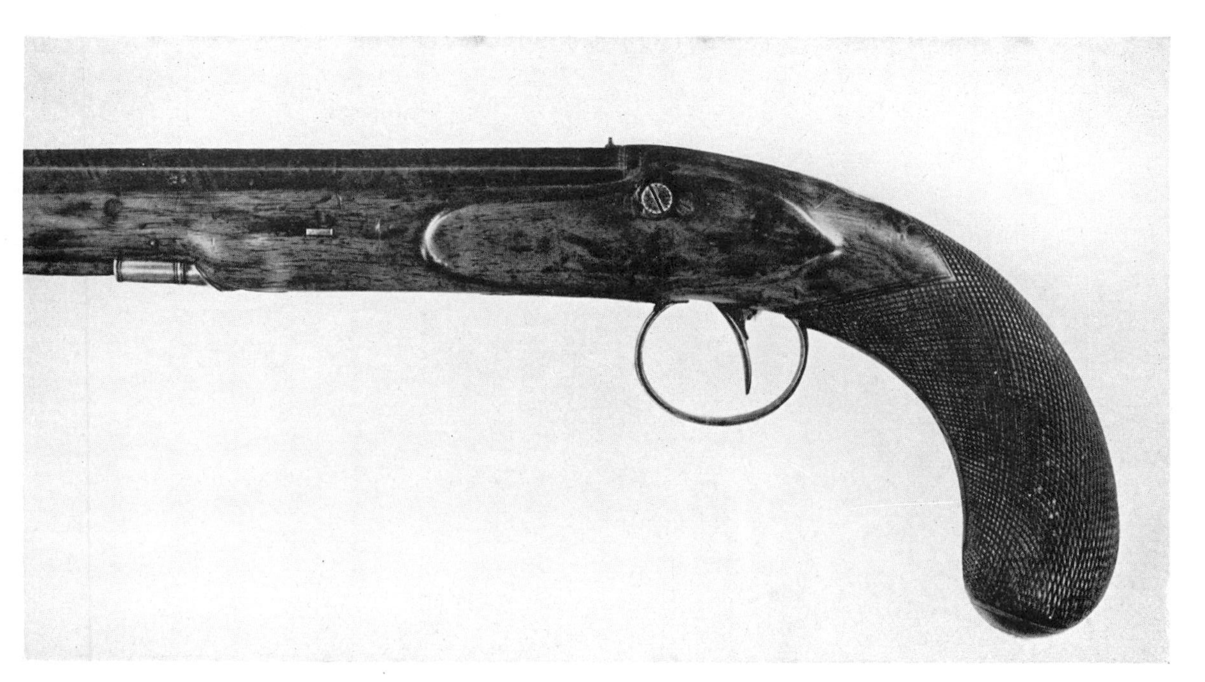

THE BUTT OF AN OLD FLINT LOCK HOLSTER PISTOL BY JOE MANTON
This is an ideal shape for the butt of a shot pistol

These two purposes are only achieved when the felt is both firm and elastic, a combination which is possessed by the very best quality felt but which becomes more and more lacking as the quality of the felt deteriorates.

If the felt is too hard, too soft, or not sufficiently "springy" or elastic, the objects of the wad are not completely fulfilled and the pattern suffers in consequence. And this in spite of the fact that both the pressure and velocity developed are satisfactory.

I have been aware of the influence of the quality of the felt wad on pattern for many years, but it was brought home to me so forcibly in 1926 that I have paid more attention to this point ever since than almost to any other in connection with cartridge loading.

I was asked out to what I knew would be a fairly heavy day's rabbit shooting, and thought I would economise by using cheap cartridges. Accordingly I bought 200 specially for the occasion. As a matter of interest I shot a few for ballistics before the day and found that the pressures and velocities were both normal, although I did notice that the felt wadding looked pretty horrid. However, I consoled myself that it was only for rabbits and hoped for the best.

In some ways that day was a tragedy. I killed rabbits all right at near distances, that is under about 20 yards; but I do not believe I killed a single rabbit clean at anything approaching long, or even medium, range. It was not that I was shooting particularly badly: I would roll a rabbit over, but it would get up and go on again and need a second barrel. And even then it would seldom be killed. This happened so continuously that I gave up anything but close shots, when I killed fairly well.

Two days later I tested some of the cartridges which I had left over for pattern in my gun. The patterns were so patchy and irregular as to be quite useless, and everything was explained. The cause of the bad patterns was proved beyond doubt to be the felt wadding, as I reloaded some of the powder with good felt wads and got excellent patterns, while cartridges loaded with some of the felt wads extracted gave bad patterns irrespective of any powder tried.

I have never forgotten that lesson: yet it is sad to think that any attempt of mine to economise in such matters seems to be doomed to inevitable failure.

And, by the way, why is it that most shooters regard any inferior brand of cartridges as "being good enough for rabbits"? I admit that I am inclined to sin in this manner myself; but it does seem rather bad luck on the rabbits.

Some years ago I found myself next to a very good shot at a covert shoot. During the first drive we were both flanking a big covert, he walking about 50 yards ahead of the beaters while I kept just in rear of their line. Several birds broke out over him and he hit them all, but did not kill one, every bird either carrying on or being a runner. The wind happened to be blowing from him to me and I caught the unmistakable smell of a particular continental powder. The smell was so pronounced that I guessed that the combustion was not satisfactory, but naturally kept silent.

Later on in the day my neighbour complained of the lack of killing power displayed by his cartridges and so I asked him whether he would mind letting me have a few to test. He kindly consented, and subsequently I found that the pressures and velocities were both very feeble owing to the incomplete combustion of the powder due to the use of an unsuitable cap. In reply to my letter telling him of the result this sportsman stated that he had a number of these cartridges left, but that he would "keep these for rabbits."

Now this is an entirely typical attitude. The great majority of shooters seem to think that anything is good enough for rabbits. But is this fair on the rabbits? After all, common though they be, they are most sporting little beasts and very tenacious of life. They do an immense amount of damage and must be killed. But I think that they deserve that every reasonable effort should be made to ensure that death is swift. Indifferent cartridges may easily mean a large proportion of wounded rabbits which die later in their holes.

But I seem to have left the subject of wadding.

There are many grades of felt used for wadding, but of actual felt the white is by far the best, although even this varies in quality. The cheaper felts are brown, and the very cheapest can be pulled apart easily with the fingers. Wads made of this last grade of felt are almost useless if any sort of quality of pattern is desired.

Sometimes the felt wad and the over-felt card wad are combined in one, the card wad being replaced by a disc of thick paper which is glued to the felt. This type of wad is widely used in America, one theory in its favour being that as the ordinary card wad does not expand effectively during the passage of the charge up the bore it is advantageous to replace it by felt, retaining only a piece of stout paper to separate the shot pellets from the felt.

But there is also the theory that a more effective sealing of the bore is obtained by compressing the felt wad between two flat card wads than between one such wad and the shot charge.

I fancy that the truth is that the nature of the felt is of far more importance than the exact thickness of the wad, and that when the same quality of felt is used there is little to choose between the results obtained by either method. Further, that the combination of the over-felt card and the felt wad in one simplifies the work of the loader or the loading machine, and that this last is the controlling factor in the determination of the single-wad system.

Until 1937 the only serious substitute for actual felt which had any success was cork, and cork wads have been dealt with so fully in Volume II that their further consideration is unnecessary. But in 1937 Imperial Chemical Industries, Ltd., brought out their new air-cushion wad, which has also been dealt with at length in the Second Edition of Volume II. These wads tend to reduce irregularity to a minimum, for the real elastic substance in them is ordinary air than which nothing can be more consistent in behaviour and density, and I am inclined to believe that they can take their place alongside high grade felt as a first class type of wad.

Brown felt was also improved greatly in quality at about the same time and at present I doubt whether there is much to choose between the very best grades of either white or brown felt and air-cushion wads.

The wads should all be inserted absolutely squarely into the case when loading, as slanting wads tend to throw the pattern to one side and scatter it.

I do not think that the thickness of the over-shot card wad has any noticeable effect on pattern, but have always expressed a possibly unreasonable preference for as thin a card wad as possible.

The felt wad is believed by some to be forced at times into the middle of the shot charge when the latter is just clear of the muzzle. This would naturally ruin the pattern, and to overcome this risk some loaders use two thinner felt wads instead of one thicker one with a very thin card wad in between them so as to prevent any risk of their sticking together. This idea is by no means new, and is also adopted by various American loaders with the exception that they use felt wads with stout paper discs stuck on the ends and leave out the thin card wad.

This principle cannot possibly have any ill effect, and it seems probable that it is an improvement in that it reduces the risk of a single heavy wad being forced into the shot charge and so increases the chances of regularity in pattern. The only disadvantage about it is that it increases the work of loading, and so adds slightly to the cost of the cartridges.

Anything in the nature of loose wadding is fatal to the pattern, as the powder gases force their way past the wads and scatter the shot charge. Loose wadding is probably one of the most fruitful causes of "balling," a phenomenon which will be considered in the next chapter.

The actual effects of good and bad wadding are shown in the diagrams in Fig. 3.

POWDER. Many gunmakers and many writers on shooting matters have declared that the kind of powder used has a great influence on pattern, some powders producing much better patterns than others. I am, however, very doubtful as to the truth of this common belief. I have, for example, been told by one gunmaker that a particular powder never gave bad patterns

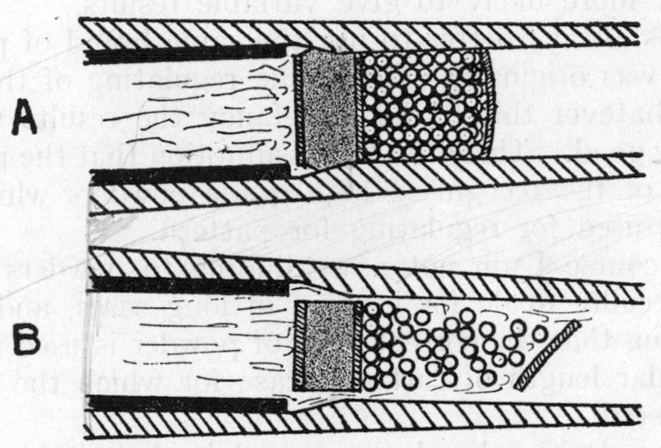

FIG. 3.—How wadding affects the pattern.

A—Good-quality felt wadding. The felt wad has expanded and sealed the entrance to the bore, thus preventing any escape of gas.

B—Loose wadding. The diameter of the felt wad is too small to permit effective expansion, and the gases force their way round it and break up the shot charge.

If the felt wad is too hard the effect is similar.

N.B.—For purposes of clarity the pitch of the chamber cone has purposely been greatly exaggerated. A section of the breech end of the bore drawn to scale is shown in Fig. 4.

and have been told just the opposite by another gunmaker of equal reputation, experience and standing. I fancy that the truth is that there is little to choose between any of the various kinds of really high grade powders, and that all are, on the average, equally good.

It frequently happens that batches of the same powder vary in violence, and if one gunmaker wants to try a change of powder and happens to get hold of rather a violent batch he will probably get less regular patterns than usual. Quite naturally he will blame the powder and never use it again if he can avoid doing so, when all that really happened was that he was unfortunate in the particular batch he tried.

No matter how careful the powder maker is, certain degrees of variation in combustion are almost inevitable between different batches. But the better the grade of powder the greater the degree of control which can be exercised in manufacture, and the less the difference between batches. For this reason very cheap powders are far more likely to give variable results.

It is always better to use the same brand of powder which was originally used in the regulating of the gun, and whatever this brand is I fancy the results will be equally good. This is on the assumption that the powder is one of the recognised high grade powders which are always used for regulating for pattern.

Of course I am not now alluding to powders which are specially made for loading in long cases, and I am assuming that the correct type of powder is used for the particular length of cartridge-case for which the gun is chambered.

CAP. It has already been explained that the proper matching of the cap to the powder can have the greatest influence on the resulting ballistics. Pattern must be included in these. But the effects of the cap are indirect as they are caused by the resulting variation in pressure and velocity.

So any sportsman whose guns give good patterns will be ill-advised to use cartridges fitted with caps of a different nature or type from those which he has used previously without first testing his guns most carefully for pattern.

WEATHER AND TEMPERATURE. The weather and temperature can together constitute a most powerful factor in connection with pattern, but here again their effect is indirect, the actual cause of the variations produced being high pressure.

As I have already explained, shotgun powders contain a certain percentage of moisture, and this percentage is reduced by spells of hot, dry weather. The result is that the combustion of the powder becomes more violent; the pressures rise; and the patterns suffer.

It frequently happens that sportsmen complain of an excessive percentage of wounded birds during the opening of the grouse and partridge seasons, and such complaints always coincide with hot weather. Quite naturally the sportsmen think that their cartridges are weak; and they write indignant letters to their gunmakers.

But the exact opposite is the truth. The hot weather has lowered the moisture contents of the powder, which has become more violent, and the resulting high pressures have produced blown and scattered patterns, especially in guns which are not bored with an appreciable degree of choke. The result is that even a bird which is well centred in the pattern may receive but a single pellet instead of three, four, or even more; and unless that pellet strikes some particularly vital spot, such as the brain, the bird is wounded instead of being killed outright.

I have investigated very many such complaints and the results have always been the same—high pressures. But there are few things I know more difficult than to convince a shooter who is wounding birds that his cartridges are not too weak but too strong. Yet cartridges must be *very* weak indeed before they fail to kill at ordinary sporting ranges, say under 35 yards. And cartridges on the "soft" side will, as a rule, kill better at such distances than those which develop full pressures and velocities, because the reduced ballistics help to increase the density of the pattern and so a bird is hit by a greater number of pellets.

Nevertheless I know that sportsmen will continue to complain about their cartridges being "weak" in hot weather until the end of time.

There are two remedial measures: the use of guns which are, at the very least, quarter choked; and of a powder which is not so sensitive to variations in temperature.

Size of Shot. There is a very general belief that guns will give better patterns with some sizes of shot than others, owing to the fact that layers of certain sizes fit better into the case or bore ; but I am inclined to doubt whether this variation is anything like so great as is frequently imagined. No. 5 shot, for example, has often been given a bad name, but I have tried several well-bored guns for pattern with this size and the results have been just as good as could be expected. There are fewer pellets of No. 5 in a charge than of No. 6, and so the pattern with the larger size cannot be so dense as when the smaller is used. Many men, when they are assessing patterns, seem to be influenced unconsciously by the obvious reduction in density and then declare that that particular gun will not shoot with No. 5. The truth is that while it may have been giving an approximate 50 per cent. pattern of, say, 142 with No. 6, it will only give a pattern of 114, or 49 per cent., with No. 5. The difference in the looks of patterns of 142 and 114 is certainly great, and the larger size is condemned in spite of the fact that the percentage of pellets in the 30-inch circle was practically the same as before.

As I explained in the last chapter, one cannot expect to obtain the exact theoretical percentage of density every time, and patterns must always be assessed with an open mind.

Even distribution is of first importance, and if a gun gives evenly distributed patterns with any particular size of shot, the fact that the density may be even 5 per cent. below the theoretical standard can be disregarded ; especially if the correct density is attained with another size of shot.

But if the distribution of the pattern is patchy and uneven it should be condemned at once. For a patchy and uneven pattern of 140 is not so useful as a perfectly distributed pattern of 120.

I am, of course, writing of the means of series of shots : the result of a single round should never be relied upon.

As a rule very large shot, such as BB, seems to give better and comparatively denser patterns than the ordinary sizes. This is probably because the large pellets suffer less from distortion. Very small shot, on the other hand, gives irregular results because the pellets are naturally more affected by deformation.

But with normal shot sizes I am inclined to the view that there is little practical difference in the patterns given by a well-bored gun with different sizes of shot beyond the natural reduction in density.

HARDNESS OF SHOT. Very soft shot is more liable to deformation than hard shot, and on this account soft shot does not give such regular patterns as hard.

In actual practice, however, at the present time almost all makes of shot, both British and foreign, are of such a similar degree of hardness that the variations in patterns due to this cause can be regarded as non-existent.

SHAPE OF SHOT. A certain amount of deformation in a proportion of the pellets in every shot charge is inevitable, but this is no reason why the most careful precautions should not be adopted in manufacture to ensure that the pellets are perfectly spherical. If the pellets are badly shaped in the first place, there is not the same chance of getting a good pattern. So the makers of shot should pay special attention to this point.

It is equally important that the pellets should be graded accurately for size; that is the weights and diameters of the pellets of any single size should be as nearly as possible constant.

I am inclined to think that in both these respects American shot is sometimes superior to British.

LENGTH OF SHOT COLUMN. By this is meant the length of the shot charge when in the bore of the gun. In a 12-bore gun a shot charge of $1\frac{1}{8}$ must obviously make a longer column than one of but an ounce. In this case the difference is so slight as to be negligible; but when we come to "magnum" sizes—that is guns bored to take extra long cases containing charges approximately the same as those normally used in a gun at least a size larger—the difference is pronounced. A

3-inch 12-bore, for example, can fire the 10-bore charge of $1\frac{1}{2}$ ounces of shot; and a 3-inch 20-bore takes an ounce, a charge which is usually associated in British guns with a 12-bore.

It has been explained in Volume II that a long shot column tends to raise pressure, a shot charge of one ounce always giving a considerably higher pressure in a 20-bore than in a 12.

This increase in pressure must, and does, tend to scatter the pattern. But in actual practice this effect is not so serious in these magnum guns as it might be, because such guns are almost always very fully choked since they are usually intended for long-range work. So the net result probably is that the patterns from these guns are perfectly satisfactory up to a point, but they are not always quite so dense as they should be according to the theoretical capabilities of the boring.

Size of Bore. The reader will very likely wonder whether the percentages of pellets of the whole shot charge found in the 30-inch circle are really constant for all sizes of bore. It certainly does seem curious that a half choke 20-bore, for example, should only give the same percentage density of pattern as a half choke 10-bore. But the reason lies partly in the fact that if a customer orders a half choke gun the gunmaker regards this to mean that a 60 per cent. pattern is desired, and he regulates the gun accordingly. It will not always follow that 20 " points " of choke (which is a half choke) will result in a 60 per cent. pattern in any size of gun, although this relation is sufficiently true for all practical purposes. One might think that a 20-bore would show less total spread than a 12-bore, and it often does: but the difference is so slight as to be negligible. It can best be appreciated by the fact that I was once informed by a very skilful barrel-regulator that he usually found it easier to get a 70 per cent. pattern out of a full choke 20-bore than out of a full choke 12.

I have sometimes heard of a small-bore gun which could place the entire shot charge within some amazingly small circle at 40 yards. But I have never been able to get hold of such a gun. I have tested an absolutely full choked ·410, but the pattern was less than 70 per cent.

So I think we can take the percentage basis for the classification of choke as being sufficiently correct for all sizes of bores, at any rate for purposes of practical sport.

The fact that small bores seem to give a slightly greater relative spread of the shot charge in comparison to the diameter of the bore than do 12-bores is probably explained by the higher pressures which are prevalent in the smaller bores. This is also the probable explanation for the further fact that the small bores seem less sensitive in their patterns to the effects of turnover and wadding. The pressure being normally on the high side a certain amount of choke is always necessary to regularity of pattern, and this choke helps to nullify the results of vagaries in pressure and gas blast.

LENGTH OF BARREL. The movement in favour of shorter barrels which became pronounced between the years 1925 to 1935, although in reality it was but a recurrence of old ideas, may have made many shooters wonder whether the reduction in barrel length has any effect on pattern.

The shorter the barrel the nearer the muzzle is brought to zone of higher pressure in the bore, and so the greater the risk of muzzle blast. But this risk is not noticeable for barrels as short as 27 inches, at any rate, and even a little more might be taken off with impunity.

At 25 inches, however, the muzzle blast seems to make itself felt and improved cylinder guns with this length of barrel are frequently more difficult to regulate for pattern in consequence. But the adoption of a slight choke helps matters considerably.

Any reduction in length below 25 inches would increase the muzzle blast still more, and the gun would be correspondingly difficult to regulate.

If any shooter orders a gun with short barrels and is

exercised in his mind about the pattern, all that he need do is to see the gun tested. If the patterns are even and regular he need not worry further. But he should make a point of seeing such a test carried out, as very short barrelled guns undoubtedly are more prone to the effects of muzzle blast than those with longer barrels.

WEIGHT OF BARRELS. Guns fitted with very light barrels do not, as a rule, give such regular patterns as those with heavier barrels. The late Mr. R. W. S. Griffith explained this by the suggestion that heavier barrels have a larger amount of metal left at the actual muzzle which, by its resistance to expansion, acts something after the nature of a choke.

This is a point which should be remembered at the present time when gunmakers seem to be vieing with each other in the building of feather-weight 12-bores. A barrel in which the walls near the muzzle are very thin and light may be perfectly safe and may help to concentrate the total weight of the gun between the hands; but it is not so likely to give regular patterns as a somewhat thicker and heavier barrel.

STATE OF BARREL. By this I am alluding to the condition of the inside of the bore. The better this condition is, the more regular will be the patterns. Pitting, however, tends to irregular patterns as the pits in the surface of the bore may provide little channels by which the powder gases can escape past the wads.

Dents and bulges have a similar effect, and should consequently be seen to as soon after detection as possible.

Then there is the question of oil in a barrel. Should this be wiped out before the gun is used or not?

Now a shotgun barrel is designed and regulated to give regular patterns under conditions in which it will be actually used, and these conditions entail a certain amount of fouling in the barrel. An oily barrel sets up a different type of conditions from those imposed by a dry and slightly fouled barrel, and consequently the pattern from an oily barrel is not likely to be typical of those obtained when the barrel is fouled by firing.

For this reason it is always advisable to fire a round through a clean barrel before beginning any test for pattern, and it is as well to remove as much oil as possible from the bore before starting off on a day's shooting.

LENGTH OF CARTRIDGE-CASE. The cartridge-case should be of just the right length to fit the chamber. That is when the turnover is opened out the end of the case should approximately coincide with the beginning of the chamber cone. The felt wad will then enter and seal the bore (provided the chamber cone is not too long) without giving the powder gases any chance of rushing past it.

But if the cartridge-case is too short for the chamber

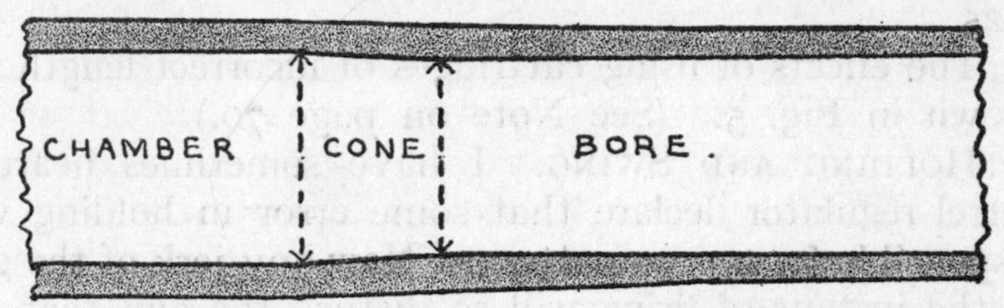

FIG. 4.—Section to scale of the breech end of a 12-bore barrel, showing the pitch of the cone.

or if the chamber cone is too long, the powder gases may be able to escape past the felt wad before the latter has entered the bore because the diameter of the felt wad is less than that of the chamber or the rear end of the chamber cone.

And when gas escapes past the wadding there is always a pronounced tendency to irregular patterns.

The Americans favour a long column of felt wadding, and this is undoubtedly a very sound view point when guns are used which are bored with long chambers, long chamber cones, or both. For the longer the column of felt wadding the less the chance of the powder gases escaping past it in a gun with a long chamber cone, or when cartridges are used which are rather short for the chamber.

But if the chamber cones are not too long and the cartridges fit the chambers, an exceptional length of felt wadding becomes unnecessary.

If cartridges are used which are too long for the chambers the pressures generated will be excessive and will cause irregular patterns irrespective of the risk of straining, or even smashing, the gun. And cartridge-cases which are even slightly too long for the chamber can tend to uneven patterns and "balling" (which will be considered in the next chapter), even though the pressures may not be unduly high.

For these reasons it is always important to use the proper length of case for any particular gun, the proper length being always stamped with the Proof Marks on the flats of the barrels in all British guns since 1925.

The effects of using cartridges of incorrect length are shown in Fig. 5. (See Note on page 70.)

HOLDING AND SWING. I have sometimes heard a barrel regulator declare that some error in holding was responsible for a poor pattern. Now any jerk of the gun at the instant of firing will so disturb the aim that the direction of the trajectory of the shot charge is changed, and this will result in the pattern being placed at one side or other of the plate. When this occurs the densest part of the pattern may actually have passed to one side of the plate, and so the count of pellets in any 30-inch circle which could be drawn would obviously be smaller than the normal.

But this is a very different thing from a change in the nature of the pattern; and I cannot believe that any error in holding can be the direct cause of a patchy pattern. I have never been able to produce an intentional bad pattern with certainty; nor have I seen anyone else able to do so. I do not know how widely this idea is held; but I think it to be without any foundation of truth.

Very similar is the common belief amongst shooters that the "swing" one gives to a gun affects the pattern, imparting a similar effect on the shot to that possessed by a jet of water coming out of a hose.

This theory is quite erroneous. When water comes out of a hose, or when a string of shots is fired from a machine gun, the water and bullets continue to leave the nozzle of the hose and the muzzle of the gun while that nozzle and muzzle are constantly changing the direction in which they are pointing. Consequently the

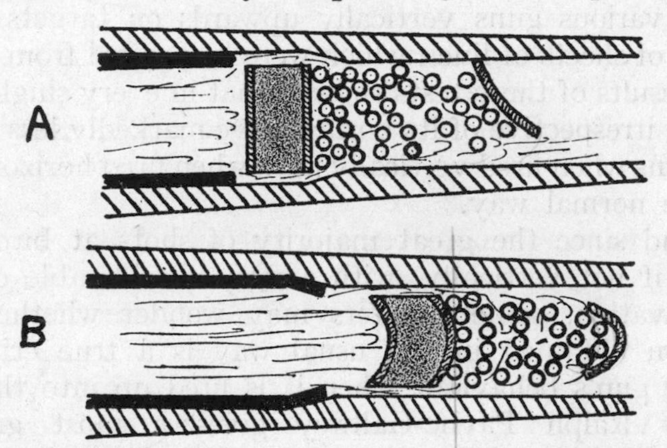

FIG. 5.—How the length of the cartridge-case affects the pattern.

A—Cartridge-case too short. The wadding is not long enough to reach the entrance to the bore before the gas escapes past it.

B—Cartridge-case too long. The wadding is squeezed over and gas escapes past it before the felt wad can effect a proper fit in the bore.

N.B.—The pitch of the chamber cone has been purposely exaggerated, as was explained in the note to Fig. 3, as have the lengths of the cartridge-cases.

water and bullets are distributed over a wider area than would be the case were the hose or machine gun stationary.

But in a shotgun the column of shot is only about one inch long when it leaves the muzzle, and the average velocity of exit is about 1,300 f.s. So the time which elapses between the departures of the head and tail of the shot column from the muzzle is appreciably less than one ten-thousandth part of a second, the average time being between 0·00006 and 0·00007 of a second.

In this small period of time the barrels of the gun would not have changed their direction to any appreciable degree, no matter how vigorously the shooter made his swing, and consequently the "water from a hose" effect could not possibly be produced.

So it can be assumed with confidence that neither swing nor any error in holding can have any effect on the regularity or density of the pattern.

Direction of Aim. In his *High Pheasants in Theory and Practice* the late Sir Ralph Payne-Gallwey describes how he carried out a number of tests for pattern made by firing various guns vertically upwards on targets composed of sheets of linen which were suspended from kites. The results of these tests showed that in every single case a gun, irrespective of its boring, gave markedly less dense patterns when fired vertically than when fired horizontally in the normal way.

And since the great majority of shots at birds are fired, if not vertically, with a very considerable degree of elevation, some shooters may wonder whether the pattern obtained in the usual way is a true criterion of the gun's behaviour when it is fired up into the air.

Sir Ralph Payne-Gallwey gives a most graphic account of the difficulties with which he had to contend during the course of these experiments: the wind carried targets away; they swung about in the air, and suffered all kinds of adventures. And I have always been lost in admiration at the author's ingenuity and pertinacity. But I have also thought that the possible sources of error resulting from this method of suspending a target in mid-air were so numerous and so potent that it was impossible to accept the results without verification.

It seemed that a simpler and far more definite test could be made by utilising one of the 120-foot towers which have been erected at various shooting schools in order to enable clay targets to be thrown high above the shooter's head, and so represent overhead pheasants.

Messrs. Holland and Holland very kindly placed their tower at my disposal, and I had a wooden frame made just over 6 feet square and with "legs" on one side. These legs were bolted as near as possible to the top of a 120-foot tower and the frame was thus held in a horizontal position nearly 40 yards above the ground at the foot of the tower. The frame was so made that it could be opened and closed so as to take sheets of stout paper, each 6 feet square, and the operation of inserting or changing a sheet of paper could be carried out quickly and with ease.

I thus obtained an excellent and rigid "vertical" target.

In order to make the comparison between the vertical and horizontal patterns absolutely exact, the distance was measured by a cord from this "vertical" target to the muzzle of my gun when it was at my shoulder and pointing at the target. This distance was rather less than 40 yards, being actually 100 feet. So for purposes of comparison a series of shots were fired for pattern in the ordinary way with exactly this distance of 100 feet separating the pattern plate from the gun muzzle.

In this way the difficulties which beset Sir Ralph Payne-Gallwey were overcome, and with them the resulting possible errors.

I anticipated experiencing some difficulty in centering my pattern on the "vertical" target, but to my surprise found it no more difficult to do so than on the ordinary plate. I may say that the pattern showed up very distinctly when viewed from underneath, the holes in the thick paper being very clear when seen against the sky.

It was thus possible to fire a series of vertical patterns very quickly, the paper being changed after every shot by an assistant who came down to the next lower stage of the tower while I fired.

When the series was completed the targets were spread out in turn on a table where they could be examined at leisure and the circle drawn round the densest area.

The result of this test with three different guns was that there was no practical difference whatever between the mean densities of the vertical and horizontal patterns, while the vertical patterns were equally even and regular. So I think that it is but reasonable to attribute Sir Ralph Payne-Gallwey's results to some extraneous circumstances, and to assume that the direction of aim makes no practical difference in pattern.

NOTE. The American standardisation of the 2¾-inch 12-bore cartridge-case with a crimp turnover for all shot charges of 1¼ ounces and less raises the question of the effect on patterns when 2¾-inch cartridge-cases are fired in guns with 2 9/16-inch chambers. Owing to its very nature the crimp turnover needs a longer case than the ordinary turnover and over-shot card wad; and in practice a 2¾-inch paper-tubed case with a crimp turnover gives a finished cartridge which is no longer than that given by a 2 9/16-inch case with an ordinary turnover and over-shot wad.

Early in 1939 I fired sixty consecutive patterns with crimp turnover cartridges loaded with 1 1/16 ounce of shot in 2 9/16-inch cases from a quarter choke barrel which normally gives a regular pattern of about 160, or 55 per cent. The mean result was 172, or 60 per cent.

Two months later I repeated the experiment with crimp turnover cartridges loaded as before but with 2¾-inch cases, using the same barrel for the first fifty consecutive patterns and then a full choke barrel for a further twenty-five. The pressures and velocities developed by these two different lots of cartridges were, for all practical purposes, identical. The average pattern from the quarter choke barrel was 139, or almost 50 per cent., and from the full choke 209, or 73 per cent. Every one of these 155 patterns was evenly spread and there was no sign of cartwheel.

Although it would be unwise to regard these tests as final, especially in view of the variations which can occur (see pages 144 and 145), they do suggest that the crimp turnover seems to counteract the drawbacks of a paper case slightly too long for the chamber, particularly if there is ample choke. Even with the quarter choke there was not a single bad pattern, although the 2¾-inch case resulted in a reduction in density of 5 per cent. on the normal instead of an increase of 5 per cent.

CHAPTER III

SOME MORE PROBLEMS OF PATTERN

IN the last chapter I have tried to deal with the principal factors which affect pattern, but the reader should realise that the subject is almost inexhaustible and a lifetime would be far too short for a complete investigation of the subject by any individual. On April 26th, 1897, the late Mr. R. W. S. Griffith, who was then Superintendent of the Schultze Gunpowder Company's Factory, delivered a lecture on Shotgun Patterns at the Royal United Service Institution. And in the course of his opening remarks, when he was explaining the complexity of the subject, he said:

"If anyone is ambitious of carrying out a complete series of tests for patterns I would suggest the following as a fairly complete scheme for the purpose.

"Let him try guns of five calibres, of three different weights, with three lengths of barrel, and two kinds of cone with three methods of boring; and let him use three kinds of cartridge-case, with three strengths of cap, loading with, say, six kinds of powder, with three charges, and powders to show four different qualities as to strength and rate of combustion. The wadding to be of eight different kinds between powder and shot, and of three kinds over shot; the shot to be of three kinds, and of five different sizes, adapted to lie in the case or not. Let the turnover be of four kinds and shoot the whole at six different ranges.

"To take a single shot under each of these complications will involve a series of more than three thousand million rounds; and as at least six shots are required for a test, let us say in round numbers eighteen thousand millions."

This is by no means an over-estimate of the case and so both sportsmen and gunmakers should try to remember that if any individual results are obtained which may at first appear to contradict the general principles I have suggested, they should proceed with caution before concluding that these are wrong. For it may well happen that one, or more, additional complications may be in existence all unexpected, and that it is these extraneous circumstances which have really brought about the contradictory result.

So far I have only dealt with what may be regarded as normal types of pattern, both good and bad. But there are two phenomena which are well known in connection with patterns, but which are quite different from anything that has yet been considered. These phenomena are Cartwheel Patterns and Balling.

CARTWHEEL PATTERNS

It sometimes happens that the total spread of the shot charge is double the normal, and when this occurs there is no definite centre to the pattern, and the pellets seem to become distributed around the circumference of an imaginary wheel. Hence the name "Cartwheel."

Since the pellets in such a pattern are distributed over at least four times the normal area it is obvious that the density of the pattern must be reduced greatly. The reduction is in fact so pronounced that any bird could fly through the very centre of the pattern without receiving a single pellet.

Such patterns are consequently useless except through a lucky fluke in which the bird happens to be struck by the outside pellets of a badly placed shot which would have missed altogether had the spread been normal. But such flukes cannot be regarded as a merit, and the cartwheel pattern is nothing but a serious disadvantage.

The correct explanation for the cause of a cartwheel pattern was for very many years a matter of conjecture, but the generally accepted theory was that there were two factors which were, in all probability, the most important of the root causes of true cartwheel or badly scattered patterns. These were the inefficiency of the wadding between the powder and the shot ; and a wad being caught up by the shot charge immediately after

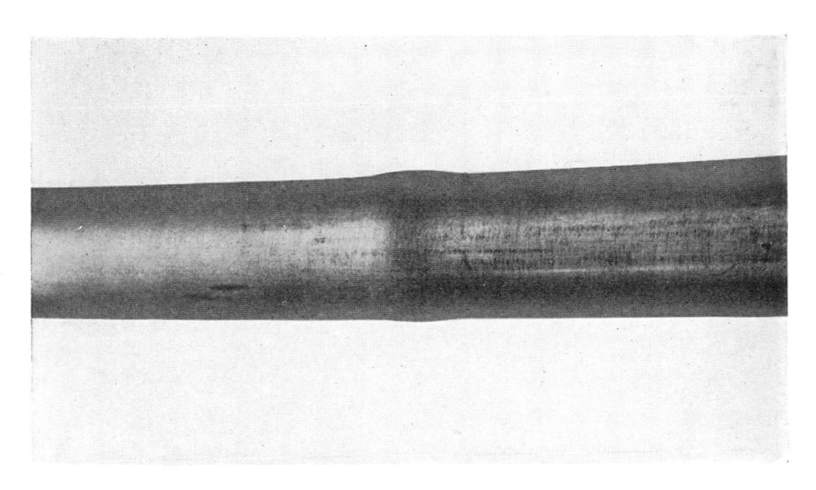

(A) A "RING BULGE" IN A SINGLE BARREL CAUSED BY AN OBSTRUCTION IN THE BORE

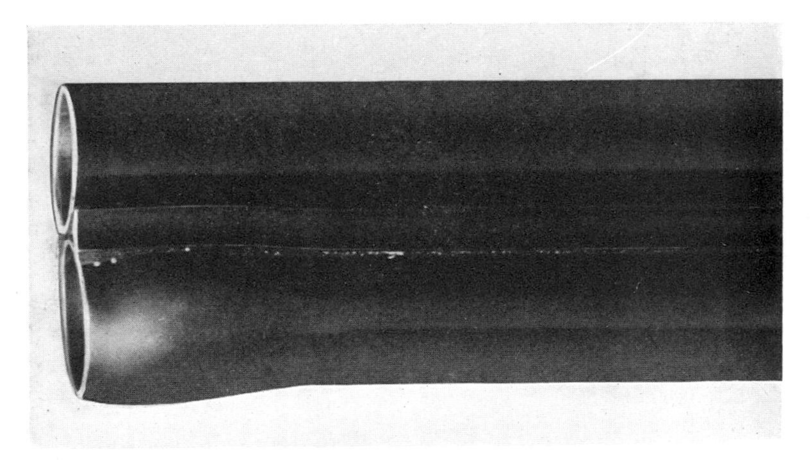

(B) A "RING BULGE" NEAR THE MUZZLE OF A GUN CAUSED BY SOME MUD STICKING IN THE BORE

It should be noticed how the rib is bent at the site of the bulge

the exit from the muzzle and so breaking up the normal cohesion of the pellets.

If the wadding between powder and shot fails at any instant to seal the bore effectively against leakage of the powder gases during the passage of the shot charge from the cartridge-case to the muzzle of the gun, the pattern will be "blown." A long column of wadding is probably a help, as the more wadding there is the less the effect of any irregularity in elasticity of one part of the wadding, and this was probably the basic cause for the long column of wadding which is such a feature in many American cartridges. But if perfect elasticity can be assured—and the best types of modern wadding are very good in this respect—the long column of wadding would seem to be unnecessary. But there is not the slightest doubt that good wadding is essential, as I have already emphasised on many occasions.

But the over-shot card wad still remained, and although cartwheel and scattered patterns were reduced to almost negligible quantities by the combination of good felt wadding and heavy chokes, which certainly helped the cohesion of the shot charge, these uncertain patterns were still an ever-present possibility.

The years 1935 to 1939 saw the gradual development of the crimped turnover and the consequent elimination of the over-shot wad and at the same time the elimination of the cartwheel pattern. Previous experience had sounded the warning against jumping to conclusions too hastily, but the development of spark photographs brought a new aid to investigation.

The over-shot wad sometimes tends to tilt in the barrel during its passage up the bore, and immediately the shot charge leaves the muzzle its lightness causes it to lose speed more quickly than the shot itself. Usually it falls away, but if it is badly tilted it is caught up by a few pellets when the others drive round it. The shot charge is thus thrown out of its proper cohesion and a "cartwheel," "scattered" or "blown" pattern is the result.

This is no longer theory for a wonderful series of American spark photographs have shown every phase of the over-shot wad and the shot charge during their initial flight from the muzzle of the gun.

Incidentally this discovery would also seem to explain why the heavier the choke the less the risk of scattered patterns. For in the case of a true cylinder gun there would be no corrective to a tilted over-shot wad, but on encountering the cone of a choke a slight tilt would tend to be corrected since the choke imposed a check on the wad and the shot charge behind it. The heavier the choke the more pronounced the check and consequently the more pronounced the correction to any tilt in the wad.

The discovery of the *effect* of the crimp turnover—crimp turnovers have, of course, been known for very many years and have been used for sealing blank rifle and revolver cartridges almost since the earliest days of the solid-drawn brass case—is of supreme importance to all who are interested in shotguns. I do not think that it is too optimistic to declare that the combination of first-class modern wadding and the crimp turnover will be found to have ended the menace of the cartwheel pattern.

BALLING

It sometimes happens that a certain number of pellets in a shot charge become jammed together in little clusters which make big splashes on the pattern plate. This phenomenon is known as Balling.

As a general rule these clusters consist of anything from two to six pellets, but they are occasionally bigger. The worst example I have ever seen was a splash on the plate nearly the size of a halfpenny in which the marks of eight pellets could be distinctly seen, while there may have been more.

Balling is a very serious fault, as when it occurs there are usually several clusters in almost every pattern. The results are that the even spread of the pattern must suffer through the concentration of so many pellets in groups; that there is a risk of mangled game, should a bird happen to be struck by one of these shot clusters; and that there is danger to beaters, spectators, passers-by and other guns owing to the increased range which these clusters must have as well as on account of the uncertain direction of their flight.

There are two principal causes of Balling: first, the *welding* together of shot pellets; and secondly, the *fusion* of the shot itself.

Welding is caused by the violent impact of the shot pellets together which is produced by a high pressure, while the softer the shot the greater the liability to welding.

The fusion of pellets is the result of the hot powder gases escaping past the wads and getting in amongst the pellets of the shot charge.

A badly designed square-cut chamber cone can increase the force of the impact on the shot charge during its initial entry into the bore, and so assist the welding together of the shot pellets. But this point is now so well understood by gunmakers that it need hardly be considered. Should any particular gun, however, show a marked tendency to ball with different lots of cartridges the chamber cones must come under suspicion and be examined critically.

The most fruitful causes of balling are high pressure and gas getting past the wads. Both of these can be helped by the use of more springy wads which will expand more readily, seal the bore, and reduce the force of the impact on the shot caused by the high pressure by acting as a buffer or cushion.

So it will be seen that balling can generally be attributed to high pressure, indifferent wadding, or a combination of both together.

Choke possibly helps to reduce balling as the constriction of the shot charge during its passage of the choke may help to break up any clusters which may have formed. It was for this reason that the late Mr. Griffith declared that true cylinder barrels were far more prone to balling than those bored with choke, and believed that the greater the choke the less the tendency to ball.

There is a common belief amongst shooters that the whole shot charge sometimes adheres together in a single ball. I will not go so far as to declare that this has never happened: but I can say quite definitely that no record of such a thing has ever been noted on any pattern plate since the plating of guns first began; that I do not believe it has ever happened anywhere; and that I do not believe it ever could happen.

If a bird is struck by a cluster of six pellets the resulting wound would be terrific and there would certainly be a big hole right through the body which would give an impression of the passage of a bullet. If the cluster consisted of a dozen pellets the hole would be still larger—one has but to see the splash of such a cluster on the pattern plate to realise this. If the entire shot charge did "ball" and hit a bird the result would not be a hole so much as the complete disintegration of the bird, a phenomenon which has yet to be reported. And in this connection it must be remembered that a cluster of even four pellets is quite enough to cut the head of a bird clean off. Should any reader wish to ascertain for himself the effects produced by the balling of the entire shot charge, let him shoot a bird at a rise of under 12 inches.

What must be the most remarkable case of balling on record was reported in the *British Medical Journal* of June 23rd, 1888, by the surgeon who attended the injuries of the wounded man. This report was as follows:

"W. L., when leading a horse and cart along the road, heard two shots in quick succession; the second struck him in the face and caused a roundish wound, large enough to admit a finger. The jaw was broken, and some teeth were carried away; and there was also a small wound on the cheek, which might have been made by a single pellet of shot. . . . The probe detected some hard substance, which was grasped by forceps, but crumbled under its grip. Withdrawal of the forceps was accompanied by a shower of shot falling to the floor. The blades held a lump of four pellets firmly stuck together, and much of what was then and subsequently removed consisted of pellets in twos and threes. The amount recovered was one-third of an ounce. The shot was fired from the raised bank of the Trent across a field, the distance to the road being 133 yards. It was fired at and killed a pheasant. The shooter saw the cart, but said it was out of the line of fire.

"The points worthy of note are: 1, the distance—133 yards; 2, the amount of shot recovered—one-third of an ounce; 3, the statement that the man was out of the line of fire. In regard to point 3, I have been told of two other cases of strong pellets hitting persons quite out of the line of fire. As to point 2, the shot was carried in a lump; and this perhaps explains point 1.

"M. R. J. BEHRENDT, L.R.C.S. and P. Ed.

"Burringham, Doncaster."

In view of the date of the occurrence—1888—it is probable that soft shot was being used; and other possible factors were a true cylinder gun, too abrupt a chamber cone, bad wadding, and a high pressure. I do not think that such an extraordinarily large cluster would be in the least likely to occur with the harder shot of the present day.

The combination of one-third of an ounce of shot—90 pellets of No. 6—and a wound which would receive a finger may seem to refute my suggestion that a cluster of but six pellets would make a comparatively large hole in a bird. But this particular cluster struck the bone of a human jaw, which is very heavy and hard in comparison to the body of a game bird. If this cluster had hit the pheasant instead of the unfortunate "W. L." the pheasant would have been blown to bits.

PATTERNS DENSER THAN 70 PER CENT.

It will have been noticed, perhaps, that I have suggested a pattern of but 70 per cent. as being the extreme normal capability of a full choke, and this in spite of the fact that patterns of 75, and even 80, per cent. are not infrequently claimed in advertisements. I have suggested the 70 per cent. limit not because of ignorance of these claims, but because I think that they are inclined to be misleading.

When indicating the general standard of behaviour

likely to be attained by any particular type of boring it is essential that normal conditions should be assumed. For instance, the patterns would have to be obtained with the sizes of shot in common use ; the ballistics of the cartridges ought to be standard ; and the patterns should be typical rather than exceptional.

It is perfectly possible by firing a series of patterns with a batch of cartridge which develop low ballistics to obtain an occasional, and almost isolated, result which gives a count of fully 75 per cent. of the shot pellets in the 30-inch circle, especially if the gun were particularly well bored.

If such a pattern were photographed it would be within the limits of strict truth to advertise the result as having been obtained with the particular gun in question. But to imply, as is sometimes done, that such a pattern is typical of what one can expect from similar guns with ordinary cartridges is to indicate, at the very least, an extremely optimistic temperament on the part of the advertiser.

It is, however, quite possible to obtain patterns of over 70 per cent. in long-chambered guns by loading with a special powder which is made for this purpose. But such powders cannot be used in ordinary 2½-inch cases because the space available for the powder is insufficient. Consequently it is most misleading to make any inference as to the possible pattern obtainable in a 2½-inch 12-bore which has been based on the extreme capability of a 2¾-inch 12-bore. In my classifications of pattern and boring I have purposely adopted densities which can be obtained with ordinary British game guns.

With very big shot, such as BB and larger sizes, it is possible to obtain extraordinarily dense patterns, especially when the velocity developed is low. But such conditions cannot be regarded as typical in any way, any more than those which pertain when using long-chambered guns and special powder.

These foregoing remarks all apply to what I may term "ordinary" cartridges loaded with over-shot wads and the usual type of turnover. As I have already explained on page 35, the crimp turnover definitely tends to give denser patterns for all types of boring and with cartridges sealed in this way I would expect a 75 per cent. pattern as the normal from a full choke.

So I do not think it unreasonable to suggest that a pattern of 70 per cent. is the limit of density which can ordinarily be achieved by a full-choke game gun which has been bored for cartridges of the normal length used in Great Britain.

In any case I think that a 75 per cent. pattern represents the normal extreme limit of density which can be expected even with long-chambered guns and special powders.

TOTAL SPREAD OF THE SHOT CHARGE

So far we have confined our consideration to that part of the shot charge which is found to be distributed within the 30-inch circle at 40 yards. It is, however, both useful and interesting to know the approximate diameter of the spread of the entire shot charge both at 40 yards and intermediate distance. These values were obtained a good many years ago from the study of innumerable experiments conducted over a number of years. The average results were condensed into a most instructive table by Mr. Max Baker and was formerly published in that most excellent little booklet, *The Shooter's Year Book*, to which I have already alluded on page 33.

The following is Mr. Baker's Table, which I take the liberty of quoting with every acknowledgment and gratitude.

It must be emphasised that these results hold approximately true *for all gauges of guns*. There is a very common but quite incorrect belief that small-bore guns concentrate their entire charges into a much smaller area than guns of larger bore. But this is not the case, and in actual practice there is little to choose between the mean diameters of the total spreads of the shot charge from all sizes of guns in normal use. I do not mean to suggest that the diameter of the total spread of a 4-bore is no bigger than that of a ·410, as it undoubtedly is. But the difference is far less than is generally believed, and for all practical purposes it can be assumed without any serious inaccuracy that the diameters of the total spreads of the shot charge are the same for the sizes of guns generally encountered in the shooting field.

TABLE VIII

DIAMETER IN INCHES OF THE SPREAD AT VARIOUS RANGES OF THE WHOLE CHARGE OF A GUN

Boring of Gun	Range in Yards.						
	10	15	20	25	30	35	40
True cylinder	19	26	32	38	44	51	57
Improved cylinder	15	20	26	32	38	44	51
Half choke	12	16	20	26	32	38	46
Full choke	9	12	16	21	26	32	40

This Table can be regarded as a sufficiently accurate guide within reasonable limits, and for all practical purposes, for all sizes of guns. But it is only a guide to average behaviour under normal conditions. Individual results may frequently be found to differ from the figures given, but such results must not be forced too far, especially without sound evidence of the ballistics generated. For, as has already been emphasised several times, pressure and velocity can influence the total spread of the shot charge just as they influence the pattern in the 30-inch circle at 40 yards.

SPREAD BEYOND 40 YARDS. The spread of the whole shot charge at ranges beyond 40 yards is very difficult to judge owing to the wide dispersion of the pellets. It can, however, be assumed that both improved and true cylinders are of no practical use at such distances, 40 yards being their limit of efficiency.

At 45 yards the diameter of the spread may be taken

as being 4 feet for a full choke, and 4 feet 6 inches for a half choke.

And at 50 yards these figures become 5 feet for the full choke and 5 feet 6 inches for the half choke.

Here again these values must not be regarded as being rigid but merely as typifying the extent of spread to be expected with these two types of boring.

Beyond 50 yards the limits of the spread even of a full choke become so indefinite that it is of little use to give any measurements.

SPREAD AT VERY CLOSE RANGES. It may sometimes happen that information is useful on the subject of the spread of the shot charge at very close ranges. Some actual photographs of shots fired through card targets with cylinder and choke guns from ranges of 2 inches to 6 feet were published in the *Field* of October 13th, 1888. These showed that up to 12 inches the total diameter of the shot charge even in the case of a true cylinder was about one inch, while it was slightly less in the case of a choke.

At 2 feet the respective diameters were about 1¼ and 1 inch, and at 3 feet 1½ and 1¼ inches.

At 6 feet both types of boring began to give signs of a few outside pellets being separated from the main bulk of the charge, and at a range of about 10 feet this separation of the whole charge into individual pellets is generally almost complete.

At 6 feet the diameters of the main bulks of the charges, neglecting the small number of outside pellets, is about 2¼ inches for the cylinder and 1½ inches for the choke.

The intermediate degrees of choke will naturally give results between the two extreme limits which have been quoted for each distance.

PATTERNS NEARER THAN AND BEYOND 40 YARDS

If a combination of gun and cartridges give a pattern at 40 yards which is sufficiently dense to ensure a kill there need obviously be no anxiety about the nearer ranges, although shooters are often interested to know what patterns their guns do give at 30 and 35 yards. But beyond 40 yards is a very different matter and shooters will frequently want to know what chances of success they are likely to have at these longer distances. As has already been stated, a killing pattern is one in which the density of the distribution of the pellets is sufficient to ensure some vital spot being struck and in which the individual pellets have sufficient velocity to ensure penetration.

The question of penetration is more simple than that of density because the striking velocities of shot are known quantities and have been tabulated in Volume II. The distribution of the spread, however, follows no laws and is consequently largely a matter of assumption based on known average behaviour.

If the pattern of a gun is known at 40 yards, the following Table provides a sound guide to the *approximate* number of pellets likely to be found in the 30-inch circle at all ranges from 30 to 60 yards.

TABLE IX

PERCENTAGES OF THE 40-YARDS PATTERN IN 30-INCH CIRCLE AT DIFFERENT RANGES FOR ALL TYPES OF BORING

Range in Yards	30	35	40	45	50	55	60
Percentage of 40-yards pattern in 30-inch circle .	140	119	100	82	67	55	45

WHY CHOKE AFFECTS PATTERN

We have now reached a stage in our investigation of the complex problems arising from the questions of Boring and Pattern when it may be of interest to consider why it is that the choke in a barrel affects the pattern in the way it does.

Various theories have been formulated from time to time but some of these can be refuted at once. For example, it has been suggested that the passage of the choke results in the outside pellets of the charge being completely deformed and welded into a sort of outer casing for the rest of the charge which then travels almost like a bullet for some distance before the casing gives way and the rest of the pellets are free to scatter.

This can be disproved by anyone who takes the

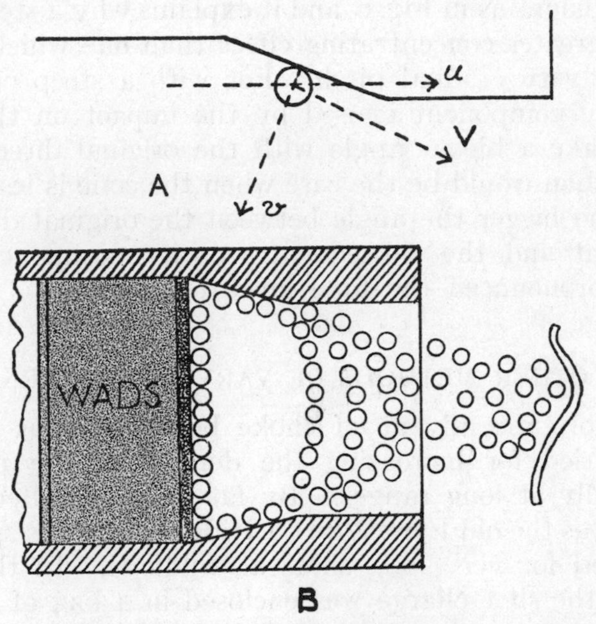

FIG. 6.—Diagrams to illustrate General Journée's theory of the effect of choke on pattern.

A—The velocity components of a single pellet before and after impact with the cone of the choke. The original velocity is u, but the impact with the cone imparts a component velocity, v, and the resultant velocity after impact is V.

B—The effect of the inward velocities imparted by the choke on the outside pellets of the shot charge.

trouble to fire a few shots at a pattern plate at 25 or 30 yards, when it will be found that the number of shot marks on the plate is very nearly the same as the number of pellets in the original charge. If the "outer casing" theory were correct a very large percentage of pellets would be lost.

By far the most reasonable explanation of the action of choke is that suggested by General Journée in his

Tir des Fusils de Chasse, which is that when the outside pellets strike the cone of the choke they are given a velocity at right angles to the surface of the cone. This component causes these outside pellets to have a final inward resultant velocity, and so checks their tendency to spread.

This theory will readily be understood with the help of the diagrams in Fig. 6, and it explains why a steep cone has a greater concentrating effect than one which is cut with a very gradual pitch. For with a steep cone the velocity component caused by the impact on the cone will make a bigger angle with the original direction of flight than would be the case when the cone is less steep. And the bigger the angle between the original direction of flight and the subsequent velocity component, the more pronounced the final inward effect.

OTHER METHODS OF VARYING PATTERN

Before the advent of choke boring various devices were tried for increasing the density of the pattern, especially at long ranges. By far the most effective of these was the old Eley Wire Cartridge which was specially designed for very long shots at wildfowl. In this cartridge the shot charge was enclosed in a bag of netting made of soft copper wire. This bag was open at the front which was covered by a wad and the whole was encased in a paper wrapping. This wrapping helped to keep the wad in position and also prevented the escape of the bone-dust which was used for filling up the spaces between the pellets of the large shot which was invariably employed.

This bag of wire netting carried the pellets together almost as a single projectile for a long distance and then burst after the manner of time shrapnel shell.

These wire cartridges proved efficacious and extremely long shots were brought off with their help. But they were not altogether certain in action owing to the variation in the range at which the "burst" occurred, and

PLATE V

(A) An Obstructional Burst in the Right Barrel of a 12-bore Gun about 8 inches from the Muzzle

Evidence of a "ring bulge" is clear. The top rib, which is farther from the camera, is bent at the site of the burst; and the bottom rib (nearer the camera) is bent downwards and actually fractured at the same place. The severed portions of the barrel protrude outwards all round its circumference and have assumed a funnel-shaped appearance; while the fractured strip of barrel at this point of rupture is plainly bent down and then up. The left barrel has also been affected by the local wave pressure resulting from the obstruction and has been bent at the site of the burst as may be seen from its divergence from the straight edge of the ruler.

(B) An Obstructional Burst about half-way up the Right Barrel of a 12-bore Gun

Evidence of a "ring bulge" is equally clear in this photograph. The top rib (nearer the camera) is bent at the site of the burst, and the fractured ends of the barrel are splayed outwards all round the circumference of the barrel, and have assumed a funnel-shaped appearance similar to that seen in Plate V (A). The general similarity of these two bursts is very marked.

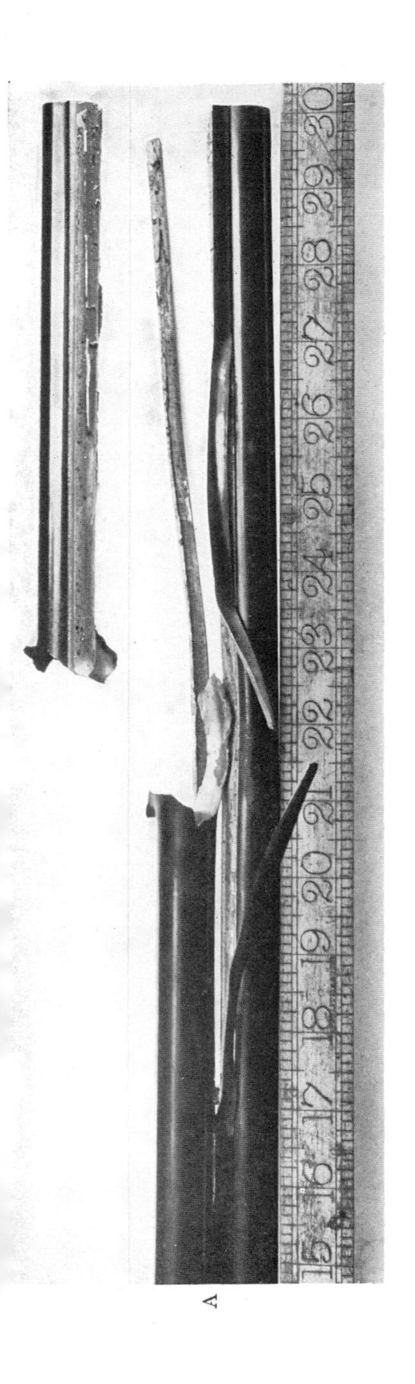

A

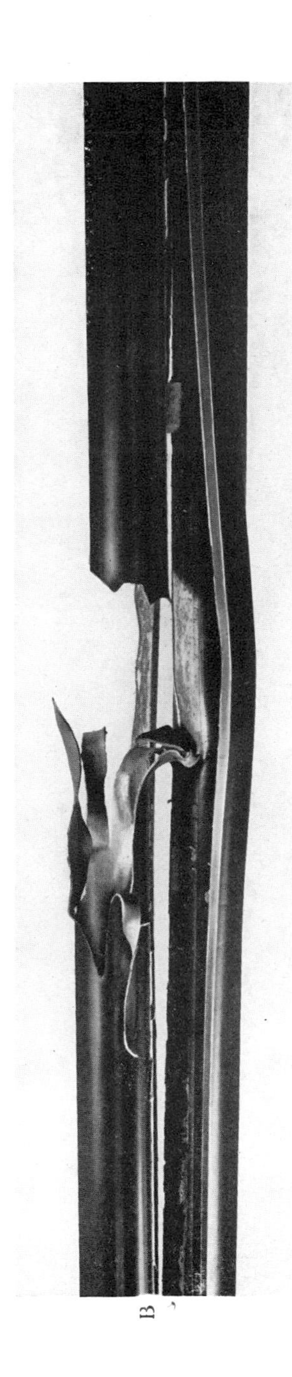

B

they were killed by the invention of choke as they could not be fired through a choked gun without serious risk of injury to the gun.

There was a modification of the wire cartridge known as the "Universal" in which the shot charge was enclosed in a paper cylinder instead of wire-netting. These were made in all standard bores and were intended primarily for those who loaded their own cartridges.

But the idea has survived in a plan which one frequently hears suggested even at the present time. This plan is to cut the paper tube of the cartridge-case right through all round its circumference just about half-way down. On firing the severed front part of the case flies forward and acts as a container for the shot charge, the theoretical effect being similar to that produced by the wire cartridge.

But this plan is most dangerous because the external diameter of the paper cartridge-case is larger than the internal diameter of the bore of the gun which takes that cartridge. The result is that the pressure generated must always be excessive, and frequently dangerous.

Then if the gun is choked there will be a big check in the velocity of the "projectile" which will very likely bulge, or even burst, the barrel at the muzzle.

There is also the risk of the forward part of the paper tube being left behind in the bore when a serious burst might result by the next round being fired.

I have often heard of this cutting through of the case being done and have always marvelled at the soundness of the guns which have withstood the pressure without seeming strain. But the fact that it has been done with impunity does not make the custom anything but highly dangerous, and one which should never be attempted, especially by anyone who places the slightest value on his gun.

A much better and safer plan is to make up a projectile for a 12-bore gun out of a 16-bore cartridge-case. A length of about 1¼ inch should be cut off a 16-bore case and used as a container for the shot charge. The shot can be held in position by means of a thin card wad at either end, each wad being held by a light turnover. A sectional sketch of such a projectile is shown in Fig. 7 which is self-explanatory.

This projectile can then be loaded in a 12-bore cartridge-case and held in position by the usual over-shot card wad and turnover.

The pressure developed by such a projectile is normal as the external diameter of the 16-bore case is slightly less than the internal diameter of a 12-bore barrel.

But although the diameter of the case is less than that of the bore, it is greater than that of the muzzle end of the bore if the barrel is even moderately choked. So in a choked gun there will be a marked check in velocity when the projectile is forced past the choke and a bulge at the muzzle might easily result.

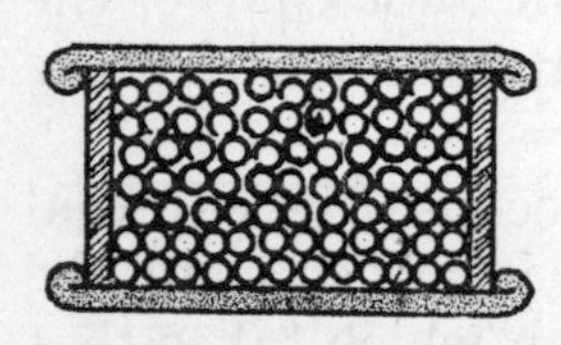

Fig. 7.—A projectile for a 12-bore gun made out of a part of a 16-bore cartridge-case.

Consequently this type of projectile should only be used with extreme caution, and it would be safer to confine its use to true cylinder, or at most improved cylinder, barrels.

And in any case its action is so uncertain that the possibility of gaining any practical advantage is extremely doubtful. It has, however, been suggested that this might be a useful method of destroying nests of grey squirrels, sparrow hawks, crows and rooks when necessary, as the effect of the projectile when hitting a nest would be similar to that of percussion shrapnel on hitting a brick wall—very efficacious if you are on the right side of the wall, and most unpleasant if you are on the wrong side.

In 1869 Messrs. C. Lancaster invented the "Concentrator," which was a hollow conical cylinder of very hard paper. This was slipped down on the shot before the over-shot wad was inserted. This wad was then put in position on top of the concentrator, and the turnover made as usual.

A sectional diagram of a concentrator in position is given in Fig. 8.

These concentrators increased the density of pattern in a true cylinder gun by about 25 per cent., but the regularity of spread was not nearly so good as that obtained by a good choke. This, together with the fact that they could not be fired in choked guns, resulted in their use dying out when choke boring became general.

But recently a patent has been taken out for an entirely new type of concentrator by Mr. W. Edwards, who has been so kind as to give me full particulars of his invention and to send me samples of the Edwards Shot Concentrator.

This concentrator consists of a capsule of special aluminium alloy, closed at the front by a dished head, which is also reinforced by a special movable disc, and open at the rear. The diameter depends on the gauge of the gun and the length on the weight of the shot charge which it is to contain.

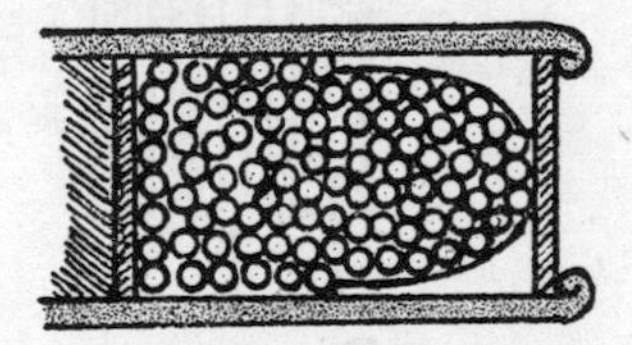

FIG. 8.—Messrs. C. Lancaster's Concentrator.

The capsule is corrugated longitudinally, and these corrugations serve a double purpose: to give strength to the wall of the capsule itself, and to permit the concentrator being fired through a full choke. For only the apex of each corrugation touches the bore of the gun, what may be termed the "apex diameter" of the capsule being that of the gauge, while the "trough diameter" is smaller than that of the muzzle end of the bore of a fully choked gun. These thin and fine corrugations thus ensure full contact with the bore during the passage along the barrel, but are compressed to allow easy passage through the choke. This compression of the corrugations can be seen clearly when examining fired capsules which have been recovered.

On discharge the concentrator behaves at first almost like a single projectile, but after a certain range it drops out of the trajectory leaving the shot charge to continue on its own.

The range at which the concentrator drops away can be controlled by the number of perforations in the dished head, four being the number found to be best to give the maximum range before separation between the concentrator and the shot charge.

Fig. 9 shows the general construction of the Edwards Shot Concentrator. The corrugated capsule (A) is shown with a part of the wall cut away so as to show the movable

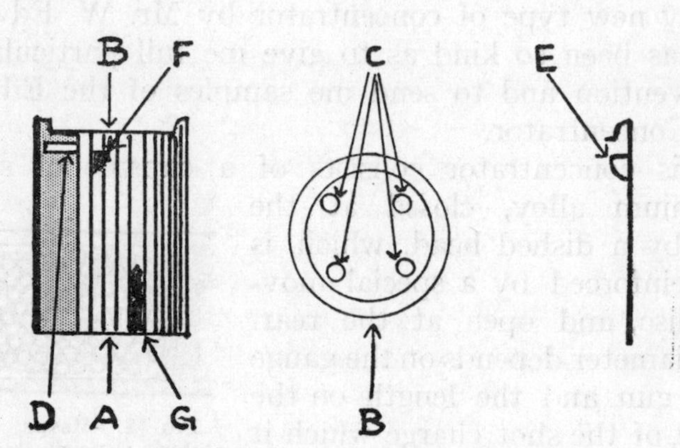

FIG. 9.—The Edwards Patent Shot Concentrator.

Left.—Side view of the corrugated capsule with a portion of the wall cut away to show the movable disc in position.
Centre.—The front end of the capsule showing the dished head and the holes for controlling the range.
Right.—One of the lugs which supports the movable disc.

disc (D) in position under the dished head (B). The head is dished, by the way, partly for strength and partly to receive the over-shot wad. The holes in the dished head are marked C in the middle diagram.

The dished head is supported by four lugs (E) which are formed by stamping out the wall of the capsule and turning the points inwards as shown in the right-hand diagram.

The movable disc is thus held securely but loosely under the dished head.

The holes resulting from the formation of the brackets serve as vents (F), for experience showed that the presence of the movable disc and these vents were needed to ensure satisfactory results.

There are also four slots (G) in the rear part of the wall of the capsule which enable it to expand in a somewhat wide bored gun without suffering irregular deformation.

Private tests have resulted in an ordinary $2\frac{1}{2}$-inch 12-bore game gun placing 100 per cent. of the charge of BB shot within the 30-inch circle at 65 yards, while a 10-bore, which normally gave 62 per cent. and 71 per cent. patterns from the right and left barrels, placed the entire charge of $1\frac{3}{8}$ ounce of No. 3 shot within the 30-inch circle at 60 yards.

The capsule needs greasing round the rear end with melted candle grease or a smear of vaseline before loading it into the case, and when it is in position the over-shot wad is added and the cartridge turned over in the usual way.

At the time of writing it has not been possible for manufacture in bulk to be arranged and the war naturally interrupted all such work and full-scale experiments and tests. It does, however, seem possible that this concentrator may prove the greatest boon to the wildfowler.

Some shooters pour melted tallow on the shot when loading their cartridges and then insert the over-shot wad and make the turnover. Here again the idea is to obtain greater cohesion of the pellets for long range, but the plan cannot be recommended because the additional weight of the tallow is liable to increase the pressure, and there is also the risk of a bulged muzzle if any choke is present.

Besides, the results are very irregular and uncertain.

Very similar in general principle is the addition of a few drops of oil to the shot charge. This is perfectly safe and the patterns certainly do become rather more dense, while the regularity is not too bad.

In practice, however, the oil soaks through the case and dries up, so the effects are not lasting. And in any case they are not very reliable.

So far I have only dealt with devices for increasing

the density of the pattern. I will now describe briefly one for decreasing the density.

This device is called a spreader and is intended for use in heavily choked guns when the shooter thinks an increase in the spread of the charge would be an advantage.

The spreader merely consists of two pieces of card which are fitted together so that the final cross-section is a cross. The spreader is placed in position lengthways in the cartridge case before the shot is inserted. When the shot is put in it is thus divided into four longitudinal sections, the cross-sectional area of each section being a quadrant of a circle. These spreaders can be used in full chokes with safety, but they do not give very regular results and I have not heard of them being used since 1914.

MINIMUM NECESSARY PATTERNS

The next point to consider in our study of patterns is the question of what constitutes the minimum density of pattern necessary to make reasonably sure of a clean kill. If we were in a position, for example, to say definitely that a pattern of 120 pellets in the 30-inch circle was the smallest number essential for an expectation to kill a bird at 40 yards, we would know that it would be of no avail to use a charge of 1⅛ ounce of No. 4 in a true-cylinder gun, as this combination only results in a pattern of 76. So we would have either to change our gun for a full choke, which would give a pattern of 134, or else use the same weight of No. 6 shot with which we could expect a pattern of 122.

And when experimenting with loads a knowledge of the minimum necessary density of pattern would be of the greatest help as it would enable us to work for a definite and tangible end, namely a combination of gun and cartridge which would place the minimum number of pellets in the 30-inch circle at the longest possible range at which the striking velocities of the individual pellets are sufficient to ensure penetration.

So the problem with which we are now faced is clearly one of great practical value.

The first step must obviously be to ascertain the areas presented by various game birds. And here we come up against the first difficulty, for the area represented as a target by any bird must vary according to the angle from which it is viewed. I do not think it possible to decide whether more birds are killed from one particular angle than another, but I am sure that all shooters derive more satisfaction from a high overhead shot than from any other. Now if the feathers are disregarded, as they should be, there is little, if any, practical difference in the area offered by a bird when seen from underneath from that offered when seen sideways—I have made a number of outline tracings of bodies of game birds when placed on their backs and on their sides to verify this point, and there is really nothing in it one way or the other.

A bird flying head on, or straight away, certainly offers a smaller target. But in no case does the area presented by the actual vital organs cover the whole target, and this area bears a smaller proportion to the whole when a bird is flying across or straight overhead than when it is flying towards or away from the shooter.

It must be remembered that in no circumstances is it possible to determine absolute minimum patterns with any degree of scientific accuracy. The results cannot be anything but reasonable estimations, and so it is useless to enter into minutiæ. Quite recently a friend of mine, whose general shrewdness is on a par with his great mathematical ability, said to me: "I always regard the man as a fool who has only a bit of chalk and a piece of string with which to take his measurements, and who gives his results in hundredths of an inch."

So let us assume the bird to be flying overhead.

The next point to decide is the actual area to measure. The feathers must obviously be disregarded; and so, too, those parts of the legs which stretch beyond the body. I think we might include the *humerus*, but not the other wing bones.

The sketch in Fig. 10 gives the outline of a bird, while the dotted line indicates the area which I have taken to be the target. There may be better areas to adopt for our purpose, but I do not think that the one which I have chosen can be regarded as unreasonable.

Working on this principle, I have made the most careful outlines of the plucked bodies of various game birds. These outlines were transferred to squared paper,

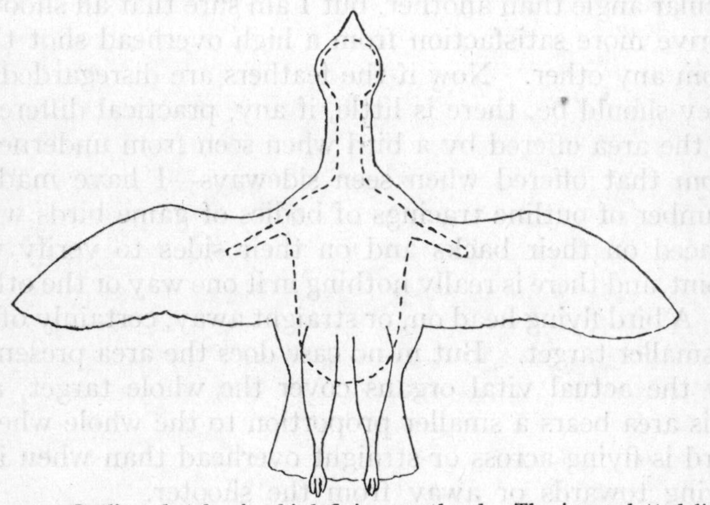

FIG. 10.—Outline sketch of a bird flying overhead. The inner dotted line indicates the vulnerable area of the body.

when the actual area was obtained by counting the squares.

In order to make certain that these values indicated the areas of average birds of each species, I weighed each bird before it was plucked ; so it is thus possible to check the likelihood of my results being typical, since the average weights of game birds are known quantities.

The actual results I obtained were as shown opposite.

Before I began operations at all I wondered whether I might not be able to evolve some empirical relation between the weight and the area, but I never hoped the results would come out as closely as they did. I only took the area to the nearest half of a square inch, and the weights to the nearest ounce except in the case of the

Bird.	Actual Weight in Ounces.	Area in Square Inches.	Area in Square Inches per Ounce of Weight.
Blackcock	48	40	0·85
Pheasant (Cock)	48	41	0·86
,, (Hen)	35	31	0·89
Mallard	42	37	0·88
Grouse (Cock)	24	21	0·88
,, (Hen)	21	18·5	0·88
Partridge (Cock)	14	12·5	0·89
,, (Hen)	13	12	0·92
Wood-Pigeon	18	16	0·89
Teal	12	11	0·92
Woodcock	12	12	1·00
Snipe	4·5	5·5	1·24

snipe. The figures in the final column are so nearly constant that I do not think we would be unjustified if we were to adopt a value for the area of a game bird as being 0·88 times its weight, and this would extend the utility of these measurements to various other game birds not found in Great Britain.[1]

[1] It would naturally be expected that the graph of the relation between the area depicted in the diagram and the weight of the bird would be a curve. I feel quite sure that this would be established were it possible to obtain similar details of a far greater number of birds varying in size right down to the wrens, and even humming birds, at one end of the scale and right up to the Great Bustard at the other end. The constancy of the results actually obtained can be explained by the comparative similarity in the weights of the birds taken as examples. The smallest birds, however, show a divergence from the constant in one direction, while the largest show a similar divergence in the other direction. So the accuracy of the relationship $A = 0{\cdot}88\,W$ will only hold for birds of round about the weights quoted. For although the graph is really a curve, and I have assumed it to be a straight line, the truth is that that part of the curve which lies within the limits of practical consideration is so nearly a straight line that the difference can be ignored. And if a greater number of hits is held to be necessary in the case of larger birds the formulæ I have suggested for the minimum necessary patterns should hold sufficiently well to make sound guides for all practical sporting purposes.

But let us now return to the question of patterns. The whole problem depends on what is regarded as the minimum number of pellets required to hit a bird in order to make certain of a kill, assuming that the pellets all have sufficient penetration. This is really a most difficult point to decide. In the *Field* of July 30th, 1910, the late Dr. H. Hammond-Smith published a most instructive article on this very subject, in which he came to the conclusion that five pellets were required to make certain of a kill. I doubt whether any other man has had greater experience in *post-mortem* examinations of game birds than Dr. Hammond-Smith, and so his opinion deserves the greatest respect, backed as it was by his professional medical training. But I cannot help thinking that five pellets is too high a number for practical sporting conditions. Let us take a partridge as an example.

Five pellets on an area of 12½ square inches at 40 yards would correspond to 283 pellets in the 30-inch circle. That is, a gun would have to make a 100 per cent. pattern with $1\frac{1}{16}$ ounce of No. 6 shot in order to make sure of a kill at this range!

This is obviously out of the question, so it may be as well to start afresh.

If the dotted outline in Fig. 9 which represents the actual body area is examined it will be seen that the vital organs (head, neck, heart, lungs and large blood-vessels) must occupy very nearly, if not quite, half the area taken. So it would not seem to be unreasonable if we began with taking two hits on the area as the required minimum.

In the case of snipe at 40 yards this would mean a necessary pattern of 258. Using $1\frac{1}{16}$ ounce of No. 8 one would expect to be able to kill a snipe at 40 yards, and yet the pattern is only 230 with an improved cylinder, although it is 287 with a half choke. So I think that we may now deduce that a snipe at 40 yards is not a *certainty* with $1\frac{1}{16}$ ounce of No. 8, unless a half choke is used.

And the theoretical necessary minumum pattern for a partridge would be 118, which does not tally badly with the 116 of a true cylinder and 145 of an improved cylinder using $1\frac{1}{16}$ ounce of No. 6. Forty yards is admittedly a long shot at a partridge, and might be just beyond the powers of a true cylinder—a fact which the theoretical figure brings out—although it should be well within the limits of an improved cylinder gun.

But with the bigger birds the results do not seem so satisfactory. A pattern of 77 for a grouse seems very open, and one of 35 for a cock pheasant is quite unreasonable.

A possible explanation for these seemingly contradictory results would appear to be the greater protection afforded to the vital organs of the larger birds by their stouter breast-bones and bigger crops. For the breast-bone covers the heart and larger blood vessels to a great extent, and the crop protects the base of the neck. If this is so, it means that the larger the bird the greater the number of hits required in order to ensure a kill ; and working on this principle, I am inclined to suggest that a reasonable value to adopt for the minimum necessary number of hits would be 2 in the case of a bird under 1 lb. in weight, and 3 for a bird over 1 lb. ; while possibly 4 might be necessary for very large and strong birds such as geese.

If this plan is adopted the results become altogether more reasonable in the case of every bird.

But even then I think that to be quite on the safe side we should increase the patterns by at least 10 per cent. to allow for any reduction in density caused by Stringing, a subject which will be dealt with in a later chapter.

These final results are given in the following table in round numbers ; but in order to avoid complications which would be impractical I have only considered the smaller hen birds in the case of both grouse and partridge. Cock pheasants are classed separately to hens because they are appreciably larger, can be readily distinguished, and are frequently shot when hens are spared. I have also made a slight reduction in the final value for the pattern for snipe so as to make it fit in better with known practice. This is quite reasonable as such small birds as snipe probably need a comparatively less dense pattern than birds the size of a partridge.

Table X confirms practical experience. A wood-pigeon would commonly be regarded as killable at 40 yards with an improved cylinder gun, and the minimum pattern is nearly that given with the standard charge of No. 6 shot by such a gun. With a choke, however, the range is obviously increased. Similarly at 40 yards both grouse and partridge are within the killing range of an improved cylinder and No. 6. If anything the patterns given are on the high side: but in working to a minimum it is ever better to play for safety rather than to suffer disappointment.

In order to obtain a rough idea as to the minimum patterns required for birds which are not included in this table, it is only necessary to divide the area of the 30-inch circle by the area of the bird in question, which can be obtained by the empirical relation between area and

TABLE X

MINIMUM PATTERNS FOR VARIOUS GAME BIRDS

Bird.	Minimum Pattern.
Blackcock	60
Cock Pheasant	
Mallard	70
Hen Pheasant	80
Grouse	130
Partridge	
Wood-Pigeon	
Woodcock	145
Teal	
Snipe	290

weight which I have already given. The average weights of almost all known varieties of game birds will be found in many books of reference. For British birds Mr. Hugh Gladstone's *Record Bags and Shooting Records* contains a mass of interesting information, while for Indian birds the *Indian Field Shikar Book* gives all the necessary data.

The actual minimum patterns are given with reasonable accuracy by the following formulæ in which a 10 per cent. allowance has been made for loss by stringing.

For birds under 1 lb. in weight.

Minimum Pattern $= \frac{1760}{W}$, where W is the weight of the bird *in ounces.*

For birds over 1 lb. and under 2 lb.

Minimum Pattern $= \frac{3000}{W}$, when W is the weight of the bird *in ounces.*

For birds over 2 lb.

Minimum Pattern $= \frac{165}{W}$, where W is the weight of the bird *in pounds.*

The values for the minimum patterns given by these formulæ should prove a perfectly practical guide which can be adopted with confidence. It might be urged that very large birds, such as geese, would need to be struck even by more than three pellets. This is quite possibly correct, although I should think that three pellets of suitably heavy shot would make certain of any goose. But if any shooter wishes to make still more certain he can take a value of $\frac{220}{W}$ for the minimum pattern necessary for birds of, say, over 4 lb., W being in pounds. The principle is the same.

It must, however, be realised that these minimum patterns are entirely independent of the question of penetration. They merely indicate the approximate density of pattern which is necessary for a clean kill, provided all the pellets which strike the bird have a sufficient capacity for adequate penetration. This capacity will always depend on the size of shot and the actual striking velocity.

CHAPTER IV

THE CHOICE OF BORING AND PATTERN

IN the three previous chapters I have done my best to establish an understanding of what is meant by the various expressions generally used both when describing the different types of boring and when discussing patterns. We have also considered the factors which affect pattern, as well as the connection between the various degrees of boring and these factors. So we have now reached a stage in our consideration of the whole subject when we can come down to the practical problem of the best type of boring to adopt in ordinary game guns.

It will be remembered that even the same types of boring have been shown to vary in their behaviour when it comes to patterns ; and for this reason it is probably better not to insist too strongly on any type of boring, but rather to base the choice on the resulting pattern, although the boring should be considered at the same time but in a less rigid manner.

It has been an almost universal custom for many years to have the right barrel bored " cylinder "—recently this has always meant improved cylinder—and the left " choke," the actual degree of choke being unspecified. But the chief point is that the boring of the two barrels has almost invariably been different, the right giving a more open pattern than the left.

This custom became established when birds were almost always walked up and the left barrel was fired at a more distant bird. As long as a gun is only used for shooting at birds which are flying *away* from the shooter the plan of having the barrels bored differently is patently excellent. But is such a condition typical of modern shooting ? I think most of my readers will agree that in Great Britain the proportion of game shot driven is far and away greater than that shot when walking up. And

I am not forgetting the fact that there are many moors in Scotland where grouse are still walked up or shot over dogs; nor that there is such a bird as a snipe; nor that there are many "rough" shoots all over the country on which driving is unknown.

I think that if an analysis could be made of all the shots fired at game during a season in Great Britain it would be found that far the larger percentage had been fired at driven birds.

Now the driven bird presents a very different problem from the bird which is walked up, as it frequently happens that the first shot is taken at a greater range than the second. In view of this fact it might be argued that the old custom of boring should be reversed, and the right barrel bored choke and the left improved cylinder. As a matter of fact this is sometimes done; but I do not believe the plan to be sound, for even at driven game one does not always fire the right barrel at a more distant bird. It is often necessary to take birds behind, when the old conditions of walking up become re-established. Then at pheasants there is seldom much in it, the bird being at approximately the same range for the second barrel if missed with the first, while the same applies to two birds coming over together or several in a bunch.

In fact the more distant shots are taken just as frequently with both barrels; and if this is the case I cannot see that any useful purpose is served by having the two barrels bored differently.

I do not think there is much dispute about this now, and I know for a fact that several of the leading gunmakers advise their customers to have both barrels bored alike in guns which are intended for use against driven game.

At the same time there is a psychological factor in having one barrel—usually the left—bored with rather more choke. Some shooters like to feel that they have a little extra range in one barrel so as to be ready for that occasional very high bird, and this feeling imparts confidence which is the most important factor of all in good shooting. In actual practice, however, the difference in boring is usually too slight to have any very pronounced effect on the patterns, and therefore on the range. So the effect is, as I have stated, more psychological than anything else. Nevertheless this aspect should not be neglected, and any shooter who thinks he would feel happier with a little extra choke in the left barrel will be well advised to follow his inclination.

But there are sportsmen who want their guns chiefly for rough shooting at home, or for sport abroad. Should they, too, adopt the modern practice ? I think the answer to this question must depend on the type of shooting they expect or the country to which they are going. In India, for example, where as many shots may be fired at flighting duck as at any other game, I can see no advantage in having the right barrel bored to give a more open pattern than the left, since flighting duck present a very similar problem to that of high pheasants. But if snipe are to comprise the principal game the left barrel might certainly be more fully choked with advantage : and this also applies to most varieties of game which are invariably walked up either at home or abroad.

So we can now draw the not unreasonable conclusion that in the case of guns wanted for driven game it is best to have both barrels, or all four of a pair, to be bored so as to give as nearly as possible similar patterns. Those individuals who have a marked bias in favour of more choke in the left barrel can follow their inclinations, but in such cases the extra amount of choke need be but slight.

For " general purpose " guns the increased degree of choke in the left barrel can be more pronounced, although even here the difference between the borings of the two barrels need not necessarily be as great as has been commonly considered necessary.

And here I will add that in the case of guns fitted with non-selective single triggers I am sure that it is a mistake to have the barrels bored differently. With such guns one barrel is always fired first, and if the two barrels are different the shooter will probably begin to wonder whether a miss was due to this difference: and such doubts will only tend to bad shooting.

The next point to consider is what the borings should be.

Variation in boring, that is in the degree of choke, has a double effect in actual shooting. The range is increased by more choke owing to the density of the pattern being better maintained at longer distances; at the same time the diameter of the total spread of the shot charge is reduced at all ranges, and consequently the permissible error in aim is reduced. In other words a heavy choke increases the effective range of a gun but necessitates a higher degree of accuracy in shooting.

The question of range, however, depends on other factors besides the amount of choke; such as the size of bird shot at, the size of shot used, and the combination of powder and shot adopted for the load. So let us first confine ourselves to the question of permissible error.

This also must vary with the range and type of boring, as it is dependent on the *effective* spread of the shot charge. The diameter of the effective spread is less than that of the total spread except at very close ranges, since the extreme outside annulus is not sufficiently dense to be effective. The width of this ineffective annulus varies with the range and the type of boring, becoming greater as the range is increased and the amount of choke is decreased. The greatest permissible error is equal to the radius of this effective spread.

The following Table gives the approximate radii of the effective spreads of the shot charge for the various types of boring at different ranges. It must be understood clearly that the figures can only be regarded as approximate, since the thickness of the ineffective annulus will vary with different guns; also the required density with the size of bird at which shots are taken. Accordingly the values given in the table should only be regarded as being typical of average results obtained with all sizes of guns.

An examination of this Table indicates immediately the great advantage in permissible error conferred by the

TABLE XI

PERMISSIBLE ERRORS OF AIM IN INCHES FOR VARIOUS BORINGS AT DIFFERENT RANGES

Type of Boring.	Range in Yards.						
	10	15	20	25	30	35	40
True Cylinder	9·5	12	13	15	18	21	24
Improved Cylinder . . .	7·5	9	10	13	15	18	22
Quarter Choke	6·8	8	9	12	14	17	21
Half Choke	6·0	7·5	8	11	13	16	20
Three-quarter Choke . .	5·3	7	7·5	10	12	15	19
Full Choke	4·5	6	7	9	11	14	18

use of a true cylinder at near ranges, and so I will deal with this type of boring first.

If shots were seldom taken beyond 20 or 25 yards, and never beyond 30 yards, this type of boring would be supreme. It has been seen, however, in the last two chapters that every single fault in patterns resulting from almost inevitable variations in cartridges is greater in a true cylinder than in any other kind of barrel. Blown, scattered and patchy patterns; cartwheels; and probably balling: these are all far more pronounced with true cylinders. So much so, in fact, that 10 per cent. of cartwheel patterns was long regarded as being an inseparable accompaniment of the true cylinder. At very close ranges such irregularities may not matter; but beyond 25 yards they begin to have their effect, while at the longer ranges they are quite fatal. The truth is that true cylinders are unreliable for any ranges much over 30 yards. The results *may* reach the standard which they should; but if the wadding is not perfect, or the ballistics of the cartridges are in the slightest degree lively, the patterns will inevitably suffer.

This fact has become so generally recognised that

really true cylinder barrels are now seldom seen, and I doubt if a single gunmaker in Great Britain would recommend a true-cylinder boring, even for a right barrel, for normal use. I am quite certain none would were the gun to be built for a customer who insisted on seeing it shot for pattern and expected regular results.

If I wanted a gun with which to shoot rabbits in thick covert and for no other purpose—except possibly driven partridges—I would certainly choose one with both barrels true cylinder. But I would not expect it to give regular effective patterns ; nor would I expect it to be reliable for shots at over 30 yards.

I am well aware that this may seem a somewhat sweeping condemnation of a type of boring which has formerly been recommended by many notable authorities.

I am also aware that arguments are frequently brought forward which quote the wonderful feats of marksmanship performed by men who use nothing but true cylinders and who kill the very highest birds. I believe the late Lord Walsingham—the joint author of the *Badminton Library* Volumes on Shooting : not his younger brother—used nothing but true cylinders. But it must not be forgotten that in his days cartridges were a very different proposition. The standard shot charge was 1⅛ ounce, which helped patterns considerably ; barrels were made heavier, which also helped ; the propellants were black powder and 42-grain bulk nitro powders which were less sensitive to climatic variations ; and there was not the demand for "high-velocity" loads which tend to higher pressures and scattered patterns. So it is useless to be guided by conditions which were prevalent sixty years ago.

Extensive experience with the pattern plate has convinced me of the constant irregularity of results given by true cylinder barrels, which irregularities are so pronounced that I cannot believe that this type of boring can be relied upon to give effective killing patterns at moderately long ranges. A bird is often regarded as "high" which is but 25 yards up in the air, and for this reason I prefer the unanswerable logic of the pattern plate to the reputed prowess of individuals.

I beg to be forgiven for being dogmatic. I only am so because my faith has been completely shattered in true cylinder boring both by numerous tests for pattern in different barrels and in the actual shooting field, for I happen to own a true cylinder gun.

And in support of my own experience I will quote that of a friend of mine who is regarded in Hampshire as being a very good shot—and that in the middle of the partridge country means much.

Some years ago this sportsman thought he would try a pair of beautiful old guns which belonged to his father, who had given up shooting as he was considerably over eighty. These guns were bored true cylinder in all four barrels, and during the partridge driving at the end of September and through October my friend was delighted with the results of the old guns. He declared that he had seldom shot better in his life and was loud in his praise of the open boring.

But when November came with its covert shoots he began to change his opinion. Day after day his experience was the same: wounded birds, and birds missed, especially if they were at any height in the air. After many disappointments he tried the guns on a pattern plate and found that up to 25 yards the patterns were very widely spread but the density sufficient to ensure killing. But at 30 yards and beyond the patterns were so scattered, irregular and uneven as to be quite unreliable, and he returned to his own guns which were more closely bored and killed his pheasants as well as ever.

This unreliability of true cylinder boring is so real that I would warn all shooters against adopting it without first making the most searching enquiries of their gunmaker as well as seeing tests for pattern carried out for themselves with ordinary commercial cartridges.

I will admit readily that all that I have said against the true cylinder applies to cartridges sealed with over-shot wads and the ordinary type of turnover; also that the crimp cartridge may cure scattered patterns even in a true cylinder as well as increase the density. I have no experience of the crimped cartridge in a true cylinder barrel and so can make no definite statement, although I am sure that the shooting would be improved. But even so there will still be vagaries of pressure to which I am confident a true cylinder will be more sensitive than a barrel with a certain amount of choke, and I find it hard to believe that a true cylinder will ever prove as reliable as a slight choke.

If I have said enough to deter the reader from selecting a true cylinder barrel for a general utility gun I will be well content; and so I will not refer to this type of boring further since I do not consider it to be a practical proposition.

The next open type of boring is the Improved Cylinder. This is, and very rightly, most popular, and I know several leading gunmakers who usually advise customers ordering a pair of guns to have all four barrels bored improved cylinder.

I have no wish to seem to be putting my opinion against what must obviously be the combined experience of numbers of shooters and expert shooting school coaches, for gunmakers will naturally be guided in their recommendations by such experiences. But at the same time I cannot help thinking that an improved cylinder is not the best boring for general purposes, and personally I prefer a gun in which both barrels are given rather more choke than is implied by an improved cylinder specification. And I have been rather encouraged in this opinion by finding that one of the firms of gunmakers which commonly recommend all four barrels to be bored "improved cylinder" adopted a boring of nearly ten points of choke giving patterns approaching 160 with the standard charge of $1\frac{1}{16}$ ounce of No. 6.

I have two reasons for this preference for a slight choke, and both are based on the question of ballistics. The first is the more important, and is eminently practical.

No improved cylinder gives good and regular patterns

unless the pressures developed by the cartridges are on the "soft" side. A study of the last two chapters will have shown that the greater the degree of choke the greater the help which the pattern receives in overcoming irregularities of pressure, velocity, turnover and wadding. An improved cylinder is very sensitive to pressure—although admittedly less sensitive than true cylinder—and a batch of cartridges which give pressures of round about 3 tons, or slightly over, will seldom yield even and regular patterns in an improved-cylinder barrel.

We have seen that the normal pressure for a 2½-inch 12-bore cartridge is regarded as lying between 2·5 and 3 tons: so 3-tonners cannot be considered as anything out of the way. Yet such cartridges will probably result in the patterns being blown over a much bigger area than the normal at 40 yards, which means that birds can escape in the open patches, or else that they will receive but a single pellet instead of the two or three which were shown to be the minimum necessary in the last chapter.

At the present time, when there are so many "high-velocity" cartridges sold, the tendency to scattered patterns is greater than ever, as some of these "high-velocity" cartridges develop lively pressures—that is pressures which cannot be regarded in any way as dangerous or excessive, but sufficient to cause scattered patterns in an improved cylinder barrel.

Then early in the season the weather is frequently hot, and this, as has been seen, tends to raise the ballistics and scatter the patterns. The effect on game is that birds are missed, or only wounded, and the shooter complains to his gunmaker that the cartridges are weak, whereas they are in reality too strong for improved cylinder guns.

Now, just as the three to five points of constriction in an improved cylinder confer a great advantage on it over a true cylinder when it comes to holding up patterns, so do a further five points of choke help a barrel to tide over the difficulties experienced by the improved cylinder. In fact a barrel bored with ten points of choke is far and away superior in holding up patterns from lively cartridges to any improved cylinder, and I am convinced that such an advantage is very real.

My second reason for preferring a slight choke is theoretical; nevertheless I think it to be sound.

I have already mentioned briefly the question of the Stringing of Shot which will be dealt with fully in the next two chapters. This stringing causes a certain loss in density in the killing pattern on a fast crossing bird. But this reduction in density is markedly less in the case of chokes than improved cylinders, as will be seen in Chapter VI.

So here again the choke has a certain advantage over the true cylinder. The advantage may be only theory, but I think that it is fairly sound theory. And I must confess to feeling happier when shooting if I believe that my gun will give the very best of whatever pattern there is, instead of only a part of it. Since confidence is everything in shooting, I prefer a gun with some choke to an improved cylinder, and personally I think that a choke of about ten points just about meets ordinary conditions. Some men may prefer more: but that is a detail which every shooter must decide for himself.

This suggestion really means that both barrels of a gun, or all four in the case of a pair, should be bored with about ten points of choke, or in other words, quarter choke.

Two objections will naturally be raised to this advice, namely that a choke adds to the difficulty of shooting and means a big percentage of smashed game.

I will accordingly try to meet these objections.

Shooting at a rapidly moving object must always be a difficult art owing to the diversity of the problems presented. But these difficulties can roughly be divided into two main categories: those arising from the object being very near to the marksmen, and those connected with a longer range. For near shots present a very different problem from long ones, and are frequently far more difficult. The latter are usually missed because the shooter has failed to judge correctly the pace of the bird, or else to allow for some angle or curl ; I believe that the actual aim is seldom much at fault, because a bird coming very high overhead, or crossing wide, usually gives one much more time than one bustling past one's head. Even though the high bird may be flying faster than the low, the low bird is shifting across the landscape more rapidly simply because it is so much nearer. The reason is the same as that which explains why a distant train travelling at 60 miles an hour appears to be moving more slowly than one which passes within a few feet at a speed of 30 miles an hour. In mathematical language the angular velocity of the nearer train is much greater than that of the distant one, although the linear velocity may be less.

The effect of this relatively more rapid change of position of the near bird is that the shooter is much more hurried, and consequently is not so accurate in his actual aim as he would be if he had more time. And so, I think it happens that near shots are missed far more through errors in aim than long ones, simply because one is hustled unduly.

If this is the case, there can be no doubt that the greater the permissible error of any type of boring the less difficult it is to kill and so there is something to be said for the first objection against choke. But let us see exactly what it amounts to.

An examination of Table XI will show that when using a full choke the permissible error is 3 inches less at 10 yards than when using an improved cylinder. This amount may not seem much, but it is quite appreciable—how often one sees a rabbit in covert missed just over its back—and proves that a full choke must be a distinct handicap for quick shots at close range. But the figure I have quoted is the difference between an improved cylinder and a full choke, while I have only advocated a quarter choke. With such a boring the difference in permissible errors compared with an improved cylinder is but 0·7 of an inch at 10 yards, and 1 inch at 15 yards and over.

This is all one stands to lose by the adoption of a quarter choke as far as the difficulty of shooting is concerned. For at longer ranges, as I have already explained, I believe that misses are due to other causes which are not helped by mere radius of spread. A really high pheasant is far more often missed by yards rather than inches, as any shooting school coach will testify.

There are, of course, other causes of missing which I have not mentioned. Such will be dealt with in a later chapter and include faulty trigger pressure, incorrect holding, incorrect swing, checking the swing, etc. But all of these faults cause one to miss by feet rather than inches and the radius of the spread of the shot charge will have little effect on their results.

Accordingly I do not think that this first objection holds much water when one comes down to actual facts. Nor have I found it hold in practice, as the experience of a number of my friends bears out my own that there is no noticeable difference in shooting with an improved cylinder or a slight choke.

Nor have I found the second objection, that of smashed birds, to be borne out in practice. Of course, if one does happen to get any going-away bird in the middle of the pattern at 10 yards it will be rendered unfit for food: but this would apply equally with any boring, and the remedy is not to fire at such birds. Rabbits, too, may sometimes be smashed; but here again I think the range has more to do with the result than the boring of the gun —that is, within reasonable limits. A full choke will certainly smash more game than an improved cylinder, as the density of pattern is even relatively greater at short ranges than at long.

And since this problem of smashed birds is not an unimportant one the following table may be of interest. This table shows in round numbers the number of pellets which will hit a bird at the nearer ranges for every single pellet which hits it at 40 yards on the supposition that the bird is centred correctly in the pattern in every case. This supposition has an important bearing on the issue as the centres of all patterns have considerably greater relative density at short ranges than long.

TABLE XII

THE NUMBERS OF PELLETS WHICH WILL HIT A BIRD AT NEARER RANGES FOR EVERY PELLET WHICH HITS IT AT 40 YARDS

Range in Yards.	Boring.				
	Improved Cylinder.	Quarter Choke.	Half Choke.	Three-quarter Choke.	Full Choke.
40	1	1	1	1	1
35	1	1	2	2	2
30	2	2	2	2	3
25	3	3	4	4	4
20	5	5	6	7	7
15	9	10	11	12	14
10	18	20	23	26	30

In Chapter I it was explained that the pattern of an improved cylinder was 145, and that of a quarter choke 160. So if a bird is hit by two or three pellets with an improved cylinder at 40 yards it is not very likely to be hit by a greater number with the quarter choke. The effect of this slight choke is to ensure the regularity of the pattern rather than to increase the density to any decided extent ; and all that the quarter choke does in the case of a partridge, for example, is to make absolutely certain that the necessary number of vital hits are secured as well as to increase slightly the range at which the minimum effective pattern can be obtained. The odds are that a bird which is hit by 2 pellets at 40 yards with an improved cylinder would only be hit by 2 with a quarter choke, when at 20 yards both would receive 10 pellets, and at 15 yards the improved cylinder would give 18 pellets and the quarter choke 20, assuming that the bird is in the middle of the pattern. There is no practical difference between these results, and even if the quarter choke gave 3 hits at 40 yards instead of the

2 of the improved cylinder, there would only be 15 pellets at 20 yards instead of 10. At 15 yards the quarter choke would put 30 pellets into the bird, and this is admittedly too many. But the difference between 3 pellets and 2 at 40 yards is an increase of 50 per cent., and a quarter choke only gives a 10 per cent. increase in pattern density at this range, and so I think that any deductions arising from a 50 per cent. increase are quite misleading.

So the fact emerges that down to 15 yards there is no appreciable difference in the numbers of pellets put into a bird by an improved cylinder and a quarter choke, which means that no increase in the danger of spoiling birds for the table is involved in the change from the former boring to the latter.

At 10 yards the bird would be filled with shot in either case.

And while we are dealing with this aspect of the matter it is interesting to make a similar comparison with the results given by a full choke. This boring will give a pattern of 200, which would mean that a partridge which received 2 pellets at 40 yards from the improved cylinder would almost certainly be hit by 3 from the full choke. But at 20 yards these numbers become respectively 10 and 21, and at 15 yards 18 and 42, which shows conclusively that the accusation of smashing birds which is generally levelled at a full choke can be true. Yet even so it should be remembered that these are extreme examples and that they only hold good when the bird is hit with the very centre of the pattern. If a bird is caught by the fringe of the pattern alone it will not be smashed to any extent.

There is, however, no comparison in this respect between quarter and full choke, and it is the former which I have suggested for the boring to replace the improved cylinder for general purposes.

All the patterns and numbers of pellets which can be presumed to hit a bird which I have quoted are obviously for the ordinary type of cartridge with an over-shot wad. The crimped cartridge would certainly make a slight difference. But this difference would be constant for all types of boring and the only practical effect would be that the distances which I have given would all be very slightly increased in every case. For example 40 yards might become 42; 35 might become 37; and so on. There would be no real change in the conclusions which can be drawn.

It will have been noticed that I have been quoting figures for the ordinary $2\frac{1}{2}$-inch 12-bore alone. I have done so because actual examples were necessary for an adequate consideration of the problem. But the principle is the same for all bores: in fact, a heavier choke than a quarter becomes almost essential in the case of the smaller bores if the minimum necessary pattern for ordinary game birds is to be obtained at 40 yards without changing to a smaller size of shot than No. 6. This aspect of the case will, however, be dealt with in another chapter.

So far we have only considered in detail the requirements for boring demanded by ordinary game shooting in Great Britain on the assumption that this will be chiefly at driven game. The man who wants a gun for all-round rough shooting in which shots at driven birds are so infrequent as scarcely to need consideration is faced with an entirely different problem. In such circumstances the very close shot is the exception, and the long shot is the rule; and so the gun should be bored more suitably for long shots than close. This must mean that the right barrel should, at the very least, be a half choke, while the left may be with advantage either three-quarter choke or full. Personally, if I were returning to India I think I would buy a gun with both barrels full choke, as I am sure it would be more generally useful than any other combination unless I was going to a district in which snipe were the only game. For flighting duck and general walking up I am certain that a full choke in both barrels is an advantage.

Where money is not a primary object it is not at all a bad plan to get two pairs of barrels for every gun, and if this were done I would be inclined to recommend one pair bored with both quarter choke, and the other pair both full choke. The latter pair would frequently be invaluable abroad, and at home would be most useful for walking up wild grouse or partridges ; when after duck or wood-pigeons ; or on occasions when pheasants are *really* high.

To sum up, I am inclined to suggest the following borings and patterns for ordinary 12-bores as being the most suitable for the types of shooting specified. For reasons which have already been explained in Chapter I it is always better to quote the actual pattern desired rather than any particular degree of choke, and so the specifications for choke which I give must not be regarded as being rigid. They are only intended to be a guide in conjunction with the pattern which should be obtained.

All-round Shooting in Great Britain (chiefly driving). Either both barrels quarter choke (Pattern 160), or right barrel quarter choke (Pattern 160) and left barrel half choke (Pattern 170). Personally, I prefer the former combination, but many shooters prefer the latter. In any case there is little to choose between them.

All-round Rough Shooting in Great Britain or Abroad (chiefly walking up). Either right barrel quarter choke (Pattern 160) and left barrel half choke (Pattern 170), or right barrel half choke (Pattern 170) and left barrel three-quarter choke (Pattern 187).

Smaller sizes than No. 12 should be bored similarly, but in their case the limit of range is shorter, as will be seen in the chapter dealing with this subject.

Finally, it is absolutely essential that the shooter should see his guns tested for pattern with cartridges similar to those which he uses in the field. This is of paramount importance, as it ensures that the gunmaker actually bores the gun to the desired specifications, and it gives the purchaser confidence in his gun as few other things can.

It may happen that the cartridges which are to be used in the field will not give good patterns in the gun : if the fault is in the gun the cartridges should give good patterns in other barrels; but if the fault is in the cartridges the shooter will be prevented from using inferior cartridges on game.

If the patterns are excellent, both the gunmaker and customer should take steps to satisfy themselves that the cartridges really do develop proper ballistics.

And there is another point in connection with patterns which is frequently not realised by shooters. No combination of gun and cartridges will always give identical patterns; a certain variation in the count is inevitable from round to round. The pattern quoted for any barrel is only the *average* obtained from a number of shots, and it is unreasonable to expect a gun to throw a certain exact pattern every time. Opinions differ as to what is the permissible variation. If the cartridges are beyond reproach a gun which has a variation of but 5 per cent. is a treasure as rare as a perfect horse, and one of 10 per cent. good. But a gun which has a variation of 20 per cent. should be discarded.

The fact that variations in pattern are inevitable makes the splitting of hairs waste of time, and it is for this reason that I have given the patterns recommended in round numbers. It is no use arguing whether it is better to have a pattern of 155 or 157, as I have sometimes heard men do. Nine times out of ten it will probably be neither. All the same it is astonishing what a skilful regulator can do in the way of averaging up patterns, but the shooter should be reasonable in his attitude, and if he has asked for a pattern of 160 he should be pleased with an average result of either 156 or 164, particularly if the spread is even. In such cases it is always better to leave well alone rather than to strive for exactness in what are really trivialities, and run the risk of having the regularity of the distribution of the pattern impaired.

CHAPTER V

THE STRINGING OF SHOT

SO far we have only considered the lateral spread of the shot charge during its passage through the air, for it is this lateral spread which influences the pattern. But just as the pellets become more separated laterally from each other the further they travel from the muzzle of the gun, so does their relative longitudinal distance apart increase with the range. In other words, the shot charge strings out from front to rear during its flight, and the greater the range the greater is the length of the total string of pellets.

The explanation for this stringing of the shot charge is not very difficult to understand. It has already been pointed out more than once that the pellets which go to make up one particular size of shot are not all of exactly the same weight. In every charge of No. 6, for instance, there are some pellets nearly as large as No. 5½ and others almost as small as No. 6½. And it is this variation in size which results in the variation in the weights of the individual pellets which constitute any shot charge. The extent of this variation will depend on the accuracy of grading for size during manufacture, and there can be no doubt that the more accurate the grading the more uniform the weights of the individual pellets of any particular size. But absolute uniformity is an impossible ideal.

And even if it were attainable there would always be variation in the shape of the pellets of a shot charge after its exit from the muzzle. For some pellets, especially the outside ones, will suffer more from deformation than others during their passage up the bore. Further, the abrasion against the bore must reduce the weight of a percentage of the pellets, and so it will be seen that even if every pellet was of exactly the same shape and weight when the shot charge was loaded into the cartridge, there would be a distinct variation in the shapes and weights of the pellets when they left the muzzle of the gun.

Now it was explained in Volume II that the capacity possessed by any projectile for overcoming air resistance during flight, and so retaining its original velocity, was dependent on its size, weight and shape. It will, accordingly, be clear that if the pellets of a shot charge vary in size, weight and shape their individual capacities for retaining their original velocity will also vary. This is exactly what happens; and obviously always must happen, although to a varying extent. The result is that the heaviest pellets and those which have suffered least by deformation will gradually forge ahead, while the lightest pellets and those which are most misshapen will steadily drop behind, the main bulk of the shot charge becoming strung out between these two extremes.

This fact has long been recognised by all who were interested in shotguns, but the practical shooter will be chiefly concerned with the actual effect of the stringing of the shot charge in the shooting field. And there are two questions which naturally arise.

First, does the stringing of shot mean that the back pellets have less effect on a bird owing to their lower striking velocity?

Secondly, what is the effect on the actual pattern on a fast crossing bird?

It has been argued that a bird occupies a certain position in space momentarily only, and that at the actual moment it was there it is possible for no pellet to have been there also at the same time; but that after the bird had flown on two or three pellets might have come up and passed through the space which had previously been occupied by the bird. If a pattern plate had been placed immediately behind the bird the plate would have registered all the hits irrespective of when those hits were made. In fact it has seemed possible that a pattern plate is altogether deceiving, in that it can show a perfect pattern when there are really large gaps. In other

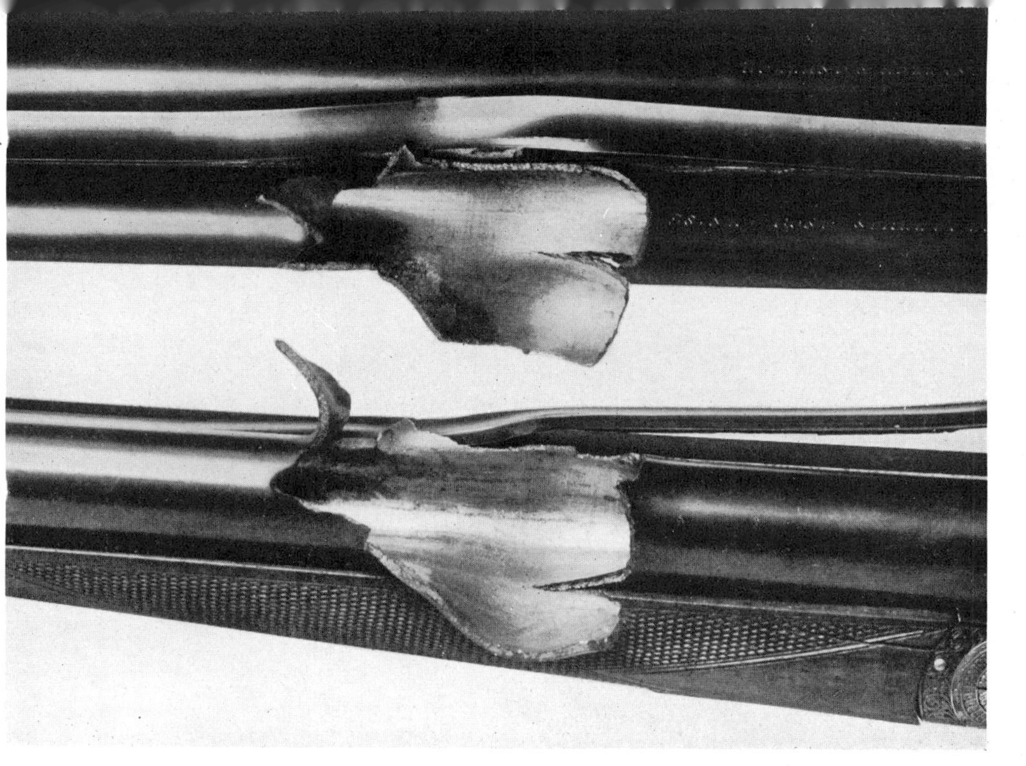

TWO VIEWS OF AN OBSTRUCTIONAL BURST NEAR THE BREECH END OF THE LEFT BARREL OF A 16-BORE GUN

In this case the burst was caused by the accidental insertion of a 28-bore cartridge in front of a 16-bore cartridge. The "ring bulge" can be clearly seen in both views. The upper photograph (A) shows how the top rib is bent at the site of the burst, and the lower photograph (B) shows the severed portion of the barrel, which has assumed a concave shape at the site of the burst

words, the bird has been believed to " fly through the pattern."

One of the chief exponents of this doctrine was the late Sir Ralph Payne-Gallwey and in his *High Pheasants in Theory and Practice* he gives an interesting example of the result of stringing of shot. The incident occurred during a grouse drive. Sir Ralph fired at and killed the leading bird of a covey, when to his astonishment he saw another bird, following some way behind the one he had picked out, also crumble up and fall dead. No one else had fired and Sir Ralph had only fired one barrel. The only possible explanation was that the second bird flew into the tail of the shot charge and was killed. From this incident Sir Ralph argued that there must be gaps in the real pattern which would never be indicated on the stationary pattern plate, and he substantiated this reasoning by an ingenious experiment.

He fixed two tin discs up at 40 yards, one immediately in front of the other, and so arranged them that the front one was pulled out of the way by strong elastic immediately it was hit by even a single pellet of shot. On firing at these discs he found that the second disc received just as many pellets as the one in front, although it could not possibly be struck by a pellet so long as the front disc was in position. Sir Ralph thus proved that the shot charge did not travel in one single plane, but that some of the pellets were behind the others.

This deduction was absolutely true, but it was no new discovery, for the experiment was conducted about 1913, and the fact that the shot charge strings out in the air had been realised for fully half a century, if not longer, before.

To my mind the argument in favour of the great loss of actual effective pattern resulting from stringing has always seemed somewhat stultified by the grouse incident just mentioned. For after all Sir Ralph killed the grouse at which he aimed, and this was what his intention had been and the gun gave a sufficiently good pattern to enable him to carry out his intention. The fact that the bird behind was also killed established the existence of a distinct tail to the shot charge: but the killing of the leading bird proved that this tail did not spoil the pattern to any very material extent.

This point of view was held by a school of thought who were altogether more optimistic and declared that stringing was a positive advantage as birds were killed by "flying into the pattern," and I have seen it stated that a moving bird must "obviously" be hit by many more pellets than a stationary one for this reason.

This line of thought always seemed to me rather difficult to follow; for it appeared more probable that the stringing out of the shot charge could not have any marked effect in view of the success which could be achieved with a gun on fast crossing birds, even though a certain loss in pattern density must clearly be inevitable.

But the important point to establish was the extent to which the pattern obtained on a stationary target could be relied upon as an indication of the efficiency of the combination of gun and cartridge on flying game.

MR. GRIFFITH'S EXPERIMENTS

The first scientific investigation of the problem of stringing of shot was conducted by the late Mr. R. W. S. Griffith in 1887. The apparatus which he designed consisted of a flat circular target, 12 feet in diameter, connected electrically with a chronograph, and kept rotating at a steady speed by steam power. For the purpose of simplifying calculations it was run at 318 revolutions per minute, which gave a rim-velocity of 200 f.s. The surface of the wheel was covered with an annular band 4 feet in width, and the rim was marked all round at points 6 inches apart from which radial lines were ruled across the face of the band towards the centre; every space between these lines thus represented $\frac{1}{400}$ of a second when the wheel was revolved at the speed mentioned.

Circular lines, 3 inches apart, were also drawn on the

face of the band, or target; and the whole face was thus divided into sections which could be numbered for reference.

For velocity work, so far as arithmetical records were concerned, these lines were sufficient. But for visual inspection the patterns thus obtained did not give such a good idea of the flight as a rectangular horizontal pattern would convey; so the sections bounded by circular and radial lines were translated into rectangular sections of 6 inches by 3 inches on a surface with parallel lines instead of the circular lines on the revolving target. The patterns were carefully plotted on this horizontal plane, and were then photographed. Thus the photographs represented a horizontal translation of the patterns actually obtained on a section of a circle.

In front of the revolving target, and as close to it as possible, was fixed a screen covering the whole of the lower half of the target, except that it was perforated with an opening 4 feet in diameter and so placed as to coincide with the 4-foot band rotating behind it. Across this opening was strained a sheet of very thin paper.

On a shot being fired the *stationary* pattern was obtained on this thin sheet of paper, while the pellets passed through it and struck the revolving target immediately behind, thus giving the *moving* pattern obtained with the same shot.

The fixed screen was whitewashed and so it was possible to tell whether the shot was a central one and whether the bulk of the pattern had entered the 4-foot aperture.

A sketch of this apparatus is shown in Fig. 11.

The experiments were made at 10, 20, 30, 40, 50, and 60 yards with cylinder and choke guns firing 42 grains of Schultze and $1\frac{1}{8}$ ounce of No. 6 shot; also with a $2\frac{3}{4}$-inch-choke gun firing 49 grains of Schultze and $1\frac{1}{4}$ ounce of No. 6 shot. So it will be realised that the scope of Mr. Griffith's research was fairly complete. Photographs of his records were published in the *Field* of April 9th, 1887, and from the measurements of some of these photographs the particulars given in Table XIII were obtained.

If these results are examined it will be seen that the main bulk of the shot charge, that is 90 per cent., flies in a comparatively compact mass, and that the remaining

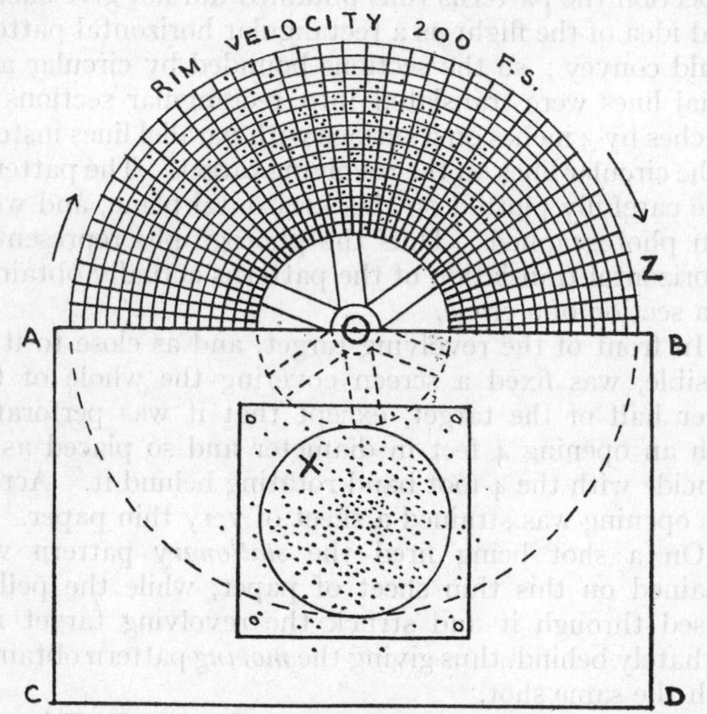

FIG. 11.—The Revolving Wheel apparatus designed and used by Mr. Griffith for measuring the stringing of shot.

Z is the revolving wheel 12 feet in diameter, and A, B, C, D is the screen covering the lower half of the wheel. X is the circular hole in this screen, 4 feet in diameter, across which a piece of thin paper was strained, and on which the stationary pattern was obtained.

In the sketch an imaginary pattern has been dotted in on both the paper screen and the revolving wheel, showing the difference between the two patterns caused by the stringing of the shot charge.

10 per cent. strings out into a tail which is roughly almost as long again as the distance from front to rear of the main bulk.

The important point to realise is that Mr. Griffith succeeded in measuring the actual length of the shot column in the air, and if this length is definitely known,

TABLE XIII

RESULTS OF MR. GRIFFITH'S INVESTIGATION OF THE STRINGING OF SHOT

Cartridges loaded with $1\frac{1}{8}$ oz. No. 6 Shot and Schultze Powder

Range in Yards.	Time in Secs. separating first Pellet and			Velocity over Range in F.S.				Actual Distance in feet separating the Front Pellets and the		
	90th-per-cent. Pellet.	95th-per-cent. Pellet.	Last Pellet.	Front Pellets.	90th-per-cent. Pellet.	95th-per-cent. Pellet.	Last Pellets.	90th-per-cent. Pellet.	95th-per-cent. Pellet.	Last Pellet.
CHOKE BARREL										
20	·0011	·0031	·0080	1,070	1,050	1,015	937	0·9	2·5	5·6
30	·0083	·0120	·0173	975	894	863	821	5·4	7·3	9·8
40	·0143	·0204	·0310	884	800	768	719	7·7	10·4	14·1
50	·0179	·0245	·0359	822	750	729	687	8·4	11·1	15·0
CYLINDER BARREL										
20	·0009	·0045	·0098	1,060	1,043	982	904	0·8	2·9	6·4
30	·0078	·0110	·0183	967	892	865	808	5·1	6·3	10·1
40	·0211	·0257	·0407	877	760	737	676	9·0	12·3	16·7
50	·0289	·0367	·0460	815	705	680	652	12·8	15·3	17·9

as well as the relative positions of a sufficient number of specified pellets, it is possible to deduce the effect of stringing both on penetration and pattern.

But before this aspect of the subject is considered it will be of interest to see what verification has since been obtained.

MR. QUAYLE'S EXPERIMENTS

Reference has already been made in Appendix I of Volume II to the spark photographs of shot charges in flight very near the muzzle taken by Mr. P. P. Quayle. Mr. Quayle also took similar photographs of the shot column at longer ranges. The principle he employed was to shoot down a darkened passage on one wall of which was stretched a large sheet of sensitised photographic film. An apparatus was fixed opposite this film which developed a brilliant electric spark when the shot charge passed by, and this momentary flash threw the shadows of the pellets constituting the shot charge on the film. When this was developed the resulting print showed the pellets in silhouette. A photograph was thus obtained without a camera; and the exposure was very brief, being but the duration of the electric spark which has been stated to be but one-millionth part of a second.

By this means Mr. Quayle measured the length of a shot column at various ranges and some of the results he obtained were published in American journals, more particularly *Army Ordnance* of May–June, 1928.

It should be noted that this method of spark photography is the only one which gives the actual measurement of the length of the shot column. In all other methods this length has to be deduced.

The Table on opposite page was one published by Mr. Quayle for a 12-bore gun.

When the variations given by the individual rounds in these measurements are considered, and a comparison is made between them and those obtained by Mr. Griffith, it will be seen that their results can be said to be practically identical. Of course both Mr. Quayle and Mr. Griffith

TABLE XIV

RESULTS OF MR. QUAYLE'S INVESTIGATION OF THE STRINGING OF SHOT

Range.	Distance in Feet between Front Pellet and			Number of Rounds.
	50 per cent. Pellets.	75 per cent. Pellets.	100 per cent. Pellets.	
40 yards . .	2·6	5·5	9·7	1
	3·2	4·1	12·6	1
	4·9	6·0	13·2	1
	3·4	5·1	10·9	1
	4·1	5·2	13·8	1
	3·6	5·2	12·0	Average 5 rounds
11 yards . .	1·0	1·5	4·2	Average 9 rounds

were measuring the same thing, but it may surprise many readers to find that the measurement of the shot string was made so accurately over 60 years ago.

By combining Mr. Quayle's and Mr. Griffith's results it is possible to give the average lengths of the different parts of the shot column at various ranges, and this has been done in the following Table.

TABLE XV

LENGTH OF THE SHOT COLUMN IN FEET AT DIFFERENT RANGES

Front Pellet to	Range in Yards.		
	30	40	50
50th per cent. pellet . . .	2·7	3·6	4·5
75th per cent. pellet . . .	3·9	5·2	6·5
85th–90th per cent. pellet . .	5·4	7·2	9·0
90th–95th per cent. pellet . .	7·2	9·6	12·0
Back pellet	9·0	12·0	15·0

This Table emphasises the fact that the main bulk of the shot charges travels in a comparatively compact column, but that there is a long, thin tail which comprises but about 15 per cent. of the total number of pellets.

Mr. Griffith stated the opinion that many experiments had convinced him that the leading pellets in the column consist of a group of about 5 per cent. of the entire charge, and that this vanguard was closely followed by a further 25 per cent. of the charge. But naturally absolute uniformity cannot exist, and Mr. Griffith's opinion should only be regarded as applying to typical average behaviour.

EFFECT ON PENETRATION

We can now come to an investigation of the practical effects of stringing in the shooting field. These effects may be detrimental both to penetration or pattern, but let us first confine ourselves to the question of penetration, which is really the simpler one to answer.

It has been seen that the shot charge strings out in

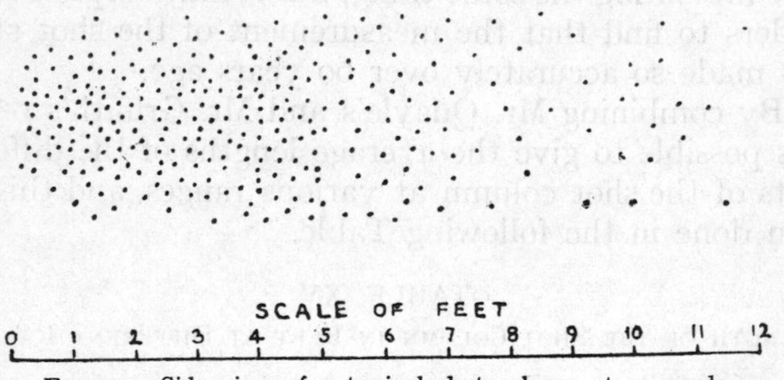

FIG. 12.—Side view of a typical shot column at 40 yards.

An imaginary sketch based on the data given in Table XV and Mr. P. P. Quayle's spark photographs.

the air because the pellets do not all possess the same capacity for overcoming air resistance and so retaining their velocity to the same extent. This means that at any specified instant the pellets of the charge have different velocities, the leading pellets having higher velocities than the more backward ones. Since the average lengths of the various sections of the shot column have been established, it is possible to calculate the actual striking velocities of the pellets comprising these sections at different ranges. The leading pellets will have a slightly higher velocity for any given distance than that of the average pellet of the charge, and the rear pellets will have lower velocities. I mention this in order to explain the seeming discrepancy between the various striking velocities given below when compared with those given in the Tables of Striking Velocities in Volume II. The Tables in Volume II were calculated on the assumption of average behaviour rather than that of the highest velocity attained by any pellet in a charge.

The following Table gives the striking velocities of the different parts of the shot column at 30, 40 and 50 yards.

TABLE XVI

STRIKING VELOCITIES AND ENERGIES OF DIFFERENT PARTS OF THE SHOT COLUMN AT VARIOUS RANGES

Standard 12-bore cartridge loaded with No. 6 shot and giving an Observed Velocity of 1,050 f.s.

Pellet.	Range in Yards.					
	30		40		50	
	Velocity in F.S.	Energy in Ft.-lbs.	Velocity in F.S.	Energy in Ft.-lbs.	Velocity in F.S.	Energy in Ft.-lbs.
Front	752	2·03	634	1·45	528	1·00
50th per cent. . . .	680	1·66	581	1·22	479	0·83
75th per cent. . . .	654	1·54	559	1·11	459	0·76
85th–90th per cent. .	621	1·39	528	1·00	432	0·67
90th–95th per cent. .	583	1·23	493	0·88	400	0·58
Back.	541	1·05	456	0·75	368	0·49

In Volume II it was suggested that a striking energy of 0·8 of a ft.-lb was the minimum necessary to ensure effective penetration ; and if this value is accepted it will be seen that at 30 yards the whole of the shot charge is effective. At 40 yards 95 per cent. of the shot charge is effective, and the ineffective 5 per cent. is made up of the most backward pellets in the extreme tail of the column. In order to be hit by this thin tail of the charge a crossing bird would need to be missed in front with the rest of the column. I do not believe that misses in front are so rare as is frequently asserted: nevertheless I think it may reasonably be assumed that the chances of a bird being struck by any of the pellets in this extreme tail are hardly worth consideration.

At 50 yards, however, the situation is different. Here only the front half of the shot column can be regarded as being absolutely effective, although the next quarter is very nearly so. But even at this range I do not think the loss in penetration resulting from stringing can be regarded as serious; for as before the ineffective portion is composed entirely of the tail of the column, although admittedly not quite the extreme end of the tail. But for a bird to be hit by any of these ineffective pellets it would have to be missed in front by the main bulk of the shot column, and the art of shooting should result in the main and effective bulk of the charge being placed just right.

All the same these 50 yards values do indicate that at this range the shot charge is reaching its limit for effective penetration; and quite possibly they explain why birds are at times undoubtedly killed between 50 and 55 yards, while at other times they may be hit but without serious effect.

An increase in the average striking velocities of all the pellets in the shot column at long range would seem to be an obvious remedy for this loss in stringing. This increase can be attained by an increase in initial velocity, and so it may be of interest to see what effect in the striking velocities and energies of the different parts of the shot column can be produced by loading cartridges to give an observed velocity over 20 yards of 1,150 f.s. These values are given in Table XVII on the opposite page.

It will be seen at once that the increase in observed

velocity has brought the whole of the shot column at 40 yards within the effective limit, but this gain is not very material, because with the standard cartridge it was only the extreme tail of 5 per cent. which lacked penetration.

At 50 yards, however, the advantage is something more real because the leading 75 per cent. of the column has now become effective instead of only the leading 50 per cent. And it is this first three-quarters of the column which is far and away the most likely part to constitute the killing pattern.

TABLE XVII

Striking Velocities and Energies of Different Parts of the Shot Column at Various Ranges

Cartridge loaded with No. 6 shot and giving an Observed Velocity of 1,150 f.s.

Pellet.	Range in Yards.					
	30		40		50	
	Velocity in F.S.	Energy in Ft.-lbs.	Velocity in F.S.	Energy in Ft.-lbs.	Velocity in F.S.	Energy in Ft.-lbs.
Front	793	2·38	671	1·62	562	1·14
50th per cent . . .	741	1·98	618	1·38	514	0·95
75th per cent. . . .	712	1·83	593	1·27	491	0·87
85th–90th per cent. .	680	1·66	563	1·14	464	0·77
90th–95th per cent. .	639	1·47	525	0·99	431	0·67
Back.	593	1·27	487	0·85	395	0·56

Nevertheless this last Table does show that at 50 yards there is an ineffective tail even when the observed velocity developed is as high as 1,150 f.s. ; accordingly, it does not seem unreasonable to place the extreme limit for the killing range of No. 6 shot at a distance of about 50 to 55 yards. And it must be remembered that this determination of the limit of killing range is only taking into consideration the question of penetration and is ignoring that of pattern.

EFFECT ON PATTERN

Having seen that up to 40 yards the effect of stringing on penetration can be regarded as negligible with normal shot sizes and cartridges, we must now consider the effect on pattern. This is really a more difficult problem, and it has been tackled in three ways.

The first of these is to calculate the time intervals between the passage of some fixed point by the front pellets and other parts of the shot column, and then to calculate the distances flown by a bird crossing at, say, 40 miles an hour in these times.

The following Tables give these results for a standard 12-bore cartridge developing an observed velocity of 1,050 f.s.

TABLE XVIII

TIME INTERVALS IN SECONDS SEPARATING FRONT PELLETS AND DIFFERENT PARTS OF THE SHOT COLUMN AT VARIOUS RANGES

Front Pellet to	Range in Yards.		
	30	40	50
50th per cent. pellet . . .	·0039	·0062	·0096
75th per cent. pellet . . .	·0059	·0090	·0139
85th–90th per cent. pellet . .	·0086	·0132	·0202
90th–95th per cent. pellet . .	·0118	·0185	·0274
Back pellet	·0158	·0249	·0381

Table XIX shows that if the head of the shot column is centred correctly on a bird crossing at 40 m.p.h. the bird will not have been able to fly clear of the column by the time the back pellets have reached it, because at all the ranges considered the radius of the total spread of the shot charge, even from a full choke, is greater than the distance flown by the bird. Of course this assumes that the bird is impenetrable to shot: if it were hit by a sufficient number of pellets it would cease to fly.

So it will be seen that a bird cannot possibly fly right through the shot column before the whole of the column has reached it; provided, of course, that the shot charge was properly placed.

This point is interesting, but it does not really decide the actual effect of stringing on the pattern likely to be

TABLE XIX

DISTANCES IN INCHES FLOWN BY A BIRD CROSSING AT 40 M.P.H. DURING THE TIME INTERVALS SEPARATING THE FRONT PELLETS AND DIFFERENT PARTS OF THE SHOT COLUMN AT VARIOUS RANGES

Front Pellet and	Distances Flown in Inches for Ranges of		
	30 Yards.	40 Yards.	50 Yards.
50th per cent. pellet . . .	2·7	4·4	6·8
75th per cent. pellet . . .	4·1	6·4	9·8
85th–90th per cent. pellet . .	6·0	9·3	14·2
90th–95th per cent. pellet . .	8·3	13·0	19·3
Back pellet	11·1	17·5	26·8

received by a crossing bird; and to settle this point it is necessary to compare the pattern actually obtained on a stationary plate with the pattern which would be obtained were the plate crossing the line of fire at the same speed as a bird is flying.

It will be remembered that Mr. Griffith obtained patterns with the help of his revolving wheel which would have been delivered on a plate crossing the line of fire at a speed of 136 m.p.h. A number of these patterns were published in the *Field* of April 9th, 1887, and a typical one is shown in Fig. 13.

From this diagram it is quite evident that there must be an obvious loss in the density of the pattern, or that part of it, received by an area the size of a bird when compared to a corresponding part of the pattern obtained on the stationary plate.

But 136 m.p.h. is an altogether extreme speed, and 40 m.p.h. is probably the highest speed at which birds actually cross the line of fire in normal circumstances. So the target velocity adopted by Mr. Griffith does not really help us much in our investigation of the effect of stringing from the point of view of the practical game shot, although this high velocity was necessary in order to obtain data for the determination of the actual length of the shot column in the air.

Nevertheless Mr. Griffith's records are so numerous and complete that it has seemed a pity not to make use of

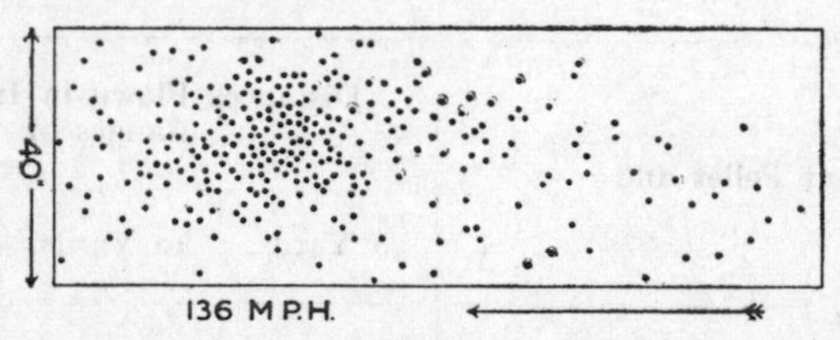

Fig. 13.—One of the patterns obtained by Mr. Griffith on his revolving wheel and translated to a rectangular target moving from right to left at a speed of 136 m.p.h.

them, and a method has been suggested for translating his 136-miles-an-hour patterns to 40-miles-an-hour patterns, when a comparison could be made with the patterns given by the same round on the stationary screen. Like most other methods of theoretical investigation into such problems, the procedure owes its existence to the late Mr. F. W. Jones.

The bedrock on which to start consists of the patterns obtained on the stationary screen and 136-miles-an-hour target by Mr. Griffith with one and the same shot. Any one of Mr. Griffith's numerous records can be taken for our purpose, and the diagram in Fig. 14 shows the procedure.

A, B, C, D is a pattern obtained on the 136-miles-an-hour target, which is the same one as that shown in Fig. 13.

A, E, F, G is the longitudinal plan of the actual shot

column in the air at the moment of impact between the front pellets and the stationary screen. In reality this shot column should be solid and standing up in the air at right angles to the plane of the target A, B, C, D; but such a position is impossible to depict in a diagram, and the effect is just the same if it is shown as it actually is in Fig. 14.

The positions of the pellets in the column A, E, F, G have been determined from a comparison of the stationary pattern (not shown here) and the 136-miles-an-hour pattern, and the column has been drawn to scale.

Now if the target were stationary the whole of the pellets in this shot column would be found on the square portion A, E, H, D; and it is only on account of the target's rapid movement from right to left that the rear part of the column is actually found E, B, C, H.

If a line is drawn joining F to B and other lines are drawn at equal intervals and parallel to this first line, it is not difficult to understand that the pellets in the shot column which lie between these lines will be found on the moving target opposite to where these lines meet the edge of that target.

It will accordingly be realised that Fig. 14 is a diagrammatic explanation of the manner in which the shot column is strung out when it strikes a crossing target.

But if the target is not travelling so rapidly the amount of stringing out will be less, and the dotted line KL marks the extreme right edge of the pattern which would be obtained with this same shot column were the target crossing at but 40 m.p.h.

So if another series of lines are drawn parallel to the line joining F to K, these lines will show how the shot column will distribute itself on the target A, K, L, D, which is crossing at 40 m.p.h.; whence it is possible to reconstruct the pattern on to this target.

This has actually been done in Fig. 15, which shows the pattern which would have been obtained on a target crossing at 40 m.p.h. by the shot which actually gave the pattern shown in Fig. 13.

There are, however, one or two admittedly weak points in this extremely ingenious translation of pattern.

In the first place it has been assumed that the pellets

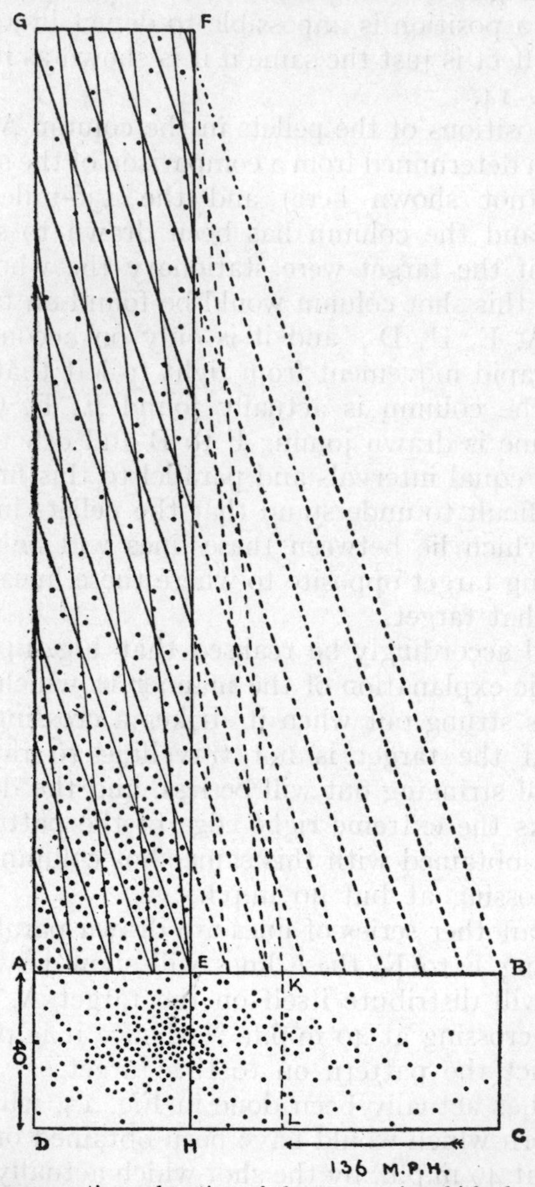

FIG. 14.—Diagrammatic explanation of the manner in which the shot column becomes distributed on a target crossing the line of fire at 136 m.p.h.

are all travelling with the same velocity, whereas in actual practice they are not. This does not in any way affect the general principle which is indicated diagrammatically with such clarity; but it would mean that in actual practice the lines drawn from the shot column to the moving target would have to be diverging as they approached the target, instead of parallel.

Then the correct placing of the individual pellets in

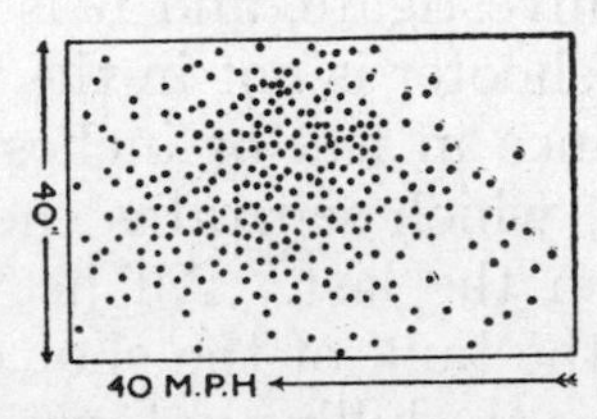

FIG. 15.—The pattern obtained by Mr. Griffith and shown in Fig. 13, but translated on to a target moving at 40 m.p.h.

the representation of the shot column must be largely a matter of conjecture and in any case one of considerable difficulty, and would require an immense amount of time and patience if it were to be done in a sufficient number of examples to give adequate information.

If no other data were obtainable this method of utilising Mr. Griffith's results would be valuable. And even as it is it can provide interesting confirmation for the recent experiments described in the next chapter.

CHAPTER VI

THE EFFECT OF STRINGING ON PATTERN

IT will have been realised from the previous chapter that the problem of the stringing of shot is not an easy one to investigate, and it is undoubtedly true that the ordinary shooter is not in the least concerned as to the exact distance in feet or inches, measured in the direction of flight, which separates the leading pellet of a shot charge from the last. All he wants to know is what happens to the bulk of the shot charge, that main portion which forms the killing pattern. It has been seen that at all ordinary sporting ranges, that is up to 40 and even 50 yards, stringing does not reduce the penetration of the main bulk of the shot charge below the necessary minimum. That is a great deal. But what about pattern? For it is of no practical use for the pellets in the shot column to possess sufficient powers of penetration if the pattern is so decreased in density that a bird can escape in the open spaces.

In spite of the calculations which have been briefly considered in the last chapter, I have always felt that the only really satisfactory way of determining the effect of stringing on pattern would be to fire series of shots on a stationary pattern plate, and then further series with the same gun on a pattern plate crossing the line of fire at 40 m.p.h., or thereabouts, which is the approximate speed of a fast bird.

There was nothing new in this idea, but it was not until quite recently that it was carried out with comparative completeness.

The first person to have conducted any experiments on this line was Mr. H. A. Ivatt, who fired a few shots—apparently four—at an iron target fixed to a railway train. The results of these shots were published in the *Field* of September 20th, 1890. The train travelled at four different speeds, 11·4, 22·8, 28·15 and 32 m.p.h.; and one shot was fired at each speed.

The primary object of the experiments would seem to have been the determination of the forward allowance necessary on a crossing target, as a bull's-eye was painted on the front end of the target and Mr. Ivatt kept swinging on this bull as it moved across his front. The distance between the centre of the pattern and the bull gave the approximate forward allowance necessary for the speed at which the shot was taken.

Not even an approximate idea of the loss in density due to stringing could be obtained because the target was only 3 feet wide, and since the range was 40 yards it was not possible to be certain that each shot had been properly centred. Further, no count of the pellets was taken. But Mr. Ivatt did mention in his account of his experiment that there was no marked difference in the patterns obtained on the moving target from those which would be expected on a stationary plate; and the actual diagrams which were reproduced in the *Field* substantiated this view.

The next experiment of this nature was conducted by Mr. W. Webster Watts, who was for many years the proprietor of the London Sporting Park. On this occasion Mr. Watts utilised an iron plate 9 feet long and 27 inches wide which he dropped from the top of a 90-foot tower and shot at it just before it reached the ground when it had acquired an estimated velocity of 75 f.s. But the narrow width of the target—only 27 inches—precluded the obtaining of any definite data, although the experiment did show that there was quite a good killing pattern on the plate, although it was naturally not possible to determine whether this was the densest part of the pattern or not. This experiment was reported in the *Field* of February 16th, 1907.

Three years later Mr. Watts tried an altogether more ambitious experiment and fixed an iron target 9 feet long by 4 feet wide on the side of a motor-car and fired some shots at it when travelling at various speeds up to 50 m.p.h.

But here again, curiously enough, Mr. Watts seemed far more interested in trying to determine the necessary forward allowance than in the question of stringing, as can be seen from his interesting account of the experiment which appeared in the *Field* of May 7th, 1910. Forward allowance depends on other factors besides the flight of the shot charge, and all of these can be ascertained with far greater accuracy by other means than aiming at a moving mark and measuring the distance of the centre of the pattern behind this mark. This method is dependent largely on the human element, which should always be excluded in any research.

On this occasion Mr. Watts's target was again too narrow for reliable tests for pattern, but his results certainly did show that a perfectly effective killing pattern could be obtained on a rapidly moving target.

It so happened that I was staying at Baynards Park, Surrey, with my friend, the late Mr. C. E. Allan, during December, 1925, for one of his most enjoyable covert shoots, and I happened to mention how keen I was to carry out some really comprehensive experiments to try to determine the actual effect of stringing on pattern. Mr. Allan seized on the idea with enthusiasm with the result that as soon as the shooting season was over, that is in February, 1926, we began work in earnest.

The car used for the experiments was an ordinary Ford lorry which normally fulfilled efficiently the duties of a luggage car. Mr. Allan had the engine generally overhauled and tuned up so as to ensure regular running at comparatively high speeds.

A vertical sheet-iron target, 6 feet high by 12 feet long, was fixed to the off side of the car. I may mention that Mr. Allan and myself between us made the whole of the target frame and attached the target ourselves, the work taking about three days. The general method of attachment can be seen from the photograph given in Plate II. In order to counter-balance the weight of the

PLATE VII

(A) An action and stock of a best-grade gun smashed by a very excessive pressure. The bar of the action is cracked as can be seen, while the head of the stock is broken. The barrels, however, are absolutely intact and exhibit no signs of distress in any way. This case shows how, in a best-grade gun, the barrels are stronger than the action, especially if the latter is not fitted with a top extension.

(B) A double obstructional burst. In this case some cleaning material was left behind in both barrels. The first shot of the day burst the right barrel, when the left barrel was jarred off, which also burst. In both barrels the wave pressure was so intense that it completely severed the barrels in two; but evidence of both " ring bulges " is plainly shown by the bands in the rib at the points 1 and 2, as well as by the tendency to a funnel-like appearance shown by the severed portions of the barrels.

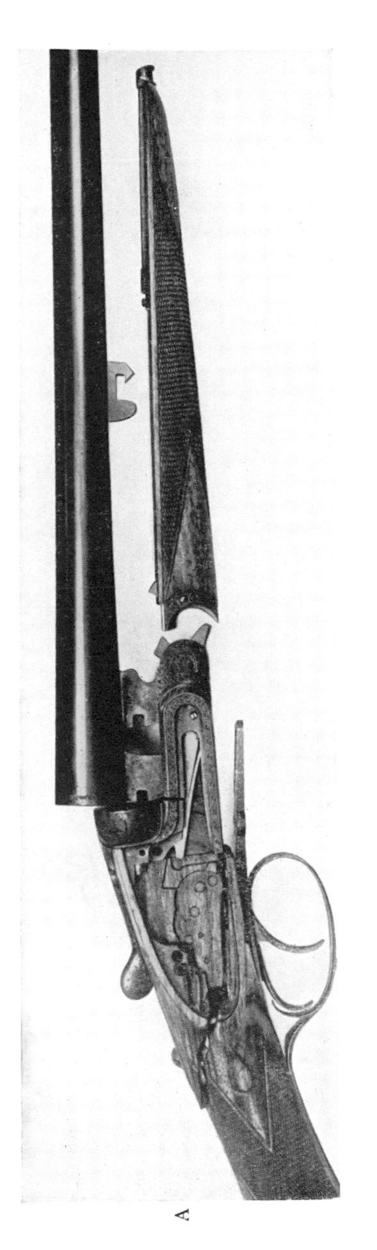

A

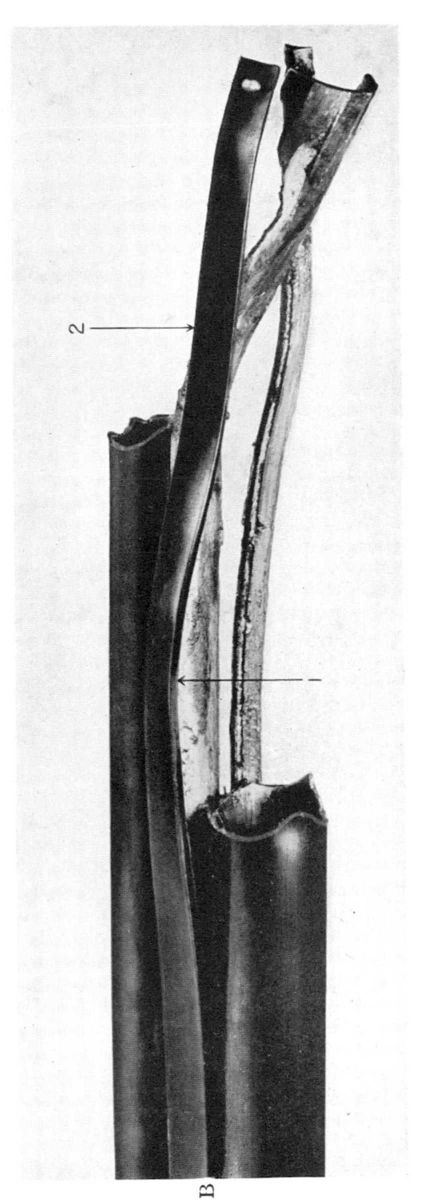

B

target four heavy iron bars were lashed to the ends of the horizontal wooden joists on the near side of the car, while an anvil placed inside the body, also on the near side, completed the necessary amount of counterpoise.

As a precautionary measure, and in order to protect the front wheel and radiator from any stray pellets, an additional piece of sheet iron was bolted on to the front edge of the main target and held in position by wooden supports behind. The three main longitudinal wooden supports for the whole target were purposely left protruding to the rear with a view to simplifying the attachment of any additional light sheet iron or canvas target should the existing length of 12 feet prove insufficient to catch all the pellets in the extreme tail of the shot charge when the car was travelling at 40 m.p.h. A very few shots, however, proved that this additional precaution was unnecessary.

In passing it may be mentioned that the car steered easily and that there was no serious wind pressure on the target ; the engine ran perfectly throughout, while no hitch of any sort occurred in connection with the target attachment.

Before any reliance could be placed on the results obtained it was necessary to check the accuracy of the speedometer, a new instrument specially fitted for the experiments, at different speeds. With this end in view a furlong was taped out along a level road and the car was driven over this furlong twice at 20, 30 and 40 m.p.h.

Speedometer Reading.	Time over One Furlong.	
	Correct Time.	Observed Time.
20 m.p.h.	22½ secs.	22 secs.
20 ,, ...	22½ ,,	22⅖ ,,
30 ,, ...	15 ,,	14⅗ ,,
30 ,, ...	15 ,,	14⅗ ,,
40 ,, ...	11¼ ,,	11⅕ ,,
40 ,, ...	11¼ ,,	11⅙ ,,

respectively, while the time was in each case taken with a stop-watch. The results of this speedometer calibration were as tabulated on the previous page.

SCOPE AND CONDUCT OF THE EXPERIMENTS

Our main, in fact almost our whole, object in these experiments was to ascertain as definitely as possible what effect the stringing of shot had on the killing pattern in ordinary sporting circumstances. It was clear that there must be some loss in pattern density when the target was moving rapidly across the line of fire, and we wished to determine whether this loss was sufficiently great as to nullify the utility of ordinary tests for pattern on a fixed plate.

We also thought that it might be possible to obtain some data as to the length of the shot column in the air. It must be remembered that these experiments were carried out before Mr. Quayle had taken or published his spark photographs, and the only scientific information on this subject was that obtained by Mr. Griffith thirty-nine years before.

But we realised that a speed of 40 m.p.h., which was the maximum the car could attain with regularity and certainty, was insufficient to permit of any accurate computations being made as to the length of the shot column. And in any case we felt that the practical effects of stringing in the actual shooting field were really of more importance to sportsmen.

With this end in view we collected a number of ordinary good shooting 12-bore game guns, all of which were regularly used in the actual shooting field. Of the total number of barrels four were bored improved cylinder and all the others with varying degrees of choke. The cartridges used were loaded with 33 grains of Smokeless Diamond powder, best felt wadding, and $1\frac{1}{16}$ ounce of No. 6 shot. Both the powder and shot charges were checked by weight, and I took a number of cartridges haphazard from the whole lot and shot them for pressure and velocity, when I found that the ballistics were normal and regular.

I had always thought it possible that the effects of stringing might be enhanced by a long shot column in the bore owing to the greater proportion of pellets which would be on the outside and suffer from abrasion, and so we borrowed an American 20-bore chambered for the special 3-inch cartridge, and a best-grade pigeon gun by Holland and Holland which was chambered for the $2\frac{3}{4}$-inch case holding $1\frac{1}{4}$ ounce of shot.

As a further check we also tested an ordinary 12-bore game gun which had been specially regulated for an ounce of shot, as this lighter charge would cause a slight reduction in the length of the shot column in the bore.

Every gun was first fired for pattern at the stationary target at 40 yards, and the number of pellets in the selected 30-inch circle was counted as usual, a mean of a series of five rounds being taken as the average. Series of five shots were then fired at the moving target at 40 yards when the car was travelling at speeds of 30 and 40 m.p.h. Here again in every single case the number of pellets in the 30-inch circle was counted, while the height and width of the whole pattern, with the exception of the outside straggling pellets, was measured as accurately as possible in order to determine the degree of elongation in the whole pattern resulting from the movement of the target.

In addition photographs were taken of a great number of the patterns obtained on both the stationary and moving targets.

(*N.B.*—In order to avoid confusion in the description of the results obtained, I propose to refer to the elongation of the whole pattern on the actual moving target as "tailing," while the longitudinal spreading out of the actual shot charge in the air will still be referred to as "stringing.")

Before any shots were taken at the moving target some difficulty was anticipated in hitting the target in a central position, but as a matter of fact the shooting was easy; very much easier than it looked. It did provide, however, a most important object lesson in the supreme importance of swing; and it was most interesting to see the effect of even the slightest check in the swing. Such a check would result in the shot being centred quite 6 feet farther back, and proved that if a bird is missed through a check in swing, it is not missed by inches but by yards.

Mr. Allan and myself fired every shot between us, but he fired about 75 per cent. of the total while I occupied myself with measuring the vertical and horizontal spreads of the whole charge, counting the patterns, recording all results and taking photographs.

Fears as to stray pellets puncturing the tyres proved to be unfounded and everything worked without a hitch from start to finish.

The sound of the discharge of the gun and that of the shot striking the sheet-iron target were so drowned by "Tin Lizzy's" ordinary everyday noise that the effect seemed no more than that of an airgun being fired, while the skill displayed by Mr. Alec Mackay, the actual driver of the car, who drove with constant regularity of speed in an identical track again and again, helped very materially to the success of the experiments.

The late Mr. F. W. Jones was Mr. Allan's guest as well as myself during the whole conduct of the actual firing at the moving target, and helped us much with his advice; while Mr. Eric Parker came over one day and watched the experiments.

THE RESULTS OBTAINED

Mr. Allan insisted on the honour of the first shot at the moving target being mine, while he rode in the car beside the driver in order to check the speed indicated and to find out what the noise made by the impact of the shot on the plate was like when the car was travelling.

So as to make quite sure of not losing any "tail" of

the pattern off the target the first shot was taken at 30 yards while the speed of the car was only 20 m.p.h.

I will never forget my feelings of excitement as I waited in position while the car approached the spot at which the shot was to be taken. They were akin to those which one experiences when firing the opening shot in the Elcho Match at Bisley. Mr. Jones stood beside me in silence, but I could see he was just as excited as I was myself.

I took the shot in exactly the same way as I take a crossing hare: that is, just swung through the spot where I wanted to place my pattern and pressed the trigger. We then all hurried to examine the result, and I was gratified to see that the shot had been placed just where I had intended.

This one shot saved us a lot of trouble, as the pattern was absolutely indistinguishable from that obtained on a stationary plate! There was no tail of any sort! So we immediately gave up all ideas of making tests at under 40 yards range or at speeds lower than 30 m.p.h.

I then fired one shot at 40 yards at the target travelling at 30 m.p.h. as a check, and once again there was not any noticeable tailing. This enabled us to proceed in earnest.

But since the attainment of a speed of 40 m.p.h. needed a considerably longer run with consequent delays the greater part of the shooting was carried out while the target was crossing at 30 m.p.h. Although this speed is undoubtedly exceeded by many game birds it proved quite sufficient to indicate whatever tendency there was towards elongation of the pattern owing to the movement of the target. Accordingly a great number of series of shots were fired from the different guns at the target moving at 30 m.p.h., and the higher speed of 40 m.p.h. was only used in a more limited number of series in order to confirm the results which had been obtained at 30 m.p.h. As it was the experiments occupied nearly a fortnight and well over 100 shots were fired at the moving target, the whole pattern being measured and the pellets in the 30-inch circle being counted in every single case.

But because there was no pronounced tailing with ordinary game guns, it did not necessarily follow that it might not be produced by magnum loads with their long shot columns in the bore of the gun. Unfortunately it was not possible to obtain all the evidence for which we had hoped on account of the poor shooting qualities of the magnum 20-bore which has already been mentioned. Series were fired with this gun at the target when stationary and moving, but the patterns were so variable and irregular that it was not possible to draw any definite conclusion. Excellent results, however, were obtained with the 12-bore pigeon gun firing $1\frac{1}{4}$ ounce of shot, and both barrels gave results which were similar to those given by ordinary 12-bores bored with choke. The additional length of the shot column in the pigeon gun due to the extra $\frac{3}{16}$ ounce of shot made no noticeable difference of any sort from the point of view of tailing. Similarly, there was no reduction in tailing caused by firing an ounce-shot charge from an ordinary 12-bore, although in this case the difference in the length of the shot column was so slight that no difference in results was thought possible.

I think, therefore, that it may be assumed that a long shot column does not have any tendency to increase the effects of stringing. Many, including myself, had thought this possible.

But although there was no tailing as such, it must not be imagined that the patterns on the moving target were identical with those made on a fixed plate. As a matter of fact, there was a very slight elongation of the pattern at 30 m.p.h., which became slightly more pronounced at 40 m.p.h. In order to check my first shot one complete series was fired at the target travelling at 20 m.p.h. but as the patterns obtained both individually and on the average were exactly similar at 40 yards to stationary ones, further firing at this speed was abandoned as being mere waste of time.

Taken as a whole, the average elongation of the pattern due to a speed of 30 m.p.h. was just under 4 inches ; and just over 5 inches at a speed of 40 m.p.h. in the case of choke barrels.

With improved cylinder barrels the average elongation was about one inch more than that of the choke at each speed.

It should be clearly understood that only the main bulk of the pattern is referred to when considering elongation. In every pattern there will be a few isolated pellets right outside the others ; these were ignored in each case. At 40 m.p.h. a common feature of the patterns was the presence of six or ten pellets just clear on the left showing that it was these few pellets which had formed the end of the string of the charge, since the target travelled from left to right throughout the experiments. At 30 m.p.h. these lagging pellets were not so noticeable.

Since it was thought possible that a small proportion of the pellets had lagged so far behind that they were never caught on the target at all, every single shot-mark on the target was counted in a number of instances with the 40-miles-an-hour patterns, and in no case were there more than ten pellets unaccounted for out of the whole charge, while in one instance every single pellet of the charge reached the target. Even when firing at a stationary target it is seldom that every pellet can be counted, and the number of pellets lost was never greater than would be expected when plating a gun in the ordinary way, and so cannot in any case be due to the stringing of the shot.

Yet although there was no pronounced tailing, and only a slight elongation of the patterns, there was one difference between the actual patterns obtained on the moving and stationary targets which was both marked and persistent ; and that was the reduced density of the moving target compared to that of the stationary one. The number of pellets in the 30-inch circle was unquestionably reduced by the movement of the target.

It might be that single shots would not show this reduction as much as others; but patterns will always vary slightly from round to round, and in every case when the average of each series was taken the number of pellets in the 30-inch circle was noticeably less in the case of the moving target than it was on the stationary one.

This reduction of density was naturally more pronounced at 40 m.p.h. than at 30 m.p.h., but it existed at the lower speed none the less, and was really the natural outcome of the elongations already mentioned, slight though they were. In the case of the moving patterns the same number of pellets was distributed over a slightly larger area, and so the concentration in any given area was reduced.

There was, however, another interesting fact which gradually became evident as the experiments were continued; and that was that the loss in density due to the movement of the target was considerably more pronounced with improved-cylinder barrels than with the choke barrels, irrespective of the degree of choke.

These results can best be realised with the help of the following Table. It should be remembered that the numbers given for the various patterns are averages of series of shots in every instance. In some cases the series consisted of seven or eight shots, but in the majority five shots constituted a series. In every case except that of the pigeon gun the gun was an ordinary 12-bore $2\frac{1}{2}$-inch game gun, and the cartridges were loaded with the standard load as has already been mentioned, except in the two instances specified. No. 6 shot was used throughout.

It will be noticed that No. 1 barrel (improved cylinder) was fired twice with somewhat different results. The first results obtained at a speed of 30 m.p.h. were obtained on the first day of firing. On the second day this barrel was used for the 40 m.p.h. test. A very regular series of eight shots was obtained at this speed which gave a mean pattern of 127, which was slightly more dense than the mean pattern (123) which had previously been obtained at 30 m.p.h. This was so contradictory that completely new series were immediately fired at the stationary plate and the target moving at speeds of 20 and 30 m.p.h. These fresh results gave average

TABLE XX

PATTERNS OBTAINED ON TARGETS MOVING AT 30 AND 40 M.P.H.

Barrel.	Pellets in 30-in. Circle at 40 Yds.				
	Target Stationary.	Target moving			
		30 M.P.H.		40 M.P.H.	
		Pattern.	Percentage Loss in Density.	Pattern.	Percentage Loss in Density.
Improved Cylinder					
No. 1	153	123	19·6	—	—
,, 2	157	124	21·0	—	—
,, 3	148	122	17·6	—	—
,, 1 (repeat)	163	142	12·9	127	22·0
,, 4	158	131	17·1	—	—
Choke					
No. 5	214	208	2·8	191	10·75
,, 6 (1 oz.)	142	138	2·8	—	—
,, 7 (1 oz.)	158	155	1·9	146	7·6
,, 7	198	184	7·0	—	—
,, 8	181	174	3·9	—	—
,, 9 (2¾ in., 1¼ oz.)	229	219	4·3	—	—
,, 10 (2¾ in., 1¼ oz.)	252	244	3·2	—	—
,, 11	182	167	8·2	—	—
,, 12	181	172	4·7	—	—
,, 13	218	211	3·2	—	—

patterns of 163 both on the stationary target and when it was moving at 20 m.p.h.; and an average of 142 when the target was moving at 30 m.p.h. These results fitted in with the pattern of 127 at 40 m.p.h. But the fact that a repeat was necessary shows how dangerous it is to form conclusions on single shots, or even on single series.

Every gunmaker knows that the same guns will give slightly different patterns from day to day even when the same lot of cartridges are used, and there can be no doubt that barrel No. 1 was shooting somewhat closer on the second day than on the first.

Turning to the choke barrels, it should be noted that Nos. 6 and 7 were the right and left barrels of an ordinary 12-bore game gun which had been regulated for one ounce of shot and was invariably used in the field with this charge. When firing an ounce these barrels behaved in a manner similar to the rest of the choke barrels, but No. 7 barrel undoubtedly behaved abnormally with $1\frac{1}{16}$ ounce of shot. A pattern of 158 from an ounce should correspond to one of 169 from $1\frac{1}{16}$ ounce, yet with the heavier charge the pattern was 198, which approaches that of a full choke. It would accordingly seem that little reliance should be placed on the results given by this barrel with $1\frac{1}{16}$ ounce as far as the formation of conclusions as to the behaviour of choke bores is concerned.

It should be noticed that both the elongation of, and the loss of density in, the pattern was increased the faster the target moved in comparison to the shot. That this should be the case is, after all, obvious. But since the car was not capable of maintaining a higher speed than 40 m.p.h. with any regularity, the only practical method of increasing the speed of the car in comparison to that of the shot was to reduce the velocity of the shot. It will be realised that the elongation due to the target's motion will vary with the velocity of the shot column at the moment of impact so long as the speed of the target is constant. That is, the governing factor is the striking velocity of the shot charge for the range at which the shot is taken, and this becomes lest as the range is increased. At 40 yards the striking velocity of what can be termed a standard charge of No. 6 shot is 623 f.s., and at 50 yards the striking velociys is 518 f.s.

So when the target was moving at 30 m.p.h. the

shot charge was travelling just about fourteen times as fast as the target at the moment of impact. And when the target was travelling at 40 m.p.h. the velocity of the shot charge was roughly eleven times that of the target at the moment of impact. But if the range were increased to 50 yards the striking velocity of the shot would become only nine times that of the target when the latter was moving at 40 m.p.h.

It was accordingly determined to try a series at 50 yards and 40 m.p.h. Various barrels were first plated on the stationary target, but it was found that only a full choke could be relied upon to give a sufficiently close pattern. In the case of improved-cylinder barrels the total spread was more than 6 feet in diameter, and since the target was but 6 feet high, no tailing of the shot charge would be visible, as it would be impossible to tell how much of the shot charge had missed the target altogether above and below.

The following Table gives the average results of series of seven shots at 50 yards, one series being that obtained when the target was stationary and the other when it was moving at 40 m.p.h.

TABLE XXI

PATTERNS OBTAINED AT 50 YARDS ON TARGET MOVING AT 40 M.P.H.

Barrel.	Pellets in 30-in. Circle.			
	Target Stationary.	Target moving 40 M.P.H.		
		Pattern.	Percentage Loss in Density.	Elongation of Main Pattern due to Movement of Target.
No. 5	132	123	6·8	7 in.

Here again we find a comparatively slight elongation of the main pattern due to the movement of the target, but quite an appreciable loss in density, although this loss is perhaps not as great as might have been expected.

As has already been stated, a very considerable number of photographs were taken of the patterns; but since all these photographs really tell the same story I have selected a few typical examples which are shown in Figs. 16 to 23 so that readers may see for themselves exactly what changes are produced in patterns owing to the target moving at 30 and 40 m.p.h.

It will be seen that apart from a certain loss in density there is very little difference between those made on stationary and moving plates, and these experiments certainly proved that the method which has been in universal usage for so long, that of assessing a gun's capabilities by plating it on a fixed pattern plate, is in actual fact a very excellent one. The general characteristics of the pattern are not in any way changed by the movement of the target. A gun which gives close patterns on the fixed plate will not throw open spaces through which a bird can escape when flying across the line of fire; nor can a gun which gives patchy and irregular patterns produce any better results on a moving object. In fact, the pattern plate was vindicated and the ghost of the evil effects of stringing was laid.

ANALYSIS OF THE RESULTS

If Table XX is studied it will be noticed that both the improved cylinder and the choke barrels gave results at 30 m.p.h., which were on the whole remarkably consistent. The difference between the two types of boring is that the improved cylinders gave a decidedly greater loss in density of pattern than did any of the chokes. The greatest loss in density yielded by an improved cylinder was 21 per cent., while the lowest was 12·9 per cent., and, as has already been explained, the barrel which gave this last result showed a loss of 19·6 per cent. under identical conditions on the previous day. Accordingly, if we take the average of these losses

12-BORE IMPROVED CYLINDER AT 40 YARDS

Load: 33 grains Smokeless Diamond and $1\frac{1}{16}$ ounce No. 6 shot.

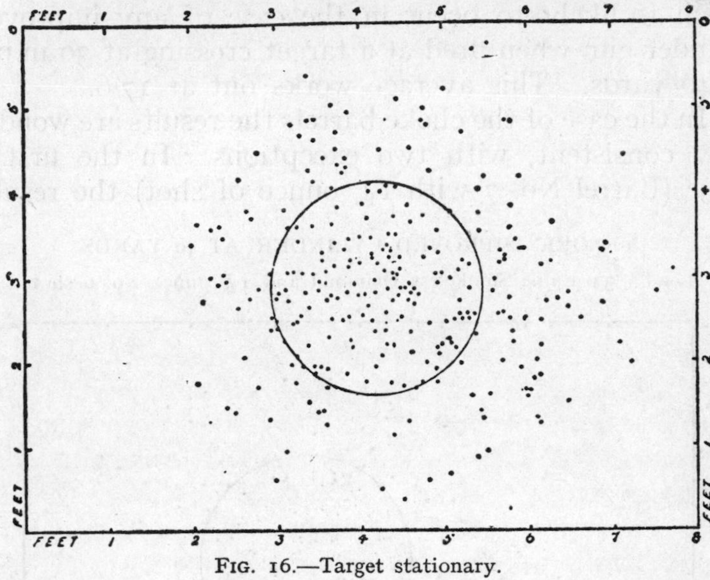

FIG. 16.—Target stationary.

Pellets in 30-in. circle: 152.

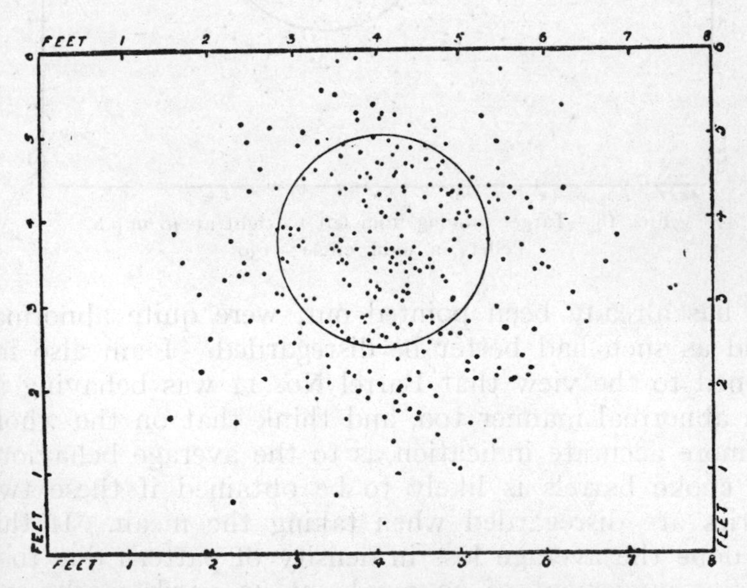

FIG. 17.—Target moving from left to right at 30 m.p.h.

Pellets in 30-in. circle: 141.

it will not be unreasonable to suppose that the figure obtained denotes the probable average loss in density which is likely to occur in the case of any improved-cylinder gun when fired at a target crossing at 30 m.p.h. at 40 yards. This average works out at 17·6.

In the case of the choke barrels the results are wonderfully consistent, with two exceptions. In the first of these (Barrel No. 7 with $1\frac{1}{16}$ ounce of shot) the results,

12-BORE IMPROVED CYLINDER AT 40 YARDS

Load: 33 grains Smokeless Diamond and $1\frac{1}{16}$ ounce No. 6 shot.

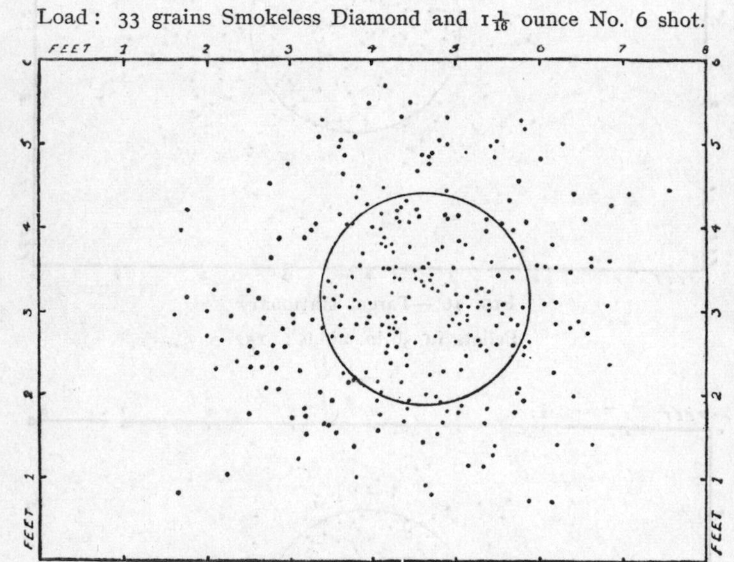

FIG. 18.—Target moving from left to right at 40 m.p.h.
Pellets in 30-in. circle: 130.

as has already been pointed out, were quite abnormal and as such had better be disregarded. I am also inclined to the view that Barrel No. 11 was behaving in an abnormal manner too, and think that on the whole a more accurate indication as to the average behaviour of choke barrels is likely to be obtained if these two series are disregarded when taking the mean. If this is done the average loss in density of pattern due to a target movement of 30 m.p.h. at 40 yards works out at 3·35 per cent. for choke barrels. And even if the two

12-BORE FULL CHOKE AT 40 YARDS

Load: 33 grains Smokeless Diamond and $1\frac{1}{16}$ ounce No. 6 shot.

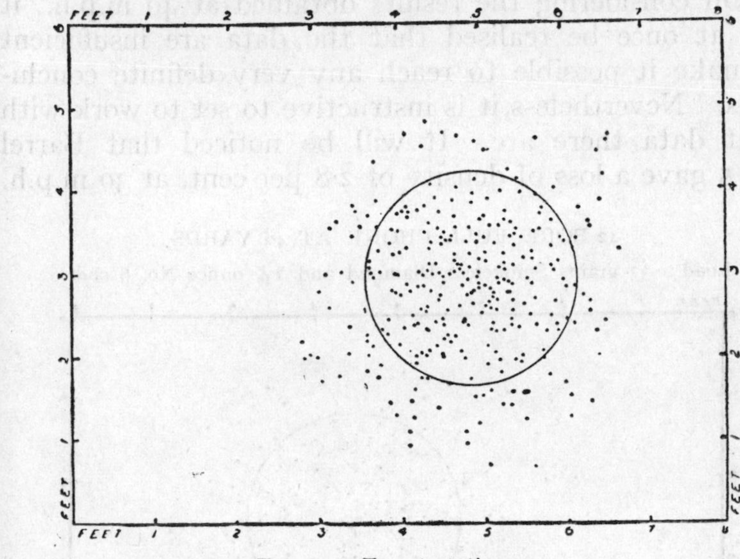

FIG. 19.—Target stationary.

Pellets in 30-in. circle: 212.

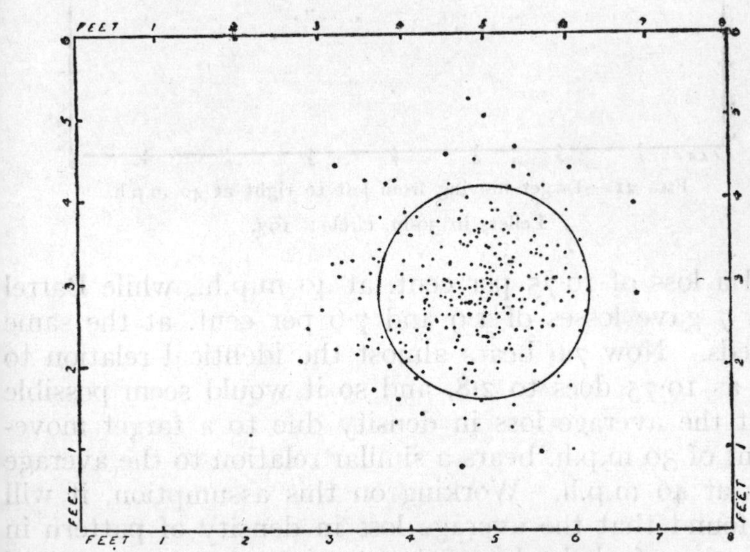

FIG 20—Target moving from left to right at 30 m.p.h.

Pellets in 30-in. circle: 206.

seemingly abnormal results are included the average loss is only 4·2 per cent.

On considering the results obtained at 40 m.p.h., it will at once be realised that the data are insufficient to make it possible to reach any very definite conclusions. Nevertheless it is instructive to set to work with what data there are. It will be noticed that Barrel No. 5 gave a loss of density of 2·8 per cent. at 30 m.p.h.

12-BORE FULL CHOKE AT 40 YARDS

Load: 33 grains Smokeless Diamond and $1\frac{1}{16}$ ounce No. 6 shot.

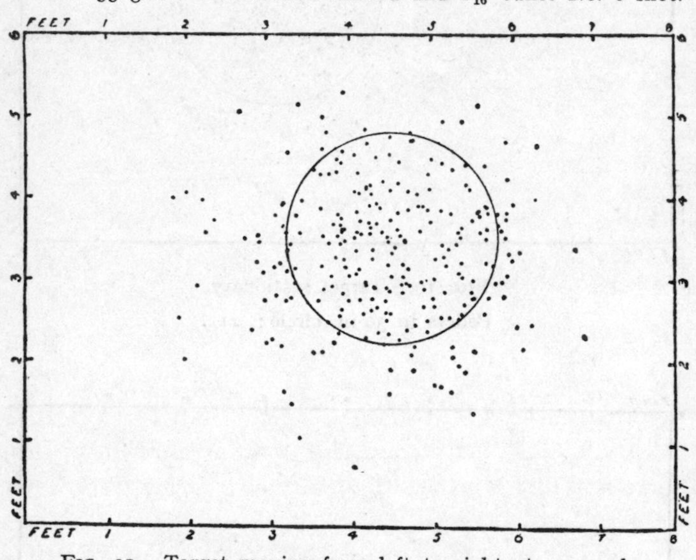

FIG. 21.—Target moving from left to right at 40 m.p.h.

Pellets in 30-in. circle: 197.

and a loss of 10·75 per cent. at 40 m.p.h., while Barrel No. 7 gave losses of 1·9 and 7·6 per cent. at the same speeds. Now 7·6 bears almost the identical relation to 1·9 as 10·75 does to 2·8, and so it would seem possible that the average loss in density due to a target movement of 30 m.p.h. bears a similar relation to the average loss at 40 m.p.h. Working on this assumption, it will be found that the average loss in density of pattern in the case of choke bores due to a target movement of 40 m.p.h. at 40 yards is 13 per cent.

Similarly, if we assume that in the case of improved cylinders the average loss in density at 40 m.p.h. bears the same relation to the average loss at 30 m.p.h. as 22 bears to 12·9 (the results which were actually obtained with Barrel No. 1), we find that the average percentage loss at the higher speed is 30.

For the sake of convenience these results are given in round numbers in the following Table.

TABLE XXII

PERCENTAGE LOSS IN DENSITY OF PATTERN DUE TO MOVEMENT OF THE TARGET AT RIGHT ANGLES TO THE LINE OF FIRE AT 40 YARDS

Type of Boring.	Percentage Loss in Density.	
	30 Yards.	40 Yards.
Improved Cylinder	17	30
Choke	4	13

At 50 yards the data are altogether too meagre to permit any attempt to form any definite conclusions. In the single series obtained the percentage loss in density was actually less than that obtained at 40 yards with the same barrel, but on a different day. The 50 yards results do prove, however, beyond any shadow of doubt that there is no real tailing even when the velocity of the shot charge is only nine times that of the crossing target.

Another fact which can be deduced in an approximate manner is the actual length of the main bulk of the shot column in the air at a range of 40 yards. This can be obtained by multiplying the elongation of the pattern by the number of times the velocity of the shot charge exceeds that of the target at the moment of impact, and the 40 m.p.h. results give a check on those obtained at 30 m.p.h. From the elongations recorded in these experiments it would seem that in the case of choke bores the main bulk of the shot charge has a length of about 4 feet

12-BORE FULL CHOKE AT 50 YARDS

Load: 33 grains Smokeless Diamond and $1\frac{1}{16}$ ounce No. 6 shot.

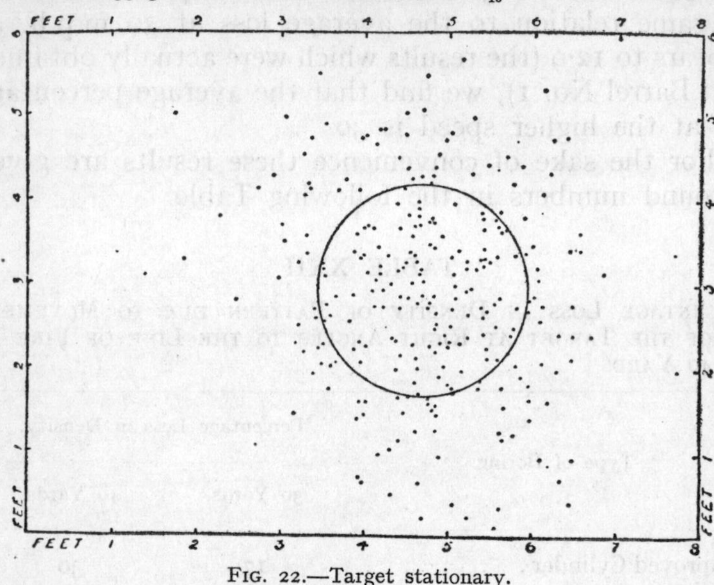

FIG. 22.—Target stationary.

Pellets in 30-in. circle: 133.

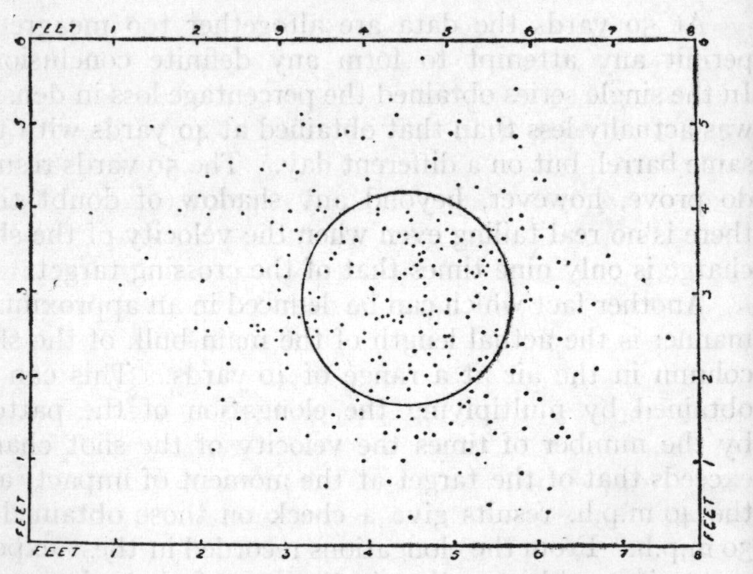

FIG. 23.—Target moving from left to right at 40 m.p.h.

Pellets in 30-in. circle: 117.

6 inches at 40 yards, while with improved cylinders the length is about 5 feet 6 inches at the same range.

With chokes the length will have increased to about 5 feet 3 inches at 50 yards.

These results are naturally somewhat rough, but they fit in very well with those given in Table XV, and so it will be realised that these experiments, together with those of Mr. Griffith and Mr. Quayle, are each confirmatory of the other.

PRACTICAL EFFECTS IN THE SHOOTING FIELD

A study of the foregoing analysis should convince the reader that for all practical purposes of sport the effect of stringing can be of little moment under ordinary conditions, although there may be occasions when the loss in density of the pattern may make just the difference between killing and wounding a bird. Such losses are, however, only liable to occur at a range of about 40 yards when using an improved cylinder gun. With a choke the loss should not be sufficient to make any material difference, except in the case of shots approaching 50 yards. In normal sport shots at even 40 yards are the exception rather than the rule, 35 yards being an average long shot, and at this range the pattern is sufficiently dense even with an improved cylinder to be able to afford a certain thinning out without loss in killing effect.

There is, however, another aspect of the case, namely that game birds frequently fly at considerably greater speeds than 40 m.p.h. and that the greater the speed of the crossing target the greater must be the loss in density of the pattern owing to elongation. Probably the best way of considering this question is to translate the speed of the bird and that of the shot charge into one common unit. I have already pointed out that at a range of 40 yards the velocity of the shot is about eleven times that of a target crossing at 40 m.p.h. If this method of comparison is amplified it will be possible to see at a glance the correct value of the shot velocity in relation to that of the target for different target speeds and at varying ranges. This has been done in the following Table. I have given the values in round numbers, and they can be taken as being sufficiently correct for all velocities normally developed in sporting cartridges, as at long ranges the variation in striking velocities is small compared to that in initial velocities, and it is only at long ranges that stringing can have any practical effect.

TABLE XXIII

RELATIVE VELOCITIES OF THE SHOT CHARGE AT DIFFERENT RANGES WHEN THE SPEED OF THE BIRD HAS A VALUE OF UNITY

Speed of Bird at right angles to Line of Fire in m.p.h.	Relative Velocity of Shot Charge.						
	20 Yds.	25 Yds.	30 Yds.	35 Yds.	40 Yds.	45 Yds.	50 Yds.
30	20	18	17	15·5	14	13	12
40	15	13·5	13	12	11	10	9
50	12	11	10	9	8·5	8	7
60	10	9	8·5	7·8	7	6·5	6

From this Table it will be seen, for example, that in the case of a bird crossing at 50 m.p.h. at 30 yards the shot has a speed ten times as great as that of the bird. It has already been proved in the 50 yards series that there is no appreciable loss from stringing when the shot is travelling nine times as fast as the target, and consequently it is quite safe to assume that a bird crossing at 30 yards will have little chance of escape owing to loss in density of the pattern, especially as the patterns of all guns have ample density in hand at 30 yards and the shot column is not so long at this range, which means that the effects of stringing would be relatively less.

In the extreme case of a bird crossing at 50 yards at 60 m.p.h. the shot is only travelling six times as fast as the bird, and consequently the loss in density due to the elongation of the pattern would be more pronounced and it is probable that at this range and speed the bird would escape in a pattern which would in any case be very open. But this is, as I have stated, an extreme case, for birds can seldom attain an actual ground speed of 60 m.p.h., and 50 yards is almost the limit of range of an ordinary 12-bore. At 40 yards the result would be doubtful, but at 35 yards the pattern should be sufficiently dense to ensure a kill, for the increased density of pattern due to a decrease in range must not be forgotten.

And there is another aspect of the matter which is in favour of the gun, namely, that a shot is comparatively seldom taken at a bird crossing exactly at right angles to the line of fire. In the great majority of shots the direction of flight of the bird makes a very decided angle with the line of fire. Even in the case of overhead pheasants it is very seldom that a shot is taken with the gun absolutely

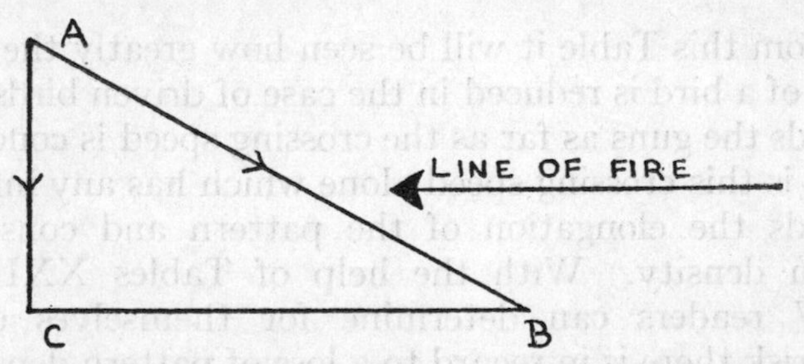

Fig. 24.—Diagram to show how the direction of a bird's flight affects the speed with which it crosses the line of fire.

vertical, and an angle of about 30 degrees with the vertical is a far more common position for the gun barrels.

If the bird were flying in direct prolongation of the line of fire it would receive exactly the same pattern as that indicated on a fixed plate, no matter whether it were flying at 60 or 20 m.p.h. The loss in density due to stringing only occurs when the target is moving across the line of fire, and if the target moves diagonally across the effect of stringing is reduced. This will readily be seen from the accompanying diagram in Fig. 24.

In this diagram AB represents the actual direction and speed of the bird, but relative to the line of fire the speed is only AC, which is considerably less.

The following Table gives the relative speeds at right angles to the line of fire for varying actual speeds.

TABLE XXIV

RELATIVE SPEED OF BIRD AT RIGHT ANGLES TO THE LINE OF FIRE FOR DIFFERENT ANGLES MADE BY THE DIRECTION OF THE BIRD'S FLIGHT WITH THE LINE OF FIRE

Actual Speed of Bird.	Relative Speed of Bird for different Angles of Flight.						
	90°	75°	60°	45°	30°	15°	0°
60	60	58	52	42	30	16	0
50	50	48	43	35	25	13	0
40	40	39	35	28	20	10	0

From this Table it will be seen how greatly the actual speed of a bird is reduced in the case of driven birds flying towards the guns as far as the crossing speed is concerned, and it is this crossing speed alone which has any influence towards the elongation of the pattern and consequent loss in density. With the help of Tables XXIII and XXIV readers can determine for themselves exactly what risk there is in regard to a loss of pattern density for different types of shots.

In this connection it should be remembered that the actual length of the shot column in the air is less at 30 yards than at 40, and still less at 25 and 20 yards. So it will be realised that stringing can have no practical effect on the pattern at all in the case of shots up to 30 yards, and even at the longer ranges only when birds fly at extreme speeds at right angles to the line of fire.

But it is at long ranges that the question of the minimum density of patterns comes in, and it was for this reason that I added on 10 per cent. to the theoretical minimum patterns in order to allow for the effects of stringing, as was explained on page 95. In view of the fact that even a choke has been seen to lose on the average 13 per cent. in pattern density at 40 yards on a 40-miles-an-hour target, this addition of 10 per cent. may seem too small. But we must make allowances for average conditions, and in the great majority of shots the bird is not crossing exactly at right angles, and its speed will not often exceed 40 m.p.h. by very much. So I do not think an addition of 10 per cent. is too little for the average type of shot that is taken at extreme range.

THE PREVENTION OF STRINGING

It will have been appreciated that the principal cause of stringing is the deformation which the pellets of a shot charge suffer during their journey from the cartridge-case to the muzzle of the gun. A certain amount of deformation is inevitable, and consequently it is impossible to prevent stringing. I only mention this point because the most extravagant claims are sometimes made that a particular brand of cartridges has a much shorter shot string than others. I have explained in Volume II the impossibility of preventing pellet deformation by giving the pellets a thin coating of copper, in itself a soft metal, and will not refer to it again.

The best way to tackle the problem of stringing is to use shot which has been most carefully graded both for the shape and weight of the individual pellets. In fact it can be taken as almost axiomatic that cartridges which give equally good patterns will give no appreciably different results in stringing.

But above all it must be remembered that the evil effects of stringing are in reality very slight, and are simply non-existent in the case of the great majority of ordinary shots at normal sporting ranges. These effects are purposely exaggerated by interested parties, who hope to persuade the sportsman to buy their particular wares, which are stated to cure an evil which does not really exist as far as ordinary practical sporting conditions are concerned. And in any case the methods by which the cure is affected are usually so patently absurd that they are not worthy of serious consideration.

CHAPTER VII

LOADS

We have now reached that stage in our investigation of our subject when we must come down to practical details and actual weights of charges of powders and shot. Our consideration of the four Ballistic Elements of a shotgun—Pressure, Velocity, Recoil and Pattern—has been completed, and it only remains to see how best we can utilise the knowledge which we have gained so as to derive the maximum benefit in the shooting field. To do this we must take at least one cartridge as a concrete example, and for this purpose I am selecting the ordinary standard 12-bore 2½-inch cartridge, partly because it is by far and away the one in commonest use by British sportsmen, at all events; and partly because it happens to be of a size convenient for the accommodation of a considerable variety of different combinations of powder and shot. Therefore any lessons which may be learned by a detailed study of this cartridge and its loads can be applied to other sizes and lengths of cartridges, when corresponding effects will be obtained.

When we speak of a "Load" for a shotgun we really mean the combination of powder and shot which is loaded into the cartridge-case, together with the suitable wadding. In actual practice, however, the wadding is not generally included in a description of a load, because it is assumed that the quality of the wadding will be of the necessary standard, and the thickness of the felt wad such that the correct amount of case is left above the over-shot wad for the making of an effective turnover. I will accordingly follow this general custom and confine myself solely to the different weights of both powder and shot charges which can be combined together in the 12-bore 2½-inch case.

But before dealing with actual weights of charges it

may be advisable to consider why variations in these weights are made, and why finality has not apparently been obtained after three-quarters of a century of experience and experimenting with the breech-loader.

It can be stated quite definitely that there are two entirely different objects in view: the first of these is Range; and the second Forward Allowance on a rapidly moving target. Both these questions are vital to all who use shotguns and every variation in the loads used has been made with the purpose of increasing Range, or reducing Forward Allowance, or both. Since, however, it can become confusing to mix up these two purposes together when considering what load, or loads, give the best results, I propose to take them in turn. It should then be possible to decide which load offers the greatest advantages and the least disadvantages.

RANGE

Let us take the question of increased range first. It does seem ridiculous that with all the modern improvements in guns, cartridges and powders we cannot kill our birds at any appreciably greater range than could Colonel Peter Hawker who was wounded in the Peninsular War! And this in spite of the fact that the effective sporting range in the case of rifles has certainly been quadrupled in the past sixty years, while the effective military range of small arms has been increased by an even greater extent. These increases in the effective ranges of rifles are due to two causes: first, the enhanced velocities developed by modern arms; and secondly, improvements in bullet design which enable the bullets to retain better the enhanced initial velocities. The second cause is admittedly of more importance in long military ranges than in the comparatively near sporting distances: but it enters even into the improvements brought about in the ranging power of sporting rifles. This is a fact which is usually ignored completely both by the average sportsman and the average gunmaker, and both attribute the increase in sporting ranges given by modern rifles entirely to the great increases in muzzle velocity.

It is, however, perfectly true that these increases in muzzle velocity are very largely responsible for the great improvements in the ranging power of sporting rifles, and so it is not surprising to find that an increase in the velocity of the shot charge has been almost universally regarded as the first step in the direction of an increased range. But it has also generally, although not quite so universally, been remembered that although birds cannot be killed with certainty when much more than 40 yards away, shot pellets will carry several times that distance, and so the mere fact of obtaining an increased *actual* range may not necessarily mean an increased *effective* range. Further reflection, however, has usually been more reassuring, for it has shown that although our shot pellets may travel four, or even five, times 40 yards they are not moving with sufficient velocity when much beyond 40 yards to be able to penetrate the feathers and flesh of a comparatively tough and heavy bird and so reach some vital organ, or else to break some big bone. So an increased muzzle velocity has become to be regarded as the panacea for shotguns which it has proved to be for rifles, especially since it is obvious that such an increase will mean an increase in striking velocity at, and beyond, 40 yards, which in turn will mean an increased power of penetration at longer ranges ; and this is only another way of describing an increase in effective range.

So far so good : but here the analogy between rifle and shotgun breaks down. The former fires a single bullet, but the latter a charge of shot consisting of a large number of individual pellets, and it has already been seen that certain minimum patterns are essential in order to make reasonably certain of a kill. If the density of the pattern falls below the necessary minimum, penetration is useless, as a kill would then be a matter of mere chance.

Consequently it should be realised that at long sporting ranges inability to kill can be due not so much to lack of penetration on the part of individual pellets as to the

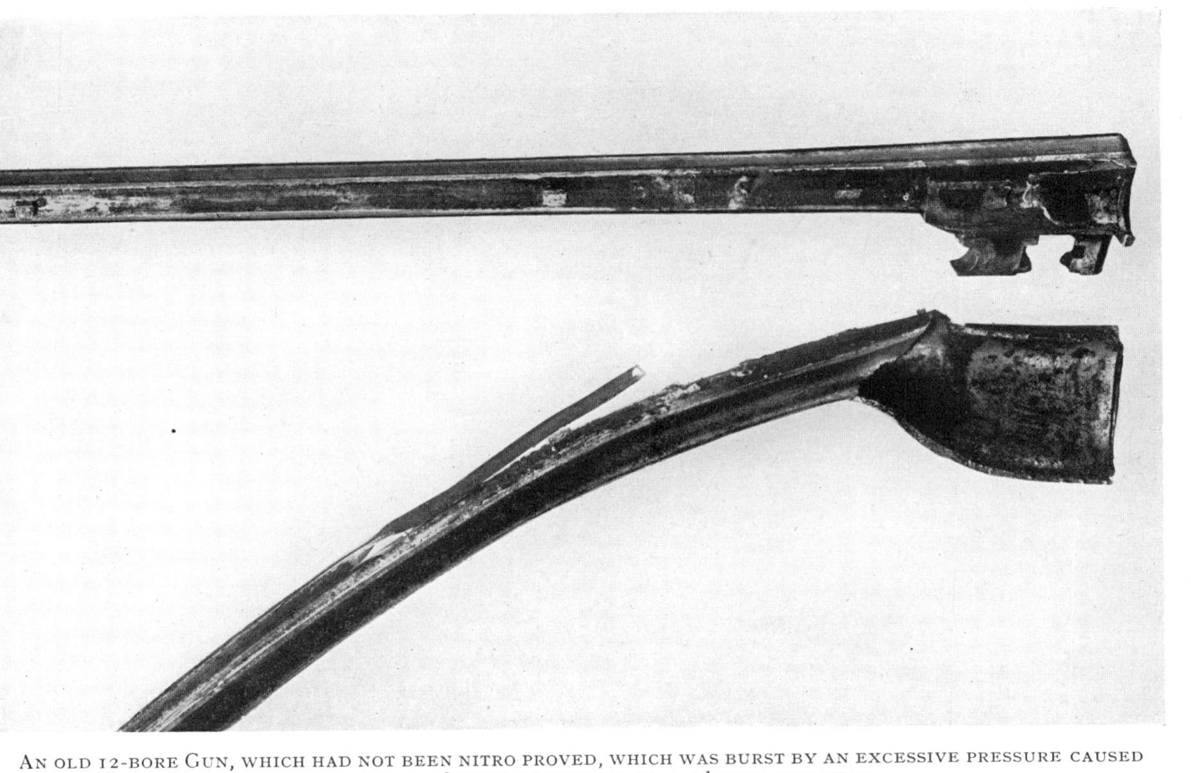

AN OLD 12-BORE GUN, WHICH HAD NOT BEEN NITRO PROVED, WHICH WAS BURST BY AN EXCESSIVE PRESSURE CAUSED BY FIRING A $2\frac{3}{4}$-INCH CARTRIDGE IN A $2\frac{1}{2}$-INCH CHAMBER

It will be noticed that the actual burst occurred along the chamber where the maximum pressure was generated

failure of any pellet to hit some vital spot because the density of the pattern has dropped below the necessary minimum.

Theoretically the ideal load would be one in which the necessary amounts of penetration and pattern faded out together, since one is useless without the other. In actual practice, however, such a load would cause a large proportion of wounded birds, since those fired at just beyond the effective range might very easily be hit by an odd pellet or two, but would not be killed because these pellets would lack penetration. Again the ballistics of cartridges will always vary slightly from round to round, and a " soft " cartridge would help the pattern at long range while the penetration would drop below the necessary minimum. This, too, would mean wounded birds. Accordingly it should be regarded as essential for penetration to last further than pattern, and probably the ideal practical combination would occur when penetration faded away at about 5 yards farther than pattern. This would allow for a reserve of power in the case of variations in velocity, or shots taken at just beyond the range limit for pattern.

Let us now turn to some concrete examples.

The load for a $2\frac{1}{2}$-inch 12-bore cartridge is 33 grains of a 33-grain powder and $1\frac{1}{16}$ ounce of shot. This combination results in an observed velocity over 20 yards of about 1,050 f.s. With No. 6 shot the limit of range must depend on the type and size of bird and the boring of the gun. In the case of birds such as partridges, grouse and wood-pigeon, the minimum necessary pattern is 130 (see page 96), and with an improved-cylinder gun the pattern will drop below this figure a little way beyond 40 yards. But the penetration of individual pellets is certainly ample—at any rate for grouse and partridges—at 50 yards, consequently it can be of little help trying to increase the effective range by improving penetration alone, as this is already sufficient, and without paying any attention to pattern. For it must be remembered that there is no practical advantage whatever in having more than sufficient penetration. If a shot pellet reaches the brain, heart or other vital organ of a bird it kills that bird just as cleanly as if it went right through that same organ and out of the bird the other side. Once a vital organ is penetrated all additional penetration is wasted. It may be argued that a bird is crumpled up and killed much more cleanly and with greater certainty at short ranges than at long. But this is not so much because the individual pellets have less penetration at long range as because the pattern has become much more scattered, with the result that at long range the bird may be struck by one or two pellets only where at some shorter range it will be struck by a dozen; and the more pellets which strike a bird the greater the odds in favour of one of them hitting some immediately vital organ. Every shooter can recall many instances of birds being killed stone dead at long ranges just as cleanly as at shorter distances, and in such cases it will always be found that fortune has favoured the shooter and a single pellet has struck a vital part.

Certain birds, however, are admittedly much tougher than others, and some of my readers may not agree with me when I state that a standard pellet of No. 6 has sufficient penetration at 50 yards. Further, there is a widespread feeling that the increased " shock " caused by a higher striking energy is a potent factor in killing cleanly, or at any rate rendering a bird incapable of movement even if a vital organ is not struck.

So it is not surprising that an increase in penetration at long range has been desired, nor that this end has been sought by the adoption of a " High-Velocity " load.

THE HIGH-VELOCITY LOAD

In Volume II it was shown that the highest observed velocity over 20 yards which was obtainable in actual practice in a 12-bore 2½-inch gun was about 1,150 f.s., and that this velocity necessitated the reduction of the shot charge to 1 ounce, the powder charge usually being 36 grains of a 33-grain powder.

This means an increase of about 10 per cent. over the standard observed velocity ; but, as has already been explained fully in Volume II, an increase of 10 per cent. in the observed velocity does not mean anything approaching a corresponding increase in striking velocity at long range as so many gunmakers and shooters seem to think.

At 40 yards the standard load with No. 6 shot gives a striking velocity per pellet of 623 f.s. ; and at the same range and with the same size of shot the high-velocity load gives a striking velocity of 664 f.s. At 45 yards these striking velocities have dropped respectively to 569 and 609 f.s. ; and at 50 yards to 518 and 555 f.s. From these figures, and from a study of Tables X and XII in Volume II, it will be seen that at long ranges the striking velocities of the high-velocity load are just about 3 yards better than those of the standard load. That is, the striking velocities of the two loads are as nearly as possible equal at 40 and 43 yards ; at 45 and 48 yards ; and at 50 and 53 yards. And if the striking velocities are the same the striking energies are the same, since No. 6 shot is being used in each case ; and it is the striking energy of a pellet which governs its powers of penetration.

So we can come to the conclusion that as far as penetration is concerned the high-velocity load has added 3 yards to the effective range.

But what about the other essential factor, pattern ?

The shot charge of the standard load is $1\frac{1}{16}$, and that of the high-velocity load but 1 ounce. Since No. 6 shot is being considered in both cases, this reduction in the weight of the charge must mean a loss in pattern density, which at first sight might appear to cancel any advantages in the matter of range derived from increased penetration. But in actual practice this does not occur because the high-velocity load must, on account of its high velocity, always be used in a heavily choked gun. As was explained in Chapter II, cartridges developing an observed velocity of about 1,150 f.s. need a half choke at the very least, while a full choke is necessary if the proper pattern percentage is to be obtained. With a half choke the pattern given by a high-velocity load of 1 ounce is approximately the same as that given by an improved cylinder and $1\frac{1}{16}$ ounce; and the three-quarter choke gives a similar pattern with the high-velocity load as the quarter choke does with the standard. It is only when the full choke is used that the proper pattern density of 70 per cent. of the whole charge can be expected in the case of a high-velocity load.

In the case of guns with more open boring than half choke the patterns given by high-velocity loads may be so blown and irregular as to be useless for long-range work.

The fact that a heavy choke is an essential adjunct to a high-velocity load counteracts the loss in density due to the reduction in the weight of the shot charge; but at the same time it constitutes a very real disadvantage, for such closely bored guns cannot be regarded as being suitable for all-round shooting.

And there is another disadvantage which is inseparable from the high-velocity load, namely recoil. The increase in 10 per cent. over the standard observed velocity means a considerably bigger percentage increase in muzzle velocity which means a corresponding increase in recoil. The total increase in recoil is reduced by the lighter shot charge; but even so the high-velocity load as specified causes an increase in recoil of just about 11 per cent. over that developed by the standard load. And such an increase is more than many shooters can stand with comfort, especially when using very light guns.

In order to overcome this disadvantage the shot charge is sometimes reduced to $\frac{15}{16}$ of an ounce. Such a reduction brings the recoil back to normal but at the same time causes such a reduction in pattern density that an absolutely full choke becomes essential. With a view to maintaining density of pattern when using this very light shot charge of $\frac{15}{16}$ ounce, No. $6\frac{1}{2}$ or No. 7 is sometimes substituted for No. 6. These smaller sizes certainly help pattern, but their adoption completely nullifies any improvement in penetration at long range owing to the feeble capacity of the smaller pellets for retaining their original velocity. In the case of the high-velocity load and No. 6½ the striking energies at 40, 45 and 50 yards are practically identical with those of the standard load and No. 6 at these ranges, as can be seen from Tables XXXVI and XXXVIII in Volume II, while the striking energies of the high-velocity load and No. 7 are actually less at these distances than those of the standard load and No. 6. So it will be seen that if we do not want to bind ourselves to the use of absolutely full choke guns we must put up with the 11 per cent. increase in recoil in order to gain an increase in range of 3 yards by adopting the high-velocity load.

Incidentally this proves that it is quite useless to expect smaller sizes of shot than No. 6 to be effective at extreme ranges, even though their use increases the density of pattern. For it is always better in every way to use a load in which pattern dies out before penetration.

We can now sum up the advantages and disadvantages of the high-velocity loads so far as we have gone, and the most convenient way to do so is to see them placed in juxtaposition, thus:

Advantages	Disadvantages
High-Velocity Load of 1 ounce of No. 6.	
Increase in effective range of about 3 yards.	(1) Necessity for half choke gun. (2) Increase in recoil of 11 per cent.
High-Velocity Load of $\frac{15}{16}$ ounce of No. 6.	
Increase in effective range of about 3 yards.	Necessity for full choke gun.

THE LOW-VELOCITY LOAD

I pointed out earlier in this chapter that the effective range of rifles had been lengthened only partly by increased muzzle velocities, and partly by improvements in bullet design which enabled them to retain their initial velocities better at long distances. In Volume II I explained that with shotguns there was no scope for improvements in the *design* of the projectile because it was made up of a number of pellets, but that an increase in the weights of the individual pellets had a similar effect to an improvement in design, as heavier pellets retained their initial velocity better at long ranges than lighter ones. It will be seen from Table X in Volume II that if charges of No. 4 and No. 6 are both propelled with standard velocities the striking velocity at 50 yards of the pellets of No. 4 is 577 f.s., while that of the pellets of No. 6 is but 518 f.s. That is, the pellets of No. 4 have roughly 60 f.s. more velocity at 50 yards than those of No. 6, although the observed velocity over 20 yards was the same in each case. Consequently the pellets of No. 4 will travel some distance farther before their velocity is the same as those of No. 6 at 50 yards, which means that No. 4 shot gives an increase in range over No. 6 as far as penetration is concerned.

And even when the velocity of a pellet of No. 4 has been reduced to the same as that of one of No. 6 at 50 yards the actual penetrative power of the larger pellet will be greater than that of the smaller, because penetration, as was explained in Volume II, is dependent on the energy of the pellet, which in its turn is dependent on the pellet's weight as well as on its velocity. Thus the change from No. 6 to No. 4 will be seen to open out promising possibilities of an increase in range provided penetration only is considered.

But penetration by itself is useless unless some vital spot is struck, and the change from No. 6 to No. 4 means a reduction in the total number of pellets in the charge, which in its turn means a reduction in the density of the pattern at long ranges, which again means a reduction in the chances of hitting a vital spot; and so the increase in the effective range is nullified by the opening out of the pattern. For when experimenting with different types of loads for shotguns it must never be forgotten that it is useless to increase penetration without maintaining the pattern at the minimum density necessary for the particular variety of game for which a load is intended.

Accordingly, if we are to continue with No. 4 shot we must maintain the density of pattern by increasing the number of pellets in the charge, or in other words the weight of the charge. But if we do this both recoil and pressure will be increased too much, and so it would seem that there is no way out of the difficulty. But is this so? Surely would it not be possible to propel an abnormally heavy charge of No. 4 at such a reduced initial velocity that neither recoil nor pressure are unduly affected, while penetration is maintained at long range?

This question is the key to the problem. Large shot retains its velocity so much better than small that it can afford to give the latter a big start in velocity at the muzzle, but at 50 yards the actual remaining velocities will be the same in each case. For example, the standard load gives an observed velocity over 20 yards of about 1,050 f.s. which means in the case of No. 6 shot a muzzle velocity of about 1,270 f.s., and a remaining velocity of the pellets at 50 yards of 518 f.s. If, however, a charge of No. 4 shot is propelled with a muzzle velocity of about 1,050 f.s., the observed velocity over the first 20 yards will be about 950 f.s. and the remaining velocity at 50 yards will be 521 f.s.

That is, No. 4 shot can be propelled from the muzzle with 220 f.s. less velocity than No. 6, and yet at 50 yards the remaining velocities of the two sizes will be the same; and since a pellet of No. 4 is nearly half as heavy again as one of No. 6, the penetration of a pellet of No. 4 will be nearly half as great again as that of a pellet of No. 6 at 50 yards.

It is obvious that if we are content with an appreciably lower muzzle velocity less force is required to push off a heavy charge of shot, which means a reduction both in recoil and pressure. As a matter of fact, both recoil and pressure are exactly the same as normal when 1¼ ounces of No. 4 are propelled with a muzzle velocity of about 1,050 f.s., which means an observed velocity over 20 yards of 950 f.s.; and tests have proved that a charge of 30 grains of Smokeless Diamond powder is sufficient to develop this velocity.

So it will be seen that a combination of 30 grains of

Smokeless Diamond and 1¼ ounces of No. 4 shot actually results in increased penetration at long range without any increase in recoil or pressure, while the additional weight in the shot charge provides a sufficiency of pellets to ensure a pattern of minimum density for the larger game birds up to about 47 yards in the case of an improved cylinder, and 50 yards in a quarter choke.

This combination of powder and shot is the "Low-Velocity" load.

The penetration of this low-velocity load is so definitely superior at long range to that of the standard, and even the high-velocity, loads that the benefit conferred by the low-velocity load would seem to be so great that further discussion might almost appear useless, especially when it is remembered that this enhanced penetration at long range has been obtained without any increase in recoil. But there is a disadvantage of this low-velocity load of No. 4 shot which needs further analysis.

I have already emphasised again and again the fact that penetration by itself is useless unless some vital spot is struck. The greatest penetration of all would be obtained by firing a single solid ball, which would retain ample penetrative power up to 500 yards, let alone 50. The only drawback to this type of projectile would be that in actual practice a bird would be so seldom hit. If there were two balls the chances of a hit would be doubled, and so on ; but as long as the pellets are so far apart that it is possible for a bird to fly in between them without being touched, an actual hit must be regarded as a matter of luck. This brings us back to the necessity for obtaining the minimum pattern essential for the particular type of bird pursued, and even with 1¼ ounces of No. 4 the pattern will drop below the minimum required long before penetration becomes too low except in the case of the larger and tougher birds. So it will be realised that although we have increased the penetration at long range by means of the low-velocity load we have reduced the pattern density, which means that there is no very appreciable increase in effective range after all except in the case of larger birds.

But in view of the fact that the principle of the low-velocity load has given us such a great increase in penetration, even over the high-velocity load, it would appear worth while to investigate whether it is not possible to obtain, by a slight reduction in shot size, a sufficiently dense pattern combined with high penetration. The obvious step is to substitute No. 4½ shot for No. 4 in our low-velocity load. The muzzle and observed velocities would be practically the same as before, being in actual fact 1,060 f.s. and 950 f.s., while the remaining velocity at 50 yards would be 506 f.s. This is very slightly lower than that of the standard charge, but the greater weight of each pellet raises their power of penetration to roughly 25 per cent. above that of standard pellets of No. 6, which is a greater increase than that given by the high-velocity load, while the pattern is well maintained and there is no increase in recoil.

In order to render easier the task of comparing the merits of the various loads mentioned, I have tabulated their respective patterns in different borings, their striking velocities and striking energies per pellet at 40, 45, 50, and 55 yards. It must be remembered when studying this Table that the patterns cannot possibly be anything but approximate, especially beyond 40 yards. In the case of the high-velocity load and 1 ounce of No. 6 I have only given patterns for guns bored with at least half choke, as guns more openly bored cannot be relied upon to give serviceable patterns. And even in the case of the half and three-quarter chokes I have purposely given patterns which are rather less dense than the theoretical standard, as these figures indicate results which are as good as can possibly be expected.

For the high-velocity load and $\frac{15}{16}$ ounce of No. 6 I have only given full choke patterns, as reliable patterns cannot be expected with this light shot charge in any guns except full choke.

Table XXV will repay careful study as it provides a

fund of information as to the extreme ranges possible for different varieties of game when examined in conjunction with Table X. For instance, it shows that with a half choke the standard load alone will give sufficiently dense patterns at 45 yards for partridge, grouse and wood-pigeon. And with this same boring better results are likely to be obtained on duck at 50 yards by using either of the low-velocity loads. At 55 yards no pattern is sufficiently dense to make certain of a partridge: for duck the best penetration is given by the low-velocity

TABLE XXV

COMPARISONS OF PATTERNS, STRIKING VELOCITIES AND STRIKING ENERGIES OF STANDARD, HIGH-, AND LOW-VELOCITY LOADS.

40 YARDS RANGE

Load.	Patterns.					Striking Velocity in F.S.	Striking Energy in Ft.-lb.
	Improved Cylinder.	Quarter Choke.	Half Choke.	Three-quarter Choke.	Full Choke.		
Standard, 1 $\frac{1}{16}$ oz., No. 6	145	160	175	187	200	623	1·40
High Velocity, 1 oz., No. 6	—	—	145	165	187	664	1·59
High Velocity, $\frac{15}{16}$ oz., No. 6	—	—	—	—	175	664	1·59
Low Velocity, 1¼ oz., No. 4	106	117	128	139	149	612	2·14
Low Velocity, 1¼ oz., No. 4½	125	138	150	163	175	597	1·73

45 YARDS RANGE

Load.	Patterns.					Striking Velocity in F.S.	Striking Energy in Ft.-lb.
	Improved Cylinder.	Quarter Choke.	Half Choke.	Three-quarter Choke.	Full Choke.		
Standard, 1 $\frac{1}{16}$ oz., No. 6	119	131	143	153	164	569	1·16
High Velocity, 1 oz., No. 6	—	—	119	135	153	609	1·33
High Velocity, $\frac{15}{16}$ oz., No. 6	—	—	—	—	143	609	1·33
Low Velocity, 1¼ oz., No. 4	87	96	105	114	122	566	1·83
Low Velocity, 1¼ oz., No. 4½	102	113	123	133	143	549	1·74

load and No. 4 shot, but the pattern with this load is too open unless a half choke is used: the best combination of both pattern and penetration is given by the low-velocity load and No. 4½ shot.

I will carry this analysis no further, merely reminding

50 YARDS RANGE

LOAD.	PATTERNS.					Striking Velocity in F.S.	Striking Energy in Ft.-lb.
	Improved Cylinder.	Quarter Choke.	Half Choke.	Three-quarter Choke.	Full Choke.		
Standard, 1 1/16 oz., No. 6	97	107	117	125	134	518	0·97
High Velocity, 1 oz., No. 6	—	—	97	110	125	555	1·11
High Velocity, 15/16 oz., No. 6	—	—	—	—	117	555	1·11
Low Velocity, 1¼ oz., No. 4	71	78	85	93	100	521	1·55
Low Velocity, 1¼ oz., No. 4½	83	92	100	109	117	506	1·24

55 YARDS RANGE

LOAD.	PATTERNS.					Striking Velocity in F.S.	Striking Energy in Ft.-lb.
	Improved Cylinder.	Quarter Choke.	Half Choke.	Three-quarter Choke.	Full Choke.		
Standard, 1 1/16 oz., No. 6	79	88	96	103	110	469	0·79
High Velocity, 1 oz., No. 6	—	—	79	90	103	504	0·92
High Velocity, 15/16 oz., No. 6	—	—	—	—	96	504	0·92
Low Velocity, 1¼ oz., No. 4	58	64	70	76	82	481	1·32
Low Velocity, 1¼ oz., No. 4½	68	76	82	89	96	464	1·05

the reader that the high-velocity load and 1 ounce of shot gives an appreciable increase in recoil and needs at the very least a half-choke gun, while the high-velocity load and 15/16 ounce of shot needs an absolutely full-choke gun.

And before proceeding I will answer now two objections which I have frequently heard raised with reference to the statements made in the preceding paragraph. It is quite common for some shooters to declare that they use high-velocity loads and 1 ounce of shot with perfectly satisfactory results in improved cylinder guns and that they notice no increase in recoil.

Let us first take the question of the results given in improved cylinder guns.

There are two explanations for this. First, the majority of driven birds shot, in the south of England at any rate, are probably nearer 20 yards than 30, and seldom much more than 30 yards away. A combination of gun and load which gives blown and scattered patterns at 40 yards may quite likely provide a sufficiently good pattern at 25 or 30 yards to ensure a reasonable chance of a kill. Since one of the chief objects of the high-velocity load was to increase the effective range, it is quite misleading to judge their efficiency by the results they give at short ranges.

Secondly, the cartridges used are "high velocity" only in name. I can say without exaggeration that since 1920 I have tested thousands of cartridges for readers, first of the *Field* and since 1932 of *Game and Gun*, and it has been my experience that as often as not cartridges which are loaded and sold as "high-velocity" cartridges develop velocities which scarcely exceed the standard. This is true irrespective of the powder charges used, for it is quite erroneous to assume, as the majority of gunmakers and shooters generally do, that because a cartridge contains 36 grains of a 33-grain powder and an ounce of shot the velocity developed will necessarily be "high." As I have repeatedly stated before, the tightness of loading and the strength of the turnover exercise just as much say in the matter as the weights of the powder and shot charges; and loose, or "soft," loading lowers the ballistics. The cartridges so loaded are perfectly effective and most satisfactory in every way: but they are not "high velocity."

The objection to the heavy recoil attributed to the high-velocity load can be answered in the same way, namely, if the cartridges are not really "high velocity" the recoil will be normal.

But at the same time it is perfectly true that many shooters do use really high-velocity cartridges without noticing any inconvenient recoil. This, however, does not prove that the recoil is not heavy ; merely that it is not too heavy for many to withstand without discomfort. In such matters there can be no hard and fast rule, and each individual must be a law unto himself. Some men are very sensitive to recoil, while others seem to be almost immune. The only way for anyone to find out is to try for themselves. And whatever the result of this trial may be it will not alter the fact that the real high-velocity cartridge does develop a higher recoil than the standard, and consequently such cartridges are for the normal individual less suitable for use in very light guns than those which give standard results.

THE MAXIMUM CARTRIDGE. Throughout this chapter I have made no reference to the crimped cartridge because I doubt whether its use can make any practical difference to the conclusions which I have ventured to draw. At best it seems unlikely to achieve more than a slight increase of a yard or two in range all round. But towards the end of 1933 an entirely new departure from the standard appeared in British cartridges which has completely changed the problem of shooting at long range. This new departure was the "Maximum" cartridge.

I have already done my best to emphasise the fact that it is the shot that kills the bird ; and that it may be better, therefore, to sacrifice powder rather than shot. The Maximum cartridge, as it is now generally known, contains the full 1¼ ounces of shot of the low-velocity load but all sacrifice of velocity is saved by the use of a special slow-burning powder called Neoflak which develops the full standard velocity but at a pressure which is normal for the standard 2½-inch 12-bore load.

In other words the 2½-inch 12-bore cartridge is given the same shot power as the 2¾-inch and all the advantages of the heavy shot charge of the low-velocity load are obtained without any of its limitations. In fact the only criticism that can be advanced is that with No. 6 shot the pattern may tend to remain almost too dense at long ranges with the necessary velocity fading out before the pattern, a condition which can tend to wounded birds. But with No. 5½ the pattern is maintained adequate up to 55 yards for both pheasants and duck with ample penetration. If any further qualms are felt about penetration the use of No. 5 will ensure all that can possibly be needed ; but a boring more open than a quarter choke should not be used in case the pattern becomes too open. Partridges and wood-pigeons can be killed with certainty up to 50 yards with No. 6 shot and a half choke.

These advantages are so definite and so real that it will be clear that there must be some disadvantage, and this will obviously be recoil. And the recoil is indeed heavy, being an increase of almost 17 per cent. above that given by the standard load. This is certainly too much for the majority of shooters to withstand when many shots are fired in rapid succession, and the cartridge was never intended for such work. It was designed for special occasions and special purposes rather than for constant use. For the rough shooter with his 2½-inch 12-bore it is ideal, and for the wildfowler a practical and useful alternative to a heavier gun.

Doubts have sometimes been raised as to the safety of using cartridges loaded with 1¼ ounces of shot in an ordinary 2½-inch 12-bore gun. It can, therefore, be stated at once that there is no risk whatever since the pressure is the same as that of the standard 2½-inch 12-bore cartridge. Similar doubts have at times been expressed about low-velocity loads and this aspect of the subject will be dealt with in Chapter XV.

CHAPTER VIII

LOADS AND FORWARD ALLOWANCE

I EXPLAINED at the beginning of the last chapter that the two objects which had always been sought by experimenters in loads was an increase in range and a reduction in forward allowance. We have considered the possibilities of increasing the effective range in detail, so let us now turn to the question of forward allowance.

This problem has already been discussed at some length in Chapter VII of Volume II, where it was explained that the amount of forward allowance which must be given on a crossing target depended on (1) the speed of that target, and (2) the total period of time which must elapse between the shooter's mental decision to fire and the arrival of the shot charge at the target. The speed of the target is naturally that with which a bird flies, and it is now known with fair accuracy that 40 miles an hour is about the highest speed which the majority of ordinary game birds can normally attain in still air. I will, accordingly, adopt this value as being typical, only adopting the higher value of 60 m.p.h. in order to indicate the most extreme examples which are likely to be encountered.

The period of time which must elapse between the shooter's mental decision to fire and the arrival of the shot charge at the bird has been shown in Volume II to to be divisible into three distinct periods, namely:

(1) The time taken from the brain's decision to fire to the actual pressing of the trigger, which can be called the "Sportsman's Time."

(2) The time taken from the pressing of the trigger to the exit of the shot charge at the muzzle, which is known as the "Time up the Barrel."

(3) The time taken from the exit of the shot charge

at the muzzle to its arrival at the target, perhaps 40 yards or more away, which is the "Time of Flight."

The first of these periods cannot be measured and must vary not only with individuals, but with individuals on different days and even at different times of the same day. It can be overcome by "swing," that is by shooting with a moving gun, and will be dealt with at greater length in the final chapter. Accordingly, in our consideration of the actual forward allowances necessary, this first period of time will be ignored.

The second period, however, cannot be ignored, although it is not nearly of so much importance as it was in the days of flint-lock muzzle-loaders. It is really made up of three elements of time: the fall of the tumbler, or hammer (about 0·0020 second); the time of ignition, which with modern smokeless powders is about 0·0010 second; and the time of movement up the barrel, which is about 0·0026 second. So the total "Time up the Barrel" amounts to 0·0056 second.

This is certainly a very small fraction of time, but a bird travelling at 40 m.p.h. will move just about 4 inches during this small period, which means that the necessary forward allowance on a bird crossing at 40 m.p.h. must be increased by 4 inches if the pattern is to be truly centred on the bird.

So the total forward allowance on a crossing bird consists of the distance the bird will travel during the "Time up the Barrel" and the "Time of Flight" added together.

The "Times of Flight" over all sporting ranges for different shot sizes when propelled at different velocities have been given in Tables XIV to XXI of Volume II. It is, accordingly, only necessary to add 0·0056 to the values given in these Tables in order to obtain the total time period which governs the amount of forward allowance needed for a crossing bird.

At a range of 20 yards a bird crossing at 40 m.p.h. will move 3·7 feet during the total time period thus obtained for the ordinary standard load developing an observed velocity of about 1,050 f.s.; which means that 3·7 feet is the forward allowance necessary under these conditions.

In the case of the high-velocity load the forward allowance necessary on a bird crossing at 20 yards at 40 m.p.h. is 3·4 feet, which means that the change from the standard to the high-velocity load has reduced the forward allowance by 0·3 of a foot, or 4 inches. A reduction of 4 inches in a total forward allowance of a foot might be appreciated, but in over 3 feet it is negligible, especially as the diameter of the spread of the shot charge has also been reduced by the necessity for a heavily choked gun. The permissible error with an improved cylinder at 20 yards is about 10 inches; with a half choke about 8 inches; and with a full choke about 7 inches. So it will be realised that even if the high-velocity load permits an error of 4 inches in forward allowance, it necessitates the charge being centred 2 to 3 inches more accurately than need be done when an improved cylinder and standard load is used, which means that the advantage given by the high-velocity load is almost nullified.

Of course, it is absurd to regard an inch—or even a foot—in forward allowance as having any practical bearing on shooting. I have merely touched on this theoretical aspect of the matter in order to show how little there is to be gained, at any rate at 20 yards, by the use of a high-velocity load. In the actual shooting field practical conditions alone count, and the man who hopes to improve his shooting by knowing the exact forward allowance necessary in feet and fractions of a foot for various ranges and speeds of birds will be doomed to disappointment. At the same time so many claims have been put forward from time to time for the high-velocity load that it is essential for us to come down to bedrock and see just what we stand to gain or lose by using different loads.

But before going any further I will meet one criticism which the reader will probably advance, namely, that I have made no allowance for the differences in the actual times of movement up the barrel of various loads. This time, it may be thought, should be distinctly less in the case of the high-velocity load on account of the enhanced muzzle velocity.

It must be realised, however, that although the actual velocity with which the shot charge leaves the muzzle may be from 150 to 200 f.s. higher, this does not mean that the average velocity of the charge during the whole of its journey up the bore is increased by this amount, for the higher muzzle velocity is only attained by a greater acceleration. It is true that the average velocity of the shot charge up the barrel is slightly higher than the standard in the case of the high-velocity load, and slightly less in the case of the low-velocity load. But the distance under consideration is so short, and the actual variations in average velocity so small, that there is no practical difference whatever in the various " Times up the Barrel " when different loads are used.

At first sight it may seem very extraordinary that the high-velocity load, which gives an approximate increase of 10 per cent. in the average velocity over 20 yards, should not result in any practical improvement in forward allowance at this range. But the truth is that a 10 per cent. increase in average velocity over the range can only mean, at the very most, a 10 per cent. reduction in forward allowance, or a reduction of 4 inches in the 40 inches which are necessary with the standard load. And when the diameters of the spread of the shot charge are remembered, it is difficult to imagine that 4 inches one way or the other can be of any material advantage or disadvantage in actual practice.

And as the range is increased, so does the improvement in forward allowance caused by the high-velocity load decrease because the percentage reduction in the average velocity over the range becomes smaller as the range becomes greater. This can be seen by studying Tables XXII to XXVIII in Volume II.

It must also be remembered that one of the objects of the high-velocity load was to gain an increase in range, and so the respective forward allowances necessary with the high-velocity and standard loads at the longer sporting ranges deserve the most careful scrutiny.

I have, accordingly, tabulated the different forward allowances necessary at all ranges, and in order to make the Table as complete as possible have included the allowances for the low-velocity load as well as those for the standard and high-velocity loads for birds crossing at both 40 and 60 m.p.h.

TABLE XXVI

FORWARD ALLOWANCES IN FEET FOR DIFFERENT LOADS AT VARIOUS RANGES

Range in Yards.	Bird crossing at 40 M.P.H.			Bird crossing at 60 M.P.H.		
	Low-Velocity Load.	Standard Load.	High-Velocity Load.	Low-Velocity Load.	Standard Load.	High-Velocity Load.
20	4·0	3·7	3·4	6·1	5·5	5·1
25	5·2	4·7	4·4	7·8	7·1	6·6
30	6·4	5·9	5·5	9·6	8·8	8·2
35	7·7	7·1	6·6	11·5	10·7	9·9
40	9·1	8·5	7·9	13·6	12·7	11·9
45	10·5	10·0	9·3	15·8	14·9	14·0
50	12·2	11·6	10·8	18·2	17·4	16·2

A study of this Table will show that just as the high-velocity load makes no noticeable or helpful reduction in forward allowance, so the low-velocity load does not add to it to any extent, nor increase the difficulty of shooting. The greatest differences will naturally be found between the allowances necessary in the case of the high- and low-velocity loads, and these will be accentuated most at extreme ranges. In round figures these allowances are 16 and 18 feet respectively for a bird crossing at 60 m.p.h. at 50 yards. When it is remembered that the diameter of the effective spread of the shot charge is from 4 to 5 feet at this range, while the forward allowance is roughly *6 yards*, can anyone believe that a difference of *2 feet* will have any appreciable effect in actual practice? With all three loads allowances of either $5\frac{1}{2}$ or $6\frac{1}{2}$ yards will result in a kill; and what shooter can estimate forward allowances at extreme sporting ranges to half a yard? Can any man hope to say for certain whether a bird is 48 yards or 52 yards away, and whether its speed is 60 m.p.h. or 50?

Personally I am convinced that such niceties and exactitudes are so impossible that their consideration is bordering on the ridiculous. For it must be remembered that the differences in figures which I have just quoted will make a bigger difference in forward allowance than can result from the greatest practical variations in loading. All that it is possible to do is to swing well through on a fast and distant bird, and in such circumstances the actual theoretical differences in allowances approximate into one indefinable average.

The truth of the matter is that with shotguns a big forward allowance will always be necessary for reasons which were explained at length in the chapters on Velocity in Volume II. We must accordingly face facts as they are and bow to the inevitable. Were shooting enjoyed on some other spheroid where there was no atmosphere and little gravity, such as the moon, the high-velocity load would come into its own: on the earth it is compelled to contend against such terrific odds in the way of air resistance that it really has not a fair chance.

I do not think it will be disputed that more birds are missed behind owing to the shooter checking his swing than from any other cause, and when this happens the bird is not missed by inches, but by yards, in which case no high-velocity load will be of any help.

It may be urged, however, that it is common occurrence for a shooter to keep on just "tailing" his birds and that in such circumstances a reduction of even 6 inches in forward allowance may make all the difference between a bird being clean killed or hit behind. But it must also be remembered that a high-velocity load needs

PLATE IX

THREE EXAMPLES OF BURST BARRELS WHICH WERE NOT BURST BY OBSTRUCTIONS

The burst barrel (A) was the result of faulty workmanship in a cheap gun, in that a longitudinal cut was made in the barrel when "striking up" the rib. This cut weakened the barrel along the line of the rib and a fracture ultimately occurred along this line.

In the two guns shown (B) and (C) the cause of the bursts was the same, namely, wear of the barrel. These were both old guns, and their barrels had been worn by use almost as thin as tissue-paper, with the result that rupture ultimately occurred.

In none of the three bursts shown is there any indication of a "ring bulge." The ribs are all perfectly straight, and there is no opening out of the severed portions of the barrels in the form of a funnel such as can be seen in the photographs given in Plates V and VII (B).

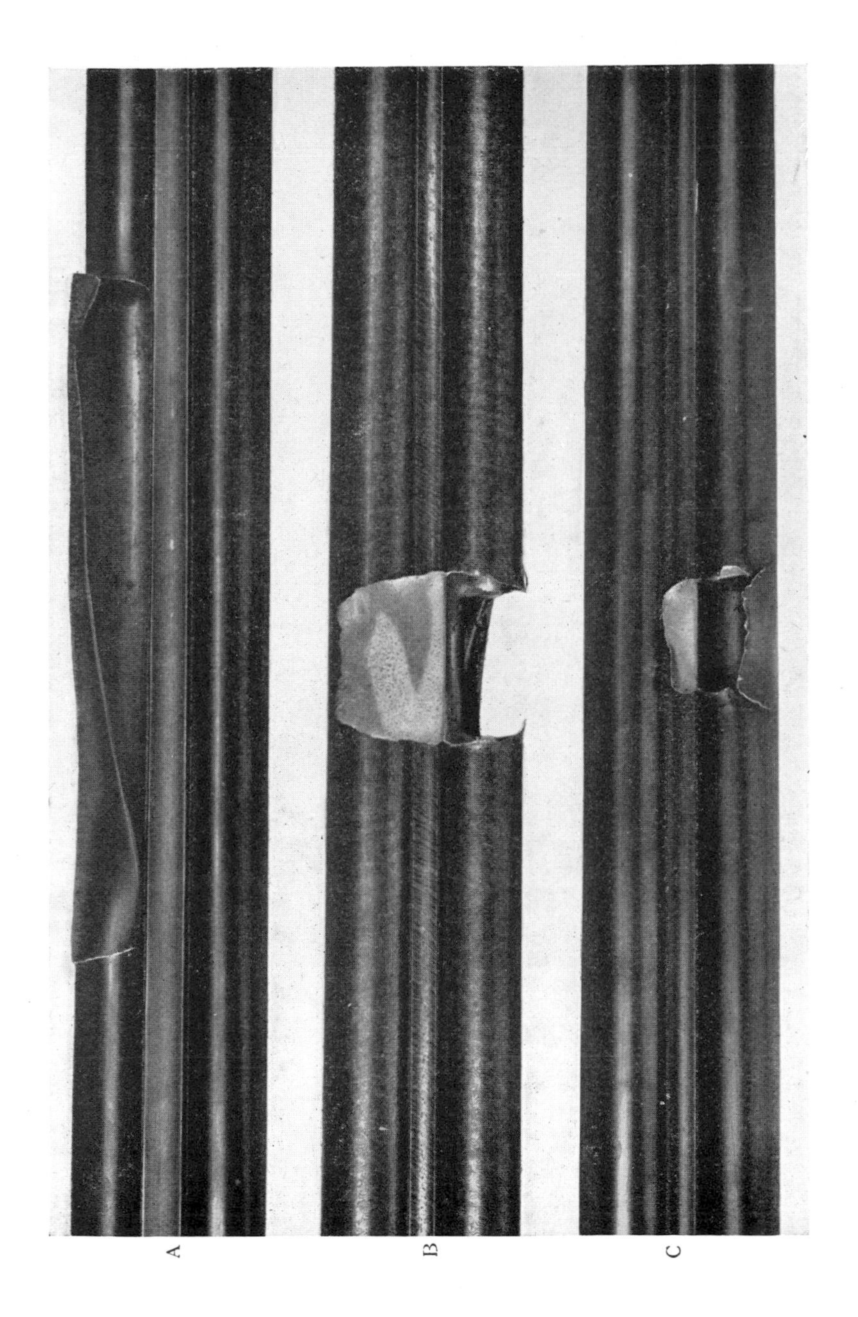
A
B
C

a fairly heavily choked gun, which reduces the spread of the shot charge, and this reduction might make a similar difference between a bird being tailed or killed clean.

Further I think it probable that tailing birds is due more to some temporary lapse from form rather than inability to judge pace. Most shooters must have experienced days, or parts of days, when things would not go right and they kept on hitting bird after bird behind. Perhaps the brain was not working quite so fast as usual ; or there was some partial check in swing—not enough to make one miss properly, but just sufficient to throw the charge a little back ; or there was some vague feeling of being out of sorts. On such occasions I cannot help thinking that the remedy lies with the shooter rather than the cartridge, for a little later he may recover his form and kill his birds well. Many shooters are too often inclined to blame their cartridges rather than themselves ; and in any case, even if the high-velocity load did make shooting easier by an appreciable reduction in the necessary forward allowance, a man who had become accustomed to this load would still be just as likely to suffer off days as when he used the standard load ; and when these off days came he would shoot behind with the high-velocity load as readily as he ever did with the standard.

There is also the fact—at least I believe it to be a fact—that birds are far more often missed in front than the great majority of shooters realise. The assumption that a bird is invariably missed behind has become so general that it is now regarded almost as an axiom. Personally I do not believe it to be anything of the sort, and would go almost as far as to say that some men miss their birds in front almost as often as they do behind. The question of the possibility of missing in front is seldom considered, and I will deal with it at greater length in the final chapter. But I am convinced of its existence, although I may be inclined to exaggerate its frequency.

The very big forward allowance which must always be necessary with a shotgun, especially at long ranges, is the chief factor which makes shooting at birds on the wing so difficult. If the high-velocity load could bring about a reduction of 50 per cent. in forward allowance, it would certainly be a load of practical value. But the reductions of but 6 to 9 inches in 7 to 10 feet are, to my mind at all events, too small to be of any real help.

FORWARD ALLOWANCE BEYOND 50 YARDS

So far we have only considered the question of forward allowance up to 50 yards, and since one of the main objects of experimenters in loading has been to increase the effective range of the ordinary game gun, the forward allowances necessary beyond 50 yards deserve attention.

At these extreme ranges the shot pellets are travelling so comparatively slowly that the forward allowance must be increased out of all seeming proportion to the range. This is because the time taken for a charge of shot to travel from 50 yards to 60 yards is just about the same as that same shot charge took to cover the first 20 yards of range. So it will be appreciated that for 60 yards the forward allowance which was correct for 50 yards must be *increased by the same amount as the total necessary forward allowance on the same bird at 20 yards*.

In round figures, the forward allowance at 60 yards for a bird crossing at 40 m.p.h. is *5 yards* in the case of low-, standard, or high-velocity loads, while for a bird flying at 60 m.p.h. the allowance is from 7 to 8 yards for all three loads.

At 55 yards the allowances are not quite so big, being actually 13·8, 13·3 and 12·5 feet for the low-, standard, and high-velocity loads on a 40-miles-an-hour bird. Or in round figures, *4½ yards* for all three loads.

Shots beyond 60 yards can affect no one but wildfowlers using special guns and heavy loads of large shot. The pellets of large shot, such as BB, have a superior capacity for overcoming air resistance and consequently their times of flight for long ranges are comparatively less than would be the case of ordinary small shot. Yet even so the forward allowances are enormous, being in round figures, 6, 7½, 9 and 11 yards for a 40-miles-an-hour bird at 70, 80, 90 and 100 yards, and correspondingly greater for faster birds.

Allowances of this nature, approaching as they must on occasions to the length of a cricket pitch, are quite beyond the capacity for estimation possessed by the average shooter, more especially as an allowance must also be made for elevation in the case of these long shots.

And then there is the further fact that the average velocity of the shot charge over these long ranges has dropped so much below the velocity of sound that the bird receives ample warning from the report of the gun and can swerve away from its original line of flight, when the most perfectly delivered shot will miss.

The truth is that air resistance must always reduce the velocity of even the largest sizes of shot pellets to such an extent that very long shots at individual birds in flight can never be anything but a pure gamble. The realisation of the very big forward allowances which are necessary at long ranges may help to convince the reader that there are other difficulties connected with very long shots quite irrespective of the problems of pattern and penetration, and that no variation in load can offer any help towards their solution.

It is far easier to design a combination of special gun and load which will give effective pattern and penetration for a large bird such as a goose at very long ranges, than it is to find a human being who can use this combination with success on individual flying birds. Bunches of wild-fowl, whether in flight or on the water, are another matter.

For all these reasons I do not consider shots at 60 yards to be practical propositions for ordinary 12-bore game guns. In fact, I am inclined to think that the actual difficulties inseperable from long shots can be taken as fixing 50 yards as the approximate limit of effective range for all except the super shot, for when trying to judge the very big forward allowances necessary it is just as easy to over-estimate as to under-estimate.

It is better to realise the limitations which are forced upon us and to concentrate on the development which is both effective within those limitations and convenient and comfortable to use, than to strive after remote possibilities and sacrifice chances at normal sporting ranges.

Throughout this chapter I have purposely dealt with the maximum forward allowances necessary, that is those for birds flying at right angles to the direction of fire. In actual practice, however, shots are far more frequently taken at birds flying at a decided angle with the line of fire, as was explained on page 157, and in all such cases the forward allowance is reduced to an extent corresponding to the reduction in the actual crossing speed of the bird which can be obtained from Table XXIV. This means that the difference in forward allowance caused by the adoption of a low-, standard, or high-velocity load is also reduced, while the spread of the shot charge remains the same. In actual practice, therefore, even the slight gain derived from the high-velocity principle of loading is less than seemed at first sight probable. Similarly, the disadvantage of the low-velocity load is not so great in practice as in theory.

In the case of very long shots, however, the time of flight factor remains the same : and a bird flying straight away will have just as much time to swerve as one flying right across the line of fire.

It will, therefore, be realised that the forward allowance is practically constant for any given range irrespective of the load, and depends only on the direction and speed of flight of the bird ; while for shots over 50 yards other difficulties enter which no type of load can possibly cure.

CHAPTER IX

GENERAL CONCLUSIONS ON LOADS

BEFORE going any further I will try to summarise the general conclusions which can be drawn from our investigation of the subject of loads as far as we have gone.

FORWARD ALLOWANCE. A slight reduction can be obtained by the use of the high-velocity load; but at short ranges at all events this reduction is counterbalanced by the necessity for using a heavily choked gun. Consequently the object of making shooting more easy has not been attained.

It must be remembered that a reduction in forward allowance *in itself* will not make it easier to hit a moving bird. If a modern magnum small-bore high-velocity rifle were used on pheasants the forward allowance would be reduced by 60 per cent., but it would be more difficult to kill one's birds.

For all practical purposes of actual sport the variations in forward allowance resulting from the various loads which we have considered make no noticeable difference. Shooting is rendered neither more easy nor more difficult, apart from any differences due to the boring of the guns used.

PENETRATION AT LONG RANGE. Here more success has been obtained, and increases in penetration of approximately 14 and 58 per cent. at 50 yards have definitely been obtained by seemingly opposite methods, namely "high" and "low" velocity loading. Of the two methods the latter is certainly the better *as far as penetration alone is concerned*, and these results can be obtained by its adoption without any increase in recoil.

INCREASE IN EFFECTIVE RANGE. Here it is probable that some slight increase has been gained, although not nearly so much as might be expected from the increased penetration. For, as has been repeatedly emphasised, range is dependent on two factors : (1) penetration ; and (2) pattern. Either is useless without the other, and in all loads there is a struggle between these two factors as to which can maintain its efficiency the longer. In the case of both the "high" and "low" velocity loads the penetration wins easily, and pattern fails first. And the range is limited by the failure of the pattern. In the case of the standard load the struggle is more even, and both pattern and penetration drop below their respective minimum limits more nearly simultaneously, the penetration outlasting the pattern by about 5 yards in the case of partridges and grouse, but by less in the case of larger birds such as pheasants and duck. This means that in all round shooting the range of the standard load is limited by the pattern rather than by the penetration.

If pattern is to be helped without raising recoil or pressure, either the size of shot must be reduced, which means loss of penetration, or else a gun with more choke must be used. It is of no more use to help pattern at the expense of penetration than it is to help the latter at the expense of the former, and so a gun with more choke is the only practical method of helping pattern. But a gun with a considerable degree of choke is not a practical weapon for the average shot for all round shooting, and so we come back very nearly to the point from which we started.

It may be suggested that the crimped cartridge can increase range by improving the pattern. But the real improvement brought about by the crimp sealing and absence of the over-shot wad is increased regularity of pattern and elimination of scatters. It is true that there is also a slight increase in density, but a 5 per cent. denser pattern will not increase the effective range by more than a yard or two at most. So I doubt if the crimped cartridge can be regarded as of much practical value for increasing the effective range.

Excellence of Standard Load. The last sentence

of the preceding paragraph but one brings us to the difficulty of improving on the standard load. The truth of the matter is that all loads are a compromise. Some combinations help the penetration, and others the pattern. It is impossible to help both without increasing the recoil beyond all practical limits as well as raising the pressure too much. The standard load is the evolution of nearly a century of practical experience with the breech-loader: it is really the outcome of millions of shots fired by thousands of shooters in the actual field: for ordinary sporting purposes it can hardly be bettered, as it provides an ideal compromise between pattern and penetration.

And this can be taken as being equally applicable to other sizes of game guns than the 12-bore which are ordinarily used in the field for normal sporting purposes. In fact it is always safe to follow the maxim: *When in doubt the standard load is best.*

PSYCHOLOGICAL FACTOR. I have alluded to the question of the psychological factor already. I believe that it is one which can have an enormous influence on shooting and consequently it deserves careful attention. I am quite convinced in my own mind that any benefits which are conferred by the high-velocity load are entirely psychological. As I have already explained, I have tested numerous batches of "high-velocity" cartridges for shooters which proved to be "high velocity" only in name and which developed ballistics indistinguishable from the standard load. Yet the shooters who used these cartridges would probably have no confidence in standard cartridges and quite likely imagine that they were missing behind on account of the much larger forward allowance which was necessary, whereas the truth would be that the forward allowance was identical.

There can be no doubt that the description "high velocity" has a comforting sound, and gunmakers instil all sorts of exaggerated ideas into their customers' heads of the great increases in penetration and reductions in forward allowance which accrue from the high-velocity load. It is but fair to add that many gunmakers do believe quite sincerely that these advantages exist, for it is only the study of ballistics which shows them to be too slight to have any practical effect.

In the same way nothing can have a worse psychological effect on the average shooter than the belief that his cartridges are "weak." For this reason the very term "low velocity" is not a happy one, and is inclined to make many shooters hesitate about using a load which gives the maximum penetration at long range. If such a load were called a "special long-range load" those same shooters would as likely as not use it with confidence and be delighted with the results.

I have used the expression "low velocity" throughout with full realisation of this disadvantage; but my sole purpose is to try to expound the truth, and the expression does convey an idea of the principle involved.

There are shooters who have become accustomed to the real high-velocity load and who miss the rather heavy recoil when using standard cartridges. Because of the lighter recoil they are inclined to think that the cartridges must be "weak," and such thoughts beget lack of confidence, and lack of confidence begets bad shooting.

So from every point of view it is advisable for the man who has a belief in the high-velocity load to use it, while those who lack this belief can make themselves happy in the knowledge that the standard load is the load which experience has shown to be most generally effective for ordinary sporting purposes.

The Low-Velocity Principle. Just as little real advantage, if any, is gained over the standard load by the adoption of the high-velocity load, so is there little to be gained by the use of the low-velocity load in an ordinary 12-bore for ordinary sporting purposes.

But it is probable that the principles of the low-velocity load could be applied with very real advantage to guns of other sizes. These sizes are the two extremes, that is large bores or ultra small bores.

In the large bore category I would include 4-bores, 8-bores, 10-bores and 3-inch 12-bores. All these guns are used almost entirely for wildfowling where shots must be taken at very long ranges, and big shot is generally used to the exclusion of other sizes. The only possible result must be that pattern will fail long before penetration, and consequently the range must be limited by the pattern. If the low-velocity principle were adopted the weight of the shot charge would be increased, while the powder charge would be reduced so as to prevent both excessive recoil and excessive pressure. This reduction in powder will cause a certain loss in muzzle velocity ; but the large size of shot used (No. 1 or larger) enables the individual pellets to retain their velocity even at the longest ranges, with the result that the struggle between penetration and pattern is rendered much more even.

This principle was advocated by the late Dr. Charles J. Heath, the President of the Wildfowlers' Association, who used it with great success in his chamberless 12-bore guns. Dr. Heath used 2 ounces of BB shot in a gun weighing but 8 lb., and $1\frac{3}{4}$ of BB shot in a gun weighing but $7\frac{1}{4}$ lb. In order to prevent the recoil from being prohibitive, he used very light powder charges which gave observed velocities over 20 yards of but 850 f.s. The heavy shot retained their velocity sufficiently well to enable kills to be made up to 90 and 100 yards when firing at bunches of fowl, while the pattern was helped by the increased number of pellets in the charge as well as by the low ballistics.

Without exhaustive experiments it is impossible to do more than suggest combinations of powder and shot for loads for all the different sizes of large bore guns ; but there can be no two opinions about the great value of the principle of the low-velocity load for wildfowlers.

In 1935 and 1936 I was able to carry out fairly extensive experiments with a view to obtaining the best possible low-velocity loads for the 3-inch and $2\frac{3}{4}$-inch 12-bore cartridges. When Modified Smokeless Diamond (a 36-grain powder) appeared at the beginning of 1933 I was at once struck by the possibilities it presented for low-velocity loads in long 12-bore cases. But it was followed quickly by Neoflak and later by the Belgian Cooppal Caulille, both of which seemed likely to be even better. So thanks to the ungrudging help of Imperial Chemical Industries, Ltd., and Messrs. J. R. Watson & Co., the British Agents for the Cooppal Powder Company, I was able to try a considerable number of loads with shot charges of 2 ounces of BB, 1¾ ounces of No. 1, and 1¼ ounces of No. 4 in 3-inch cases.

These tests satisfied me that Modified Smokeless Diamond was so much better in 3-inch cases with heavy shot charges than ordinary Smokeless Diamond that I now regard ordinary 33-grain and 42-grain powders as obsolete for low-velocity loads in cartridges longer than 2½ inches. But good as the Modified Smokeless Diamond was the Neoflak and Caulille were even better, and with 33 and 32 grains of these powders respectively and 2 ounces of BB which gave normal pressures, observed velocities of just under 850 f.s. and patterns of 70 per cent. in a full choke.

With 38 grains of Neoflak and 33 grains of Caulille and 1¾ ounces of No. 1 normal pressures were combined with observed velocities of just over and a little below 950 f.s. and patterns of 70 per cent.

With 1½ ounces of No. 4 it was found difficult to improve upon the standard " Alphamax " cartridge, which is really a 3-inch Maximum cartridge.

The results of these tests were published in *Game and Gun* and both the two low-velocity loads—the Alphamax has a standard shot charge and gives a standard velocity—proved most satisfactory, the 1¾ ounces of No. 1 being especially popular and successful.

Accordingly I then carried out further experiments with 2¾-inch 12-bore cases, again with the unstinted help of Imperial Chemical Industries, Ltd., and Messrs. J. R. Watson & Co. This time, instead of the original Neoflak I used a Modified Neoflak, which was a slightly slower burning powder than the Neoflak, and the results it gave proved that for this particular purpose it was better even than Neoflak.

With 34 grains of Modified Neoflak and 1½ ounces of shot the pressures were normal and the observed velocity averaged almost exactly 950 f.s. The patterns with No. 1 were 70 per cent. and with No. 4, 72 per cent. in a full choke barrel.

The Cooppal Caulille results were not quite so satisfactory, for the pressures were a bit low and observed velocity only just over 900 f.s. But as is so often the case with low ballistics the patterns were excellent, being round about 75 per cent. in a full choke.

These results were also published in *Game and Gun*, and the loads, especially the Modified Neoflak load, were tried out by a number of wildfowlers and gave the very greatest satisfaction.

It must, however, always be borne in mind that the *use of large shot is essential for the low-velocity principle.* To shoot large shot at a high velocity is merely to throw away killing pattern, and so from every point of view it is always better to combine large shot and a low velocity. The larger the shot the lower the velocity can be, and a very good idea of the most suitable combinations of shot sizes and observed velocities can be obtained from Tables XXXII to XXXIX in Volume II.

As a general rule it is fairly safe to assume that pattern is being wasted if any sizes from No. 1 to No. 4 inclusive are fired with a higher observed velocity than 950 f.s. ; if B and BB are fired with a higher observed velocity than 900 f.s. ; and if BBB and the larger sizes are fired with a higher observed velocity than 850 f.s.

As the velocity is reduced, so can the weight of the shot charge be increased without increasing the recoil, and the following shot charges when propelled at the observed velocity indicated, give equal recoil, the weight of the shot charge propelled with the standard observed velocity of about 1,050 f.s. being taken as unity.

From this it will be seen that as the observed velocity developed in a 3-inch 12-bore cartridge is lowered from 1,050 f.s. to 1,000 f.s., 950 f.s. 900 f.s. and 850 f.s., the weight of the shot charge can be 1½, 1⅝, 1¾, 1⅞ and

2 ounces respectively while the recoil will be the same in each case.

Observed Velocity over 20 yards	Weight of Shot Charge giving Constant Recoil
1,050 f.s.	1
1,000 f.s.	1·07
950 f.s.	1·15
900 f.s.	1·20
850 f.s.	1·30

Similarly, the standard charge of 3 ounces of shot for a 4-inch 4-bore cartridge can be raised to 4 ounces if the observed velocity is reduced to 850 f.s.

Such increases in the weights of the shot charge must help very materially towards pattern, while there will be no lack of penetration provided suitably large shot is used in each case.

The pressures will also remain approximately constant, as although the weight of the shot charge is increased that of the powder charge is reduced.

The ultra small bores, namely the 28-bore and the ·410, offer a similar problem but in a slightly different form. At present the cartridges for both these bores are loaded to develop velocities which are not much less than the standard observed velocity given by a 12-bore cartridge. This can only mean that penetration is efficient long after the pattern has failed owing to the very small shot charges used. In the $2\frac{1}{2}$-inch ·410 cartridge the shot charge is but $\frac{3}{8}$ ounce, and it is impossible for such a light charge to constitute a killing pattern at a range of over 30 yards. Yet the shot charge is given sufficient velocity to ensure penetration for individual pellets up to 40 or 45 yards. This is mere waste of velocity, and a more generally effective cartridge would ensue from loading with more shot and less powder, as the pattern would be maintained better, while there would still be ample velocity to ensure penetration as long as the pattern was sufficiently dense to render a hit something more than a pure fluke.

The use of Neoflak or Modified Neoflak opens out new possibilities for these ultra small bores and I see no reason why it should not be possible to load a 2½-inch ·410 cartridge with ½ ounce of shot to develop an observed velocity of 950 f.s. without any increase of pressure beyond the present standard. Such a cartridge would be really effective up to 35 yards against all ordinary game.

And the same applies to the 28-bore.

Although I have stated that there is little to be gained by adopting the low-velocity principle in 2½-inch 12-bore game guns for ordinary sporting purposes, low-velocity cartridges can be very useful for large birds which do not require a very dense minimum killing pattern. In Table XXV it will be seen that a quarter choke gives a sufficiently dense pattern for mallard with the low-velocity shot charge of 1¼ ounces of No. 4 at 50 yards. This, as has been seen, is about the longest practical range for ordinary shooting, and so it will be realised that the low-velocity load will be very effective against game birds of the size of mallard or larger.

The same thing applies, but in a smaller degree, to the 2½-inch 16- and 20-bores. In these guns, however, the weight of the shot charge is less and consequently the pattern will become too open unless very large birds comprise the quarry, or the shot size is reduced.

DETAILS OF LOADS

There are so many possible variations in loads that it is impossible to consider all. Frequently such variations consist of an additional grain to the powder charge. This is particularly common in the ordinary 2½-inch 12-bore cartridge, and powder charges of 33, 34 and 35 grains are often used in conjunction with 1 ounce of shot. Such variations are always the work of gunmakers and never of a factory where every effort is always made to maintain standardisation in order to simplify the work of mass production. Some shooters think that an extra grain of powder in the charge will make a great difference to the velocity. The truth is, however, that there are so many other factors to be considered besides the actual weight of the powder charge that these small variations have little, if any, effect. Cap, wadding, and above all turnover, can affect the results far more than a grain more or a grain less ; and a tightly loaded cartridge with 33 grains will develop a higher velocity than a loosely loaded one with 34 or 35 grains. It is true that many gunmakers load most excellent cartridges with 34 grains and 1 ounce of shot. But, as I have already explained in Chapter II, gunmakers, as a rule, load on the "soft" side ; and a load of 34 grains and 1 ounce loaded by a gunmaker will probably develop a very similar velocity to one of 33 grains and 1 ounce loaded at a factory. There can be no sort of harm in these small variations, but sportsmen must not expect any practical difference in the results.

Variations in the shot charge, however, can have important results, but these are all due to alterations in the pattern rather than in the velocity.

The standard shot charge for the $2\frac{1}{2}$-inch 12-bore is $1\frac{1}{16}$ ounce. Thirty years ago it was $1\frac{1}{8}$ ounce, but it was reduced because shooters found that the lighter charge did all they wanted in ordinary shooting and also gave a lighter recoil which enabled them to use lighter guns.

During the 1914–18 War the weight of the shot charge for an ordinary 12-bore gun was limited by law to 1 ounce on account of the shortage of lead. Consequently all who shot at that time were compelled to use this lighter shot charge. It was found so pleasant that it is not surprising that those who had once tried it were not always anxious to revert to the standard $1\frac{1}{16}$ ounce, especially as 1 ounce proved perfectly effective in the actual shooting field for all ordinary game, especially driving. The result is that an ounce charge is now nearly, if not quite, as common as the standard $1\frac{1}{16}$; and there can be no doubt that the further reduction in recoil which is the natural outcome of the lighter shot charge has helped the movement in the direction of lighter guns.

The velocity developed with an ounce of shot is slightly higher than that with $1\frac{1}{16}$ ounce, while the density of the pattern must be correspondingly less owing to the fewer pellets in the charge. The effect of these changes is to maintain penetration at a somewhat greater distance beyond pattern than is the case with the standard load. The actual effective range is, therefore, reduced : but this reduction is so slight as to have little, if any, practical result in ordinary shooting ; although if the game is very wild and shots at extreme range are the rule rather than the exception, the lighter shot charge cannot possibly be quite as effective as the heavier.

It will, accordingly, be seen that during the past forty years the shot charge for an ordinary 12-bore gun has been reduced from $1\frac{1}{8}$ ounce to 1 ounce, although in theory $1\frac{1}{16}$ ounce is still the standard weight. This reduction has had a great influence on recoil, and has helped as much as any other single cause towards the building of lighter guns. It is also probable that the tendency towards reducing the weight of the shot charge has been fostered by all firms which load cartridges on a big scale. This is not difficult to understand, as nine cartridges can be loaded with the same amount of shot when an ounce charge is used as can eight when the charge is $1\frac{1}{8}$. Since shot is one of the most expensive items in the composition of a cartridge the saving in cost will be appreciated when hundreds of thousands, let alone millions, of cartridges are being loaded and sold. And a reduction from $1\frac{1}{16}$ ounce to an ounce makes a correspondingly pleasant saving in expenditure. But even so the wide adoption of an ounce charge could never have been brought about unless it was a thoroughly practical and efficient load for all ordinary shooting. Sportsmen, however, should remember that an ounce must reduce the effective range to a slight extent. This reduction, however, is so slight in comparison to the benefit conferred by rendering possible the use of a lighter gun that it is probable that the majority of shooters who fire most of their shots at driven game will prefer an ounce charge to anything heavier.

It may now be of interest to summarise the particulars of the different loads which are usually adopted in 2½-inch 12-bore guns as they form a very sound guide to the possible variations in other sizes of cartridges.

In the following particulars the powder is assumed to be a 33-grain bulk powder, such as Smokeless Diamond, except in the case of the Maximum cartridge, and the velocity quoted is the ordinary observed velocity over 20 yards. The wadding in every case is assumed to be of the best felt—air-cushion wads need lighter powder charges—and the loading to be similar as regards turnover and general tightness, while it is also assumed that the different loads are all used in guns which give regular and even patterns of approximately the correct density for the various types of boring.

30 GRAINS OF POWDER AND 1¼ OUNCE OF NO. 4. A low-velocity load which has the maximum penetration at long range, but the pattern is rather open at 45 yards for birds smaller than mallard. Up to 40 yards it would be hard to imagine a more killing load for all ordinary game except snipe, and it is especially deadly against ground game. For mallard and birds of the same size or larger it is the most deadly load of all and will kill at 50 yards in a quarter-choke barrel. Can be used in any type of boring. Velocity, about 950 f.s. Recoil, normal.

30 GRAINS OF POWDER AND 1¼ OUNCE OF NO. 4½. A low-velocity load which has a sufficiently good killing pattern for pheasants up to 50 yards in an improved cylinder barrel and gives great penetration, but not quite so good as that of the previous load. A very good general load for all round shooting except snipe ; and, like the previous load, especially useful for walking up because the large shot has greater penetration on a bird shot from the rear. Can be used in any type of boring. Velocity, about 950 f.s. Recoil, normal.

33 GRAINS OF POWDER AND 1⅛ OUNCE OF NO. 6. Probably the most deadly load of any for all-round rough shooting on account of the dense pattern, and one which can be quite useful for snipe. Will kill partridges, etc.,

with certainty very nearly up to 45 yards in an improved cylinder gun, and will kill larger birds up to very nearly 50 yards, if not quite. If No. 5 shot is used instead of No. 6 the pattern and penetration become almost identical with those given by 30 grains of powder and 1¼ ounce of No. 4½. Can be used in any type of boring. Velocity, about 1,040 f.s. Recoil, heavy.

N.B.—42 grains of a 42-grain bulk powder such as Schultze probably give better results than 33 grains with this shot charge; and further, with these powders the velocity becomes about 1,060 f.s.

33 Grains of Powder and 1$\frac{1}{16}$ Ounce of No. 6. The standard load. Probably as good an all-round load for all ordinary shooting as any other, and with No. 6 shot can be quite useful for snipe, although a smaller shot size is better. Will kill birds the size of a partridge slightly beyond 40 yards with certainty, and bigger birds up to 45 to 50 yards. Can be used in any type of boring. Velocity, about 1,060 f.s. Recoil, normal.

33 Grains of Powder and 1 Ounce of No. 6 or No. 7. A delightful all-round load which is particularly useful for driven game and perfectly effective up to 40 yards for partridges and larger birds up to 45 yards. With No. 7 shot is excellent for snipe and is then the most useful all-round load when snipe are expected but do not comprise the principal game. Can be used in any type of boring. Velocity, about 1,100 f.s. Recoil, light.

N.B.—34 grains are frequently loaded by gunmakers instead of 33, but there is no practical difference in the results. (See page 196.)

36 Grains of Powder and 1 Ounce of No. 6. The best high-velocity load. Very deadly for all game and will kill partridges up to 45 yards and perhaps a little farther, and larger birds up to 50 yards. Needs a half choke. Velocity, about 1,150 f.s. Recoil, heavy.

36 Grains of Powder and $\frac{15}{16}$ Ounce of No. 5. A high-velocity load which gives penetration at all ranges which is practically identical with that given by the low-

velocity load of 30 grains and $1\frac{1}{4}$ ounces of No. 4. Will kill partridges up to 40 yards, but not beyond on account of the open pattern. Will kill mallard up to 50 yards. Needs an absolutely full choke. Velocity about 1,170 f.s. Recoil, normal.

36 GRAINS OF POWDER AND $\frac{15}{16}$ OUNCE OF NO. 7. A high-velocity load which has no advantage over the standard, as the small shot cannot retain its original velocity. Will kill up to 45 yards. Needs very nearly, if not quite, a full choke. Velocity, about 1,150 f.s. Recoil, normal.

MAXIMUM CARTRIDGE. Pre-eminently the cartridge for the rough shooter. With No. 6 will kill all ordinary game from partridges to duck and pheasants up to 50 yards, and with No. 5 will kill duck and pheasants up to 55 yards, although the pattern is a bit too open for partridges and pigeon beyond 45 yards. Velocity, about 1,050 f.s. Recoil, very heavy.

NOTE.—If snipe alone are the quarry no shot size larger than No. 8 should be used, as the minimum necessary pattern cannot be obtained with certainty at 40 yards with larger shot. It is, however, extraordinary what larger shot can do at times. For instance, although I have fired very few times at snipe with the low-velocity load of 30 grains and $1\frac{1}{4}$ ounce of No. 4, the first three shots were all kills!

The Table on page 202 suggests details of loads for all sizes of British cartridges. The list is admittedly not complete in that it does not give all the possible combinations of powder and shot which can be used in the different cartridges. But it does indicate the limits beyond which variations in charges should not be made. In the column headed "Type of Load" the letters L.V., S., and H.V. indicate respectively low-velocity, standard, and high-velocity loading. Details of high-velocity and low-velocity loads are not given for those cartridges in which any pronounced divergence from the standard is not to be recommended as likely to prove of practical value. And in the case of the long 12-bore and 10-bore cartridges the only powder suggested for low-velocity loads is Modified Smokeless Diamond because the experiments I mentioned on page 192 convinced me that this slower-burning powder is far more suitable for such loads in these larger cartridges than the ordinary 33-grain and 42-grain bulk powders. Experience has also shown that 33-grain and even 36-grain powders are less satisfactory in 4-bore and 8-bore cartridges than 42-grain, so in their cases only loads for 42-grain powders have been given. No mention has been made of Neoflak or Modified Neoflak because these powders are not sold separately and cartridges loaded with them can be obtained only from the makers. Further, it must be borne in mind that all the powder charges given in this Table are those suitable for felt wadding. Air-cushion wads need lighter powder charges to develop the same ballistics.

It will be seen that two low-velocity loads have been suggested for the 12-bore 3-inch cartridge. This has been done because of the popularity amongst wildfowlers which is enjoyed by this particular cartridge. The load utilising $1\frac{3}{4}$ ounces of shot develops an observed velocity of 950 f.s. and is very suitable for shot sizes from No. 4 to No. 1 inclusive. The load with 2 ounces of shot develops an observed velocity of from 850 to 900 f.s. and is the best to adopt when very large shot, such as BB, is considered necessary.

The same principle could be adopted in all cartridges. For instance, 28 grains of Smokeless Diamond and $1\frac{3}{8}$ ounce of shot gives an observed velocity of about 900 f.s. in an ordinary $2\frac{1}{2}$-inch 12-bore. But the loads actually given are those which are likely to prove most generally useful.

The 3-inch ·410 cartridge carries such an abnormally long shot column that pressures are excessive unless Modified Neoflak is used. The charges suggested for Modified Smokeless Diamond give the maximum pressures advisable, but the velocities are slightly on the low side and cartridges loaded with Modified Neoflak are better.

TABLE XXVII

Loads for all Sizes of British Cartridges

Cartridge.		Type of Load.	33-Grain Powders.		36-Grain Powders.		42-Grain Powders.		Ballistite Condensed Powder.		Black Powder.		Suitable Shot Sizes.
Bore.	Length of Case in inches.		Powder in Grains.	Shot in Ounces.	Powder in Grains.	Shot in Ounces.	Powder in Grains.	Shot in Ounces.	Powder in Grains.	Shot in Ounces.	Powder in Drachms.	Shot in Ounces.	
4	4¼	S.	—	—	—	—	105	3¼	—	—	9¼	3½	1 and larger
4	4¼	L.V.	—	—	—	—	95	4	—	—	8¼	4	,, ,,
4	4	S.	—	—	—	—	100	3	—	—	9	3¼	,, ,,
4	4	L.V.	—	—	—	—	88	4	—	—	8	4	,, ,,
8	4¼	S.	—	—	—	—	75	2½	—	—	8	2¾	2 ,, ,,
8	4¼	L.V.	—	—	—	—	68	3¼	—	—	7	3¼	1 ,, ,,
8	4	S.	—	—	—	—	72	2⅜	—	—	7½	2½	2 ,, ,,
8	4	L.V.	—	—	—	—	65	3¼	—	—	6	3¼	1 ,, ,,
8	3¾	S.	—	—	—	—	70	2¼	—	—	7	2⅜	2 ,, ,,
8	3¾	L.V.	—	—	—	—	62	3	—	—	6	3	1 ,, ,,
8	3½	S.	—	—	—	—	67	2⅛	—	—	6½	2¼	3 ,, ,,
8	3½	L.V.	—	—	—	—	60	3	—	—	5¾	3	1 ,, ,,
8	3¼	S.	—	—	—	—	65	2	—	—	6	2⅛	4 ,, ,,
8	3¼	L.V.	—	—	—	—	58	2½	—	—	5	2½	1 ,, ,,
10	3¼	S.	48	1⅝	52	1⅝	60	1¾	—	—	4½	1¾	4 ,, ,,
10	3¼	L.V.	—	—	43	2¼	—	—	—	—	3¾	2¼	1 ,, ,,
10	3	S.	46	1½	49	1½	56	1⅝	—	—	4	1⅝	4 ,, ,,
10	3	L.V.	—	—	40	2	—	—	—	—	3⅜	2	1 ,, ,,
10	2⅞	S.	44	1 $\frac{7}{16}$	48	1 $\frac{7}{16}$	56	1 $\frac{7}{16}$	—	—	4	1½	4 ,, ,,
10	2⅞	L.V.	—	—	38	2	—	—	—	—	3¼	2	B ,, ,,
10	2⅝	S.	38	1 $\frac{5}{16}$	42	1 $\frac{5}{16}$	49	1 $\frac{5}{16}$	—	—	3½	1⅜	4 ,, ,,
10	2⅝	L.V.	—	—	35	2	—	—	—	—	3	2	B ,, ,,
12	3¼	S.	43	1½	46	1½	54	1 $\frac{9}{16}$	—	—	4	1 $\frac{9}{16}$	6 ,, ,,
12	3¼	L.V.	—	—	42	1¾	—	—	—	—	3½	1¾	4 ,, ,,
12	3	S.	40	1 $\frac{5}{16}$	42	1⅜	50	1½	29	1 $\frac{5}{16}$	3¾	1½	6 ,, ,,
12	3	L.V.	—	—	40	1¾	—	—	—	—	3¼	1¾	4 ,, ,,
12	3	L.V.	—	—	36	2	—	—	—	—	3	2	BB ,, ,,

12	2¾	S.	36	1¼	38	1¼	46	1¼	28	1¼	3¼	1¼	6 ,, ,,
12	2¾	L.V.	—	—	36	1½	—	—	—	—	3	1½	3 ,, ,,
12	2½	H.V.	36	1	39	1	46	1	28	1	3¼	1	6
12	2½	S.	33	1 1/16	36	1 1/16	42	1 1/16	25	1 1/16	3	1⅛	5 and smaller
12	2½	L.V.	30	1¼	33	1¼	38	1¼	23	1¼	2¾	1¼	4½ ,, larger
12	2	S.	26	7/8	—	—	—	—	—	—	2¾	7/8	6 ,, smaller
12	2	L.V.	24	1	—	—	—	—	—	—	2½	1	4½ ,, larger
14	2½	H.V.	33	15/16	36	15/16	42	15/16	25	15/16	3	15/16	6
14	2½	S.	31	1	33	1	38	1	23	1	2¾	1	5 and smaller
14	2½	L.V.	28	1 3/16	30	1 3/16	36	1 3/16	21	1 3/16	2½	1 3/16	4½ ,, larger
16	3	H.V.	36	1	39	1	46	1	28	1	3¼	1	6
16	3	S.	33	1 1/16	36	1 1/16	42	1 1/16	25	1 1/16	3	1⅛	5 and smaller
16	3	L.V.	30	1¼	33	1¼	38	1¼	23	1¼	2¾	1¼	4½ ,, larger
16	2¾	H.V.	33	15/16	36	15/16	42	15/16	25	15/16	3	15/16	6
16	2¾	S.	31	1	33	1	40	1 1/16	23	1	3	1 1/16	5 and smaller
16	2¾	L.V.	28	1 3/16	30	1 3/16	36	1 3/16	21	1 3/16	2¾	1 3/16	4½ ,, larger
16	2½	S.	28	7/8	30	7/8	36	7/8	21	7/8	2¾	7/8	6 ,, smaller
16	2½	L.V.	26	1	28	1	33	1	18	1	2½	1	4½ ,, larger
20	3	H.V.	32	15/16	35	15/16	38	15/16	23	15/16	3	15/16	6
20	3	S.	30	1	32	1	35	1	21	1	2¾	1	5 and smaller
20	3	L.V.	27	1 3/16	29	1 3/16	31	1 3/16	19	1 3/16	2½	1 3/16	4½ ,, larger
20	2¾	S.	26	7/8	29	7/8	33	15/16	18	7/8	2¾	15/16	6 ,, smaller
20	2¾	L.V.	24	1	27	1	31	1	16	1	2¼	1	4½ ,, larger
20	2½	S.	24	¾	27	¾	31	¾	18	¾	2¼	¾	6 ,, smaller
20	2½	L.V.	21	7/8	23	7/8	25	7/8	16	7/8	2	7/8	4½ ,, larger
24	2½	S.	22	5/8	23	5/8	27	5/8	—	—	2	5/8	6½ ,, smaller
24	2½	L.V.	20	¾	21	¾	24	¾	—	—	1¾	¾	5 ,, larger
28	2½	S.	20	9/16	21	9/16	25	9/16	—	—	1¾	9/16	7 ,, smaller
28	2½	L.V.	16	¾	17	¾	21	¾	—	—	1½	¾	5 ,, 6
32	2½	S.	16	½	17	½	21	½	—	—	1⅜	½	7 ,, smaller
32	2½	L.V.	12	5/8	13	5/8	16	5/8	—	—	1⅛	¾	5 ,, 6
·410	3	S.	—	—	11	9/16	—	—	—	—	1	9/16	7 ,, smaller
·410	3	L.V.	—	—	8	11/16	—	—	—	—	¾	11/16	5 ,, 6
·410	2½	S.	10½	⅜	11½	⅜	12½	⅜	—	—	1	⅜	7 ,, smaller
·410	2½	L.V.	8½	½	9	½	10	½	—	—	¾	½	6 ,, ,,
·410	2	S.	9	5/16	10	5/16	11	5/16	—	—	¾	5/16	8 ,, ,,
·410	2	L.V.	7	⅜	7½	⅜	8½	⅜	—	—	½	⅜	7 ,, ,,
·360	1¾	S.	6	3/16	7	3/16	7	3/16	—	—	½	3/16	8 ,, ,,
·360	1¾	L.V.	4	¼	4½	¼	5	¼	—	—	⅜	¼	8 ,, ,,

SIZES OF SHOT

No investigation into the problem of loads would be complete without considering the advantages and disadvantages which can be conferred by adopting different sizes of shot. It is quite obvious that the smaller the shot size the greater is the number of pellets in the charge, and consequently the denser is the pattern. And since the falling of the pattern below the minimum necessary for any particular variety of bird is recognised as being one of the two principal factors in limiting range, many sportsmen advocate the use of No. 7 shot in place of No. 6 in the standard 2½-inch 12-bore load with a view to increasing the chances of a kill at long range. Those who do so, however, not infrequently forget the other limiting factor to range, namely penetration. It is just as useless to have pattern without penetration as it is to have penetration without pattern. In fact it is more useless, as in the latter case a lucky pellet will kill, while in the former it will not ; and there is no more fruitful source of wounding than pattern without penetration.

If small shot gave the same penetration as large, its use would be most advantageous on many occasions. But unfortunately it does not, and for two reasons. First, because it does not retain its velocity so well as the larger sizes owing to its poorer capacity for overcoming air resistance, with the result that the actual striking velocity of the pellets of a charge of small shot is always less at any given range than that of the pellets of a charge of large shot propelled with a similar velocity.

Secondly, because the capacity for penetration possessed by any single pellet depends on its weight as well as on its velocity at the moment of impact. The belief that small shot " cuts its way in like the edge of a razor " while the pellets of larger size fail to get through the feathers, is very common, but absolutely erroneous, as was explained in Volume II. The expounders of this theory fail to realise that the superior weight of a large pellet helps it to penetrate more than it is retarded by its

PLATE X

(A) A Gun which burst owing to a flaw in the Right Barrel

In this particular case the flaw was due to an inclusion of "slag" in the original ingot, and when the ingot was drawn, a longitudinal "seam" was produced in the metal. This "seam" begins at the point marked 1 and runs in a straight line to the point 5. The actual burst occurred along this "seam." An examination of the fractured edge of the barrel, between the points marked 1 and 2, will show that the metal of the barrel seems to consist of two layers of varying thickness, the outer layer being dark. This discoloration is due to the presence of the "slag," which produced a fissure penetrating in places to half the thickness of the wall.

The photo-micrographs of this fissure in the barrel which are shown in Plates XII, XIII (A) and XIII (B) were taken respectively at the points marked 3, 4 and 5.

(B) Another Gun which burst owing to a flaw in the Right Barrel

In this case the flaw was possibly due to an air bubble which produced a short "seam" in the metal when the ingot was drawn. Such a "seam" would cause an incipient flaw. This flaw extended from the point 1 to 2 in a straight longitudinal line, and the burst occurred along this line. The similarity of these two bursts is very marked. In both cases the site of the burst is situated along an almost straight longitudinal line, and there is no sign of a "ring bulge" such as would be produced by an obstruction.

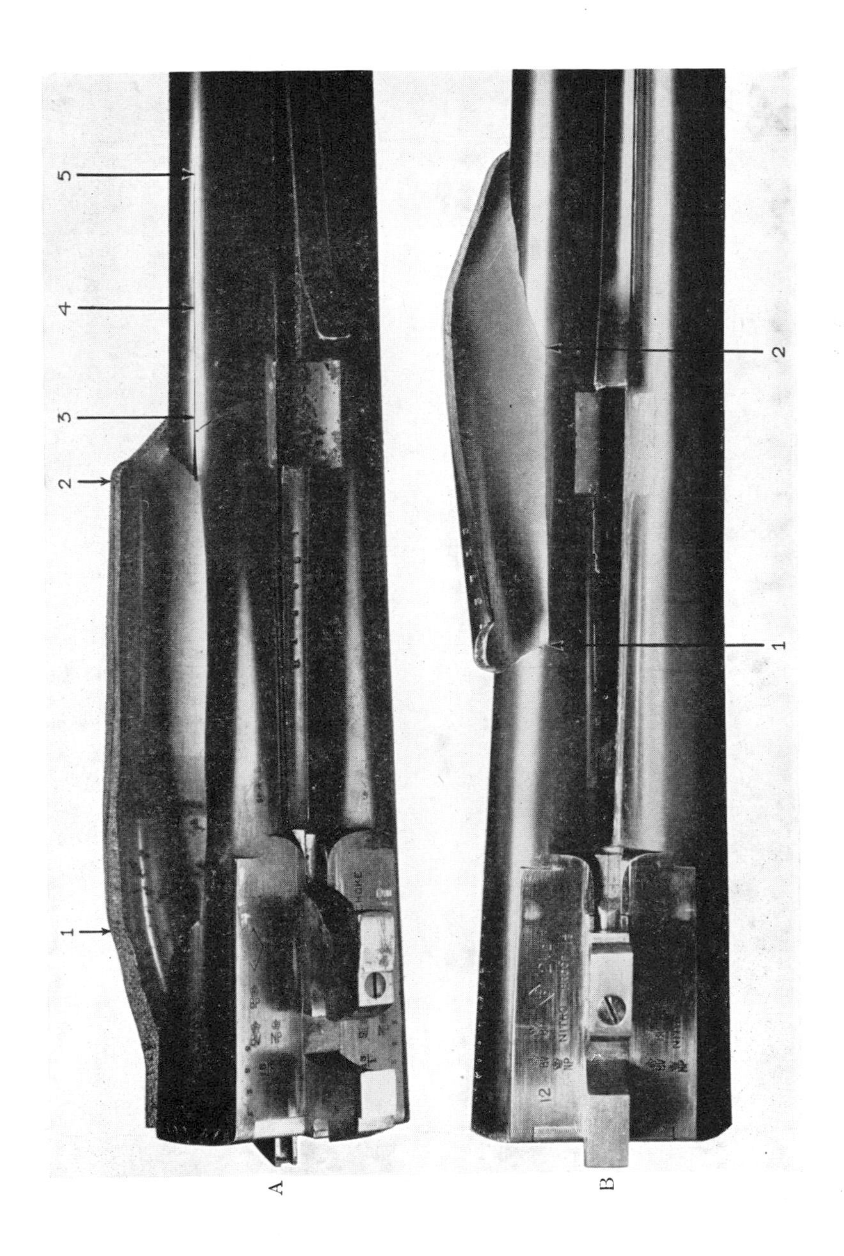
A
B

greater cross-sectional area. The capacity possessed by any pellet to penetrate a substance such as the body of a game bird is indicated more nearly by its energy than by any other means, and Tables XXXII to XXXIX in Volume II prove better than any words how feeble the penetration possessed by small shot becomes at the longer sporting ranges. In fact, as was pointed out in the last chapter, no size smaller than No. 6 can be relied upon to give sufficient penetration to produce any increase in effective range, no matter how high the initial velocity.

I am inclined to think that the question of shot size for ordinary shooting is as much psychological as anything else. Some men like to feel that they have a pattern sufficiently dense to ensure hitting the head and neck of a bird, and so use No. 7; while others are inspired with confidence by the extra smashing power possessed by the pellets of No. 5. The truth probably is that for the great majority of shots, at driven game at all events, the range is sufficiently close for No. 7 to give ample penetration and No. 5 an ample density of pattern.[1]

There is, however, one disadvantage of No. 7 for ordinary shooting which has always seemed to me unanswerable: this is the number of pellets which are put into a bird killed at close range. The No. 7 school say that one should wait until the bird gets further away before firing. But frequently one has to take a shot when

[1] In this connection it should be noted that the average area presented by the head and neck of a cock pheasant or mallard when flying overhead is approximately 6 square inches. This entails a minimum necessary pattern of 165 (including an addition of 10 per cent. to allow for loss in density through stringing) if a hit with one single pellet is to be a matter of comparative certainty. And this, in turn, means that a quarter choke gun is needed in order to place one single pellet in the head and neck of a cock pheasant or mallard at 45 yards when using $1\frac{1}{16}$ ounce of No. 7 shot. Beyond this range a hit would be a fluke unless a more closely bored gun were used. These birds should both be killed with greater certainty when using either the standard load of $1\frac{1}{16}$ ounces of No. 6 or the low-velocity load of $1\frac{1}{4}$ ounces of either Nos. 4 or $4\frac{1}{2}$ in a quarter choke gun, as all these three loads would give a bigger margin of density with superior penetration.

one can or not at all. Nor is it a fact that filling a bird with shot is due to a heavy choke, as is frequently asserted. An improved cylinder is quite capable of putting far too many pellets of No. 7 into a bird at 20 yards, and very often does.

Taking all things into consideration, I am inclined to the belief that a smaller size of shot than No. 6 confers no possible advantage in range or killing power in the case of any bird the size of a partridge or larger, while it may cause wounded birds at long range owing to lack of penetration, and it will certainly result in plastered birds at close range.

For birds smaller than a partridge, such as woodcock, teal and golden plover, No. 7 is undoubtedly a most excellent size. And if the Table of minimum necessary patterns is consulted it will be realised that No. 8 is essential for snipe unless kills at 40 yards are to become flukes rather than certainties. The density of pattern necessary for snipe will explain how easily one of these birds can be missed by its flying through the pattern when larger sizes of shot are being used.

For all-round shooting at partridge, grouse, pheasants and duck, it is doubtful whether there is any practical difference between Nos. 6, 5½ and 5 when using the standard load. In any case the result obtained must always be a compromise between loss of pattern and loss of penetration ; with No. 6 penetration fades out more nearly after pattern than with Nos. 5½ or 5. On the other hand, the pattern given by No. 5 tends to become rather too open for the smaller birds in an improved cylinder gun at 40 yards. It is probable that No. 6 comes nearest to the ideal I have previously suggested, that is, of penetration being retained for 5 yards beyond pattern. The shooter with an experimental turn of mind can plate his guns with all three sizes and see if there is any noticeable superiority in regularity of pattern given by any one size. If there is, that is the size to use. If there is not, and he cannot make up his mind, he had better toss up.

Larger sizes than No. 5 are, I think, a mistake in an ordinary 2½-inch 12-bore cartridge loaded with the standard load owing to the comparatively few pellets in the charge and the resulting loss in pattern density.

If larger sizes of shot than No. 5 are considered necessary the low-velocity principle of loading should undoubtedly be adopted or Maximum cartridges used. The low-velocity load and No. 4 is perfectly deadly for rabbits and hares, and I am quite certain cannot be bettered for these animals, especially hares.

For very large birds, such as geese, a low-velocity load of No. 1 can be very effective, but the range must be limited in an ordinary 12-bore, although it is probable that one of these would account for nearly as many geese as a larger gun in the course of a season provided shots were only taken at individual flying birds. The difficulty of forward allowance at 60 yards and over can become so terrific that the percentage of kills to shots fired at these ranges will usually be very small, except in the case of the shooter who can combine exceptional skill with long experience.

The shooter who is really interested in trying to evolve the most satisfactory load for some special type of shooting (e.g. geese, Himalayan snow cock or Monal pheasant) will find all the necessary data in the various Tables given in Volume II and the present volume. He should, however, remember that just as the low velocity principle is in every way preferable for large shot, so is large shot essential for the low-velocity principle.[1]

[1] I will give one example to indicate the general procedure which can be adopted.

Suppose it is desired to ascertain the best possible load to use for Monal pheasant in an ordinary 2½-inch 12-bore game gun bored quarter choke in the right barrel and half choke in the left.

Monal fly very fast, and long shots are the rule rather than the exception, so we must look for a killing pattern up to 50 yards, but place this range as the extreme limit for practical purposes owing to the enormous difficulties presented by more distant shots due to the extra forward allowance which must always be necessary. Monal are

But whatever shot charge is regarded as being most suitable, it must always be remembered that small shot sizes and light shot charges go together just as do large sizes and heavy charges. The purpose of a heavy charge is to increase the effective range by maintaining density of pattern. But it is equally essential to maintain adequate penetration for long range, and this can only be done by using large shot. If, on the other hand, the size of the gun demands a light shot charge it must be realised that a killing pattern at long ranges is an impossibility, and it is better to concentrate on the normal sporting ranges and select a shot size which gives the best patterns and penetration at these distances.

There is one further point in connection with the sizes of shot which is worthy of mention.

It has been seen on numerous occasions that the different sizes of shot retain their velocities to different degrees, and that their times of flight over any given

also very tough, so the maximum penetration is required. For this reason the low-velocity principle should be adopted.

The average weight of a cock Monal is 5 lb. Therefore working with the formula $\frac{220}{W}$ given on page 97 we find that the minimum necessary pattern is 44. This is to be the pattern at 50 yards which we see from Table IX on page 82 is 67 per cent. of the 40-yards pattern. Hence the necessary pattern at 40 yards is 66. The right barrel is quarter choke, so we turn to Table IV on page 38 and see that the largest size of shot which gives this pattern or over with a charge of $1\frac{1}{4}$ ounces is No. 1.

So the load we want is 30 grains of a 33-grain powder such as Smokeless Diamond and $1\frac{1}{4}$ ounces of No. 1 shot.

In order to satisfy ourselves that the penetration at 50 yards is sufficient, let us turn to Table XXXIV in Volume II, when we find that the pellet energy of No. 1 shot fired with an observed velocity of 950 f.s. is 3·28 ft.-lb. at 50 yards and 2·48 ft.-lb. at 60 yards. These values are about the same as the pellet energy of a standard load of No. 6 at 15 and 23 yards respectively, as can be seen from Table XXXVI in Volume II. We can be quite confident that the pellets of No. 6 from a standard load will penetrate a Monal at under 25 yards and so any doubts as to the efficiency of the load evolved can be set at rest.

range are consequently different. The question will not unnaturally arise whether this difference in the time of flight is sufficient to cause any noticeable change in the forward allowance.

It can be stated quite definitely that it is not.

But let us take an extreme case as an example, and suppose that we have cartridges loaded to develop standard ballistics, but some containing No. 9 shot, and the others BB. At 40 yards the forward allowance for a bird crossing at 40 m.p.h. will be 9 feet for the No. 9 and 8 feet for the BB, while the allowances for all intermediate sizes will lie between these two extreme values. A difference in forward allowance of 1 foot in 3 yards is too small to make any practical effect at 40 yards, and at shorter ranges the difference would be less.

In conclusion, I would emphasise again the importance of the psychological factor. If any shooter is satisfied with the load and shot size he is using, and has confidence in them, he would be mistaken to change. Confidence in one's guns and cartridges is as important as swing and footwork.

CHAPTER X

COMPARATIVE MERITS OF DIFFERENT BORES

HITHERTO whenever a particular cartridge has been taken as an example of any sort, the ordinary 2½-inch 12-bore cartridge has invariably been selected. As has been explained, this was partly because this cartridge is the length and bore by far and away the most commonly used by British sportsmen, and partly because it happens to be of a most convenient size for accommodating various combinations of powder and shot which differ from the standard load, but which give satisfactory results. But although the 12-bore is the most common size of gun in general use, it is by no means universal. Similarly, just as guns differ in their bores, so do cartridges in their lengths. All these different sizes of guns and cartridges have their admirers; and it is, therefore, but natural that many shooters should be perplexed as to the relative merits of the different bores and wonder whether a 20-bore, for example, really is as effective as a 12-bore, as is not infrequently claimed. A 20-bore is considerably lighter than a 12, and if it can do all that is asked of the larger gun its superiority is self-evident. Consequently the question of the comparative powers of different bores is one of the greatest practical interest and importance.

In ordinary shooting the guns usually seen are 12-bores, 16-bores and 20-bores, all of which are chambered for 2½-inch cartridges. Clay target and pigeon shots generally prefer 12-bores chambered for the 2¾-inch cartridge, while wildfowlers use 12-bores taking 3-inch cartridges and 10-bores chambered for 2⅞-inch and 3-inch cartridges. There are, of course, other sizes: 4-bores and 8-bores for wildfowling; "Magnum" 16's and 20's—that is guns of these gauges chambered for cases longer than the usual

$2\frac{1}{2}$ inches; 28-bores and even ·410's, but a detailed consideration of each is unnecessary for our purpose, which is to determine general principles for comparing the relative powers of different bores.

Now the power of a gun is really governed by the limit of its effective range. It is quite possible for two guns of different sizes to be equally effective at 20 yards from the point of view of killing a single bird. The bird will be killed by both, and the fact that it was shot with a bigger gun does not make it any more dead than if it had been shot with the smaller. But what about 40 yards and 50 yards? Will the bird be killed with equal certainty by both guns at these ranges? It is the answer to this question which determines which of the two guns is the more powerful.

The limit of effective range is dependent, as we have seen, on pattern and penetration. Pattern is governed by the type of boring used and the number of pellets in the shot charge: penetration by the initial velocity of the shot charge and the size of the individual pellets. The velocity developed by the standard load is approximately the same for all gauges and lengths of case, the larger bores generally giving somewhat higher velocities than the smaller. But in order to prevent anything in the nature of favouritism of the larger bores, let us assume that the velocity is the same for all. Then in order to make our comparison fair we must also assume the same type of boring for all the guns considered, since it is clearly illogical to compare the results given by a full choke with those of an improved cylinder. If these two factors are constant the only variables in the different guns will be the weights of the shot charges, since the powder is utilised merely to propel the shot.

It has already been explained that any type of boring gives a pattern of approximately the same percentage of the total charge, irrespective of the size of bore. So the pattern at any range will depend on the amount of shot there was in the cartridge in the first place; in other words, on the weight of the shot charge.

From this it should be quite clear that the only way of comparing the effective powers of different sizes of guns is by making a comparison of the weights of the shot charges which they fire.

Let us take the ordinary $2\frac{1}{2}$-inch 12- and 16-bores by way of an illustration. The standard charge of the former is $1\frac{1}{16}$ ounces and that of the latter $\frac{7}{8}$ ounce. If No. 5 shot is used in each gun the shot charge of the 12-bore will contain 234 pellets, and that of the 16-bore 193. And if both guns are bored quarter choke the former will give a pattern of 129 at 40 yards and the latter a pattern of 106, which means that the 12-bore gives a minimum effective pattern for a partridge or grouse, but that the 16-bore does not.

The density of the pattern, however, can be increased by decreasing the size of the shot ; and if No. 6 is substituted for No. 5 in the 16-bore there will be 236 pellets in the charge of $\frac{7}{8}$ ounce, and the 40-yards pattern will be 130. This is identical with the 12-bore pattern as regards density ; but it must be remembered that the 12-bore pattern is obtained with No. 5 shot and the 16-bore with No. 6. At 40 yards the striking energies of pellets of No. 5 and No. 6 are 1·85 and 1·40 ft.-lb. when both sizes are propelled with the standard velocity. So the superior efficiency of the 12-bore is obvious.

Now let us consider a 20-bore. Here the standard shot charge is but $\frac{3}{4}$ ounce, and so we must go down to No. 7 shot before we can get the same density of pattern with a quarter choke, and at 40 yards the striking energy of a pellet of No. 7 is but 1·01 ft.-lb., which means that the 20-bore gives a correspondingly less effective pattern than either the 16-bore or the 12-bore.

But if small birds, such as snipe or quail, are expected to figure in the bag No. 7 will probably be regarded as necessary in the 12-bore, which would mean having to go down to No. 8 in the 16-bore and No. 9 in the 20-bore if the pattern density is not to be weakened at 40 yards. The difference in penetration at this range of pellets of

Nos. 7, 8 and 9 is so obvious that the point needs no further stressing.

From this it will be clear that something else must be done besides varying the shot size if the smaller bores are to hold their own with the 12, and the only possibility is in the boring. A full-choke 16-bore will give a pattern of 135 with the standard charge of No. 5 shot, which is practically the same as that given by the quarter choke 12-bore.

But in the case of the 20-bore even a full choke will not bring it up to the level of the 12-bore, and we must use No. 5½ instead of No. 5 in order to get a pattern of 126. The difference in striking energies of a pellet of No. 5½ and one of No. 5 is admittedly not great: but still it exists, and cannot be ignored.

If we use No. 6 shot in all three guns it will be found that practically identical patterns will be given by an improved cylinder 12-bore; a half-choke 16-bore; and a full-choke 20-bore. And if the three sizes of guns are bored with these different degrees of choke their effective ranges are the same.

Such comparisons, however, cannot by any stretch of imagination be considered fair. The more choke there is in a gun the more difficult it is to take near shots. And if the shooter is so skilful that he does not feel the handicap of a full choke—and there are very few who would not be handicapped at driven partridges and rabbits in covert, for example—he could use a full choke 12-bore, which would at once increase his effective range beyond the limits possible with either a 16- or 20-bore.

So we return to the fact that the only true comparison of the powers of different guns is that given by comparing the weights of their standard shot charges. Working on this plan, and taking the 2½-inch 12-bore firing $1\frac{1}{16}$ ounces of shot as 100, it will be found that the relative powers of the various guns mentioned at the beginning of this chapter prove to be:

10-bore	3-inch	141
,,	2⅞-inch	135

12-bore	3-inch	. . . . .	124
,,	$2\frac{3}{4}$-inch	. . . . .	118
,,	$2\frac{1}{2}$-inch	($1\frac{1}{16}$ oz.)	100
,,	,,	(1 oz.)	94
,,	2-inch	. . . . .	82
16-bore	$2\frac{1}{2}$-inch	. . . . .	82
20-bore	$2\frac{1}{2}$-inch	. . . . .	71
28-bore	$2\frac{1}{2}$-inch	. . . . .	59

These figures may come as a surprise to many, but they give a true comparison between the different sizes of guns when both shot size and boring are constant, and these are the only conditions under which an absolutely fair comparison can be made.

The great advantage of a large bore is that it enables one to increase the size of shot, and so obtain better penetration at long range, without incurring any loss in density of pattern. And this is an advantage which should never be forgotten, especially when long shots are essential to success.

It is, however, but fair to point out that the advantages of a larger bore only begin to make themselves felt near the limit of the effective range. A larger gun, taking a heavier shot charge, extends this limit to a greater distance. For all ordinary shooting—especially at driven game where the majority of shots are probably nearer 20 yards than 30, and where 30 yards is a long shot—there is nothing to choose between the 12-bore and the 16, while the lack of power accompanying the 20-bore is so slight as to be almost negligible. But directly long shots become necessary the gun firing the heavier shot charge will immediately begin to show its superiority: and the greater the weight of the shot charge the more marked will that superiority be.

But we now come to a very important point which should certainly be the governing factor in the selection of any particular size of gun. Hitherto we have considered power alone. Power, however, is useless without ability to use it ; and a large bore can easily be so heavy that few shooters could handle it effectively in the field. Such a gun would, in practice, be useless be it ever so effective at extreme ranges. Trying to shoot with too heavy a gun is exactly like trying to throw a fly with too heavy a rod. Such a rod can be master of the angler, whereas the angler should be master of the rod. To use a gun effectively the shooter must be master of his weapon.

It is impossible to lay down any definite limit to the weight which any shooter can use effectively, as this weight must naturally vary with individual strength, physique and age. It is, however, a safe rule always to use a gun well within one's strength rather than near the limit, as allowances must be made for fatigue towards the end of a long day, trying weather, and heavy walking. A gun which feels light in a gunmaker's shop, or at the shooting ground, can become wondrous heavy at the end of a long day's walking through roots, heather or mud under a hot sun. And one's shooting is inclined to suffer in consequence. For this reason a gun the least bit beyond one's strength is fatal for ordinary all-round shooting.

As a general rule, I would fix $6\frac{3}{4}$ lb. as about the limit of weight for a gun for an average man for general shooting which entails a good bit of walking. And the marked tendency to lighter guns which is the chief feature of gunmaking since 1920 shows that the great majority of sportsmen are in agreement with this view. Every ounce below this weight is an advantage until the point is reached when recoil is increased by the reduction in weight to such an extent that it becomes more unpleasant than a slightly heavier gun. This point will also vary with the individual: but for the standard 12-bore load it is generally reached when the weight drops to between 6 lb. 6 oz. and 6 lb. 4 oz., or 6 lb. if an ounce charge of shot is used.

For a young boy in his early teens there can be no more fatal mistake than too heavy a gun, and it is always better to "under gun" a boy rather than to "over gun" him. Incidentally, it will help to teach him among other things not to take long shots.

There are men who find a gun of 6 to 6¼ lb. a bit on the heavy side. Such should not hesitate, but take to a 2-inch 12-bore, a 16-bore or a 20-bore. They will find their shooting improve for all ordinary shots and this should more than compensate the loss in extreme range which must accompany the change to a smaller gun.

There now remains the question of the "Magnum" gun. By this I mean a gun chambered to take a longer cartridge than the standard length for any particular bore, which enables a heavier shot charge to be used. These charges are frequently of the same weight as those normally fired by guns chambered for standard cartridges one or two sizes larger in gauge. For instance, the standard length of British cartridge for a 12-bore is a nominal 2½ inches, but a 12-bore chambered to take 3-inch cartridges fires a shot charge of the same weight as a 10-bore. Similarly, a 3-inch 16-bore fires a standard 12-bore charge, and a 3-inch 20-bore a standard 16-bore charge.

These Magnums offer no advantage in reduction in weight since the weight of the gun is governed by recoil, and therefore by the weight of the shot charge which it fires. A gun which fires 1$\frac{1}{16}$ ounce of shot cannot be built lighter than a certain weight irrespective of the gauge of its barrels ; and consequently a 3-inch 16-bore should weigh exactly the same as a 2½-inch 12-bore, and a 3-inch 20-bore the same as a 2½-inch 16-bore.

Further, so far from there being no palpable advantage in these Magnums there is a pronounced disadvantage, for the smaller diameter of the bore means a column of shot in the cartridge and barrel which is longer in proportion to its diameter. And we have seen in Volume II that a long shot column tends to increase pressure, while high pressures help to spoil pattern as well as throwing an extra strain on the action.

It is not easy to understand the purpose of these Magnums, since they confer no benefit in weight and merely raise the pressure. Even what may be called "Semi-Magnums"—that is guns such as 2¾-inch 16- and

20-bores—would seem to be superfluous. The charge in a 2¾-inch 16-bore can be fired just as effectively—in fact more so, as the pressure is lower—in a 12-bore; and the 2¾-inch 20-bore charge will be handled more comfortably in an ordinary 16-bore.

If the greatest degree of efficiency is to be obtained the weight of the shot charge and the diameter of the bore should mutually be suited so that the resulting velocity is satisfactory; the patterns the best possible with all types of boring; and the pressure sufficiently high to ensure regular velocity and pattern, but not a fraction of a ton higher than necessary. If the diameter of the shot column is too small in proportion to its length, the pressures will be high; if the length of the shot column is too small in proportion to its diameter, the pressures will tend to be too low and irregular. The standard weights of shot charges are the outcome of long experience and indicate the approximate relationship between the diameter and length of the shot column which best combines pressure, velocity and pattern.

The 2-inch 12-bore is a departure from this standard in the opposite direction. It was originally introduced as an alternative to the 20-bore and fired the standard 2½-inch 20-bore shot charge of ¾ ounce, its purpose being to eliminate the danger caused by the accidental intermingling of 12- and 20-bore cartridges, which is dealt with at length in Chapter XVII. But experience proved that this shot charge was too light. The ratio of the diameter to length was too great and it was difficult to obtain satisfactory ballistics. So the shot charge was increased to the standard 2½-inch 16-bore weight of ⅞ ounce. But even with this weight the diameter–length ratio is a bit too high and the pressures usually tend to be very low. This is sometimes thought to be an advantage and an indication of optimum efficiency, since an adequate velocity is obtained for a lower pressure than usual. But if the pressure drops too low the combustion of the powder is affected and may become incomplete when the results can be very unsatisfactory. In order to give optimum ballistics a special powder would have to be designed and this has not been done. One result of the low ballistics is to be found in the patterns, which frequently tend to be abnormally close for any given boring.

It would seem, therefore, that the best principle to adopt for selecting the most suitable bore is to be guided by the weight of shot charge which it is desired to fire. This, as has been explained on many occasions, controls also the approximate weight of the gun. If a shooter wants to limit the weight of his gun to 6 lb. 4 oz., he must be content with an ounce charge; and an ounce of shot is undoubtedly handled better by a 12-bore than by a 16-bore or 20-bore.

As a matter of fact, an ounce of shot probably makes as short a shot column as a 12-bore can carry to the greatest advantage, and a charge of between 1 ounce and 1¼ ounces is, perhaps, the best for a 12-bore. It is possible that a 14-bore might handle an ounce charge best of all: but the theoretical advantages of the 14-bore are entirely outweighed by the practical disadvantages in using a gun which takes a size of cartridge which is so rare, and supplies of which would always have to be ordered specially. A 12-bore handles an ounce charge well enough, and certainly better than a 16- or smaller bore.

There are two exceptions to this question of Magnums which should be made: the 2¾-inch and 3-inch 12-bore. The former because it takes a charge of but 1¼ ounces which only just exceeds, if it does exceed, the high limit for the most suitable shot charge for a 12-bore. The latter because it is a gun which was born of necessity. For there are countries in which larger bores than twelve are forbidden by law. But wildfowlers frequently need heavier shot charges than can possibly be carried even in a 2¾-inch 12-bore, and the 3-inch 12-bore is the result. But even so it is probable that the shot charge fired in these guns could be handled more suitably in a 10-bore, which would be no heavier, since the weight of the gun is controlled by that of the shot charge.

Magnum 12's, 16's and 20's are much used in America; but it is probable that their use is the outcome of somewhat different conditions of sport. The most usual length of 12-bore cartridge in America is $2\frac{3}{4}$ inches; guns chambered for this cartridge are quite rightly popular for wildfowl shooting; and since shooting at driven game on the scale practised in England is unknown the $2\frac{3}{4}$-inch 12-bore has become the standard in that gauge. But for small birds such as quail these guns are unnecessarily heavy, and smaller bores are the natural outcome. It is also natural that these smaller bores should be designed on the same general lines as the standard 12-bore, which explains what may be termed the "magnum attitude."

In Great Britain shooting at driven game has evolved the modern light 12-bore, which experience has shown to be perfectly effective up to 40, 45 and even 50 yards with suitable loads. And it is an undisputable fact that a gun weighing from $6\frac{1}{4}$ to $6\frac{1}{2}$ lb. and firing from 1 to $1\frac{1}{16}$ ounces of shot is the most generally effective gun for all-round shooting at game birds from snipe and quail to duck and pheasants, especially when the question of the weight of the gun is taken into consideration. And there can be no doubt that ballistically a 12-bore is the best gauge for this combination.

The only advantage of the Magnum principle which can seriously be put forward is the benefit conferred to aiming—either conscious or unconscious—owing to the barrels being of smaller diameter than those of a 12-bore. But is this advantage real? The approximate difference in width of barrels is but 0·15 inch in the case of 12- and 16-bores, which would seem to be too small a dimension to make any difference one way or the other. The barrels of a 20-bore are but about a quarter of an inch narrower than those of a 12. This is a bigger difference; and it is admittedly noticeable. Yet is it sufficiently noticeable to counterbalance the disadvantage of high pressure? This is a question which every shooter must decide for himself. I am sure, however, that nine gunmakers out of ten would recommend a 12-bore in preference to a 20 for an ounce charge of shot ; and gunmakers can be a most admirable guide in such matters, since they depend for their existence on satisfied customers.

Sportsmen should realise that from 40 to 50 yards is, in practice, the effective limit of range for shooting at fast flying individual birds ; that they will shoot better with a gun which is well within their strength ; and that it is, accordingly, a mistake to cumber themselves with heavy guns which they may not be able to use to full advantage.

The average weights for different sizes of guns are given in the following Table.

TABLE XXVIII

WEIGHTS OF DIFFERENT SIZES OF GUNS

Bore.	Length of Cartridge.	Weight of Double-Barrelled Gun.
4	4 and 4¼ inches	19 lb. to 22 lb.
8	All lengths	13 lb. to 15 lb.
10	,,	8½ lb. to 9½ lb.
12	3-inch	7 lb. 12 oz. to 8 lb.
12	2¾-inch	7 lb. 2 oz. to 7 lb. 8 oz.
12	2½-inch	6 lb. to 6 lb. 8 oz.
12	2-inch	5 lb. 6 oz. to 5 lb. 12 oz.
16	3-inch	6 lb. 4 oz. to 6 lb. 8 oz.
16	2¾-inch	6 lb. to 6 lb. 4 oz.
16	2½-inch	5 lb. 12 oz. to 6 lb. 4 oz.
20	3-inch	6 lb. 2 oz. to 6 lb. 6 oz.
20	2¾-inch	5 lb. 12 oz. to 6 lb.
20	2½-inch	5 lb. 8 oz. to 5 lb. 10 oz.
28	2½-inch	5 lb. 2 oz. to 5 lb. 8 oz.
·410	2½-inch	4 lb. 6 oz. to 4 lb. 12 oz.

The weights given are those within which guns are normally built, and in no case should lighter guns be ordered unless the barrels and stock are both abnormally short. For the length of the stock must obviously affect the weight, and the limits given in the Table permit variations in weight due to the length of stock and barrel.

In the case of the larger bores the weights will also

vary according to the length of case for which the gun is chambered.

It will be noticed that the 3-inch 16- and 20-bores are not made as light as 12-bores. The reason for this is the high pressures generated in these Magnum cartridges which render strong actions necessary. And the same applies, but in a less degree, to the $2\frac{3}{4}$-inch 16- and 20-bores.

CHAPTER XI

CHOICE OF ACTION AND BARREL LENGTH

WE have now reached a point when we can return to the actual gun itself, which was left at the end of Volume I. The whole of Volume II, and the preceding chapters of the present volume, have been intended to lead the reader up to this point ; the actual choice and purchase of a gun or pair of guns. We will, at first, leave the question of price on one side and consider only the qualities which should be possessed by the perfect gun. Having done this the reader will be able to judge for himself which of these qualities he can discard in order to meet whatever restrictions may be imposed by his purse.

The whole question of actions and their respective merits was dealt with fully in Volume I, so it only remains to see what details the would-be purchaser should study when examining any particular make of gun with a view to buying it, or placing an order for a similar gun or pair.

Such details are the following :

(1) Ease of Opening. This is one of the most important, as on it depends to a great extent the degree of quickness with which it is possible to re-load. A gun which opens stiffly is an abomination, and a really efficient " self opener " is a joy to use and handle. When testing a gun for ease of opening be sure that *both* barrels have been fired. Most guns will open by the weight of the barrels if neither lock has been fired, while the majority of guns will open much more easily when one lock only has been fired. It is, therefore, essential that the test should be made when both locks have been snapped off against snap caps.

(2) Ease of Closing. To my mind this is as important as ease in opening, and the effort required for opening and closing a gun should be balanced evenly between the

two operations. Here again the test should be made after both locks have been fired so as to make sure that every spring is being compressed which can possibly be compressed.

(3) Drop of Barrels. By this is meant the extent to which the barrels fall when the gun is opened. A wide "drop" or "gape" is a great advantage in quick loading, and a gun in which the barrels only drop just sufficiently to allow a cartridge to be slipped in over the top of the action should be avoided if possible.

Incidentally, a wide drop usually means that the gun is easy to open or close, as the greater the angle through which the barrels move, the more the work of compressing springs can be distributed, which means that the actual effort needed for the compression is reduced.

(4) Ease of Loading. Ease of loading is a very important point, and it depends on the presence or absence of a top extension as well as on the extent of the drop of the barrels. Some top extensions are very clumsy and interfere appreciably with the work of loading. So this is a point which should not be forgotten, and the sportsman should try to form his own opinion and avoid being influenced unduly by a salesman who wants to sell a particular gun.

(5) Ease of Putting Gun Together. Some guns are much more easily put together than others, and this is by no means an unimportant point to which attention ought to be paid. For a gun which is difficult to put together will almost certainly suffer from burrs and bruises in course of time ; and these will add to the difficulty of assembling as well as detract from the appearance and second-hand value.

As a general rule, the absence of a cocking cam increases the ease with which a gun can be put together.

It should be remembered that new guns are almost always rather stiff to put together, open, or close. But this stiffness soon wears off. And for purposes of testing it is better to experiment with an old gun of the same type in which no difficulty can possibly be attributed to its being new.

(6) Removal of Fore-end. The fore-end should be capable of being easily removed at all times. In some actions it is quite difficult to take the fore-end off when the locks have been fired because the mainsprings are pressing the front ends of the cocking levers against the fore-end and so holding it against the barrels. A fore-end should fit tightly to the barrels, but this tightness should be provided by the proper attachment and not by the cocking levers. This may seem a very trifling point, but the reader must remember that an occasion may arise when it becomes imperative to remove the fore-end after the gun has been fired and before it can be opened. Such an occasion may be due to a faulty cartridge-case, and is admittedly a rare occurrence. But when something of the sort does happen it is a great help to be able to remove the fore-end without having to prize it off with a turn-screw, or similar tool, which will almost inevitably mark the wood, and perhaps the metal as well.

Similarly, the fore-end should be capable of being removed when the gun is in the open position. It is extremely useful to be able to do this should the head of a cartridge over-ride the extractor and get between the extractor and the barrel. When this occurs it is not possible either to close the gun or remove the cartridge-case in the ordinary way ; and frequently the easiest method of taking out the cartridge is to take off the fore-end, unhook the barrels, take out the stop-pin and release the extractor. The cartridge can then be pushed or pulled out without any risk of bruising any metal. The operation sounds complicated, but it is really extremely quick and simple. In order to carry it out, however, it is essential that the shooter should be able to remove his fore-end without undue difficulty.

Accidents such as this may never occur : but when they do occur it is an enormous convenience to be able to deal with them expeditiously in the proper manner, and consequently it is always advisable to test the ease with which the fore-end can be taken off when the gun is open as well as closed.

Further instructions for dealing with such a *contretemps* will be found in Chapter XIV.

(7) Removal of Locks. Except in the case of the Westley Richards hand-detachable locks the locks in a box lock action cannot be removed by the ordinary shooter. Side locks, however, can be quite easily taken off by those who are competent to use a turnscrew, although the procedure is not to be recommended as a habit, even for the more experienced amateur gunsmith. But there are times when it is certainly advantageous to be able to take the locks off, and consequently it is an advantage to have a gun fitted with locks which are not too difficult to replace. Most side locks are very easily removed : but they are by no means so easily put back. In some actions the locks *must* be put back at full cock, while in others the cocking levers must be held in a certain position before the locks will slip into position. The whole question of the removal of locks will be dealt with in Chapter XIV, but the ease with which they can be taken off and put back is a point which deserves attention when choosing a gun. It is admittedly a minor point, but the simpler the operation is the less the risk of damaging the locks, and so the possibility of having to remove the locks should not be forgotten.

(8) Solid Knuckle. Some designs of actions have a more solid knuckle than others. This is an advantage in wet weather, as moisture works its way down between the fore-end and the barrels and into the action through the slots for the cocking levers. Consequently actions in which there are no such slots, or in which the slots are very small, have an advantage over those in which the slots are large.

Nevertheless I am inclined to doubt whether this advantage is really quite as great as those gunmakers whose actions have solid knuckles will declare. A solid knuckle undoubtedly eliminates one of the chief points of entry for wet into the action, but it is by no means the only point of entry, for moisture certainly gets in past the action bolt. Further, the very fact that there are slots in the knuckle enable the moisture to dry out more readily, as will be seen in the chapter dealing with the care and cleaning of guns.

I think that the truth probably is that a solid knuckle is an advantage in the case of the man who takes no proper care of his gun, or who leaves the cleaning of his gun to some inexperienced servant. But the man who takes a real pride in his weapons and either cleans them himself, or else superintends the cleaning, will find no practical benefit in a solid knuckle.

(9) Sharp Projections. The actions of some guns carry sharp projections which can easily cut or tear the hand. Such cuts may not be serious ; but they can be both annoying and painful, and should be quite unnecessary. So attention should be paid to this detail, trivial though it may appear.

I do not believe that any make of action embodies every single advantage which has been enumerated. But some go very nearly all the way, and in any case the first six points are undoubtedly far the most important.

LENGTH OF BARRELS

The next point to consider is the length to be adopted for the barrels. For many years the barrels of an ordinary 12-bore have almost always been made from 28 to 30 inches long ; but some years ago there was a revival of the controversy as to what is the best length. There is but one possible answer to this question : there is no general best length for shotgun barrels, and the best length for an individual shooter to select is the length with which he finds he can shoot best.

Very short barrels of 25 inches for 12-bores have always had their admirers, and there is nothing new in their use. In his *Modern Breech-Loaders* (page 68) the late Mr. W. W. Greener wrote of barrel lengths and stated that " some gentlemen will not have them longer than twenty-four inches"; but he went on to add "we think it unwise to shorten a barrel more than to twenty-six inches." This was in 1870, so it will be seen that the controversy was not new seventy-five years ago; and ever since it has been revived from time to time in the pages of the sporting press. But although short barrels have always had their supporters they never became generally popular, and it is only in recent years that they have been made in appreciable numbers.

The reason almost invariably advanced to explain the failure of short barrels to become generally popular in the past is that the powder of those days was not so "quick" as the modern powders and consequently it is only in recent times that short barrels have become as effective as long. This explanation, however, is quite inaccurate. In the first place the actual loss in velocity due to a reduction of barrel length from 30 to 25 inches was not sufficient even with the standard loads of black powder to make any practical difference in penetration at sporting ranges. Further, if the demand for short barrels had become pronounced it would have been easy to use a finer grain powder which would burn more rapidly.

The real explanation is entirely the matter of recoil.

The primary object of reducing the length of barrels below 28 inches has been, and is, to enable the gunmaker to build a lighter gun. The weight of the gun, however, as has been seen in Volume II, is fixed within certain limits by recoil. Black powder produces a heavier recoil than smokeless powders; and in the days of black powder the shot charge was 1⅛ ounces. Such a combination rendered a featherweight gun impossible except for the rare, but happy, individual who was seemingly immune to recoil. Such men frequently did use light guns with short barrels; but they were the exception.

A gradual reduction in recoil has been brought about by the change from black powder to 42-grain bulk smokeless powders, and then to 33-grain powders, with corresponding reductions in the shot charge from 1⅛ to

$1\frac{1}{16}$, and finally to 1 ounce. It is this reduction in recoil that has alone rendered possible the more universal adoption of light guns, and guns have been coming down in weight steadily during the past forty years. At last a point was reached beyond which many gunmakers would not go in reducing the weights of their actions, for a light action can never be so strong or so rigid as a heavier one. The demand for light guns, however, grew and the length of barrels provided an obvious starting-point for further reductions in weight, since it helped the gunmaker to balance his guns better when they were built with very light actions.

There can be no two opinions as to the joy of shooting with a light gun, and the recent change to barrels shorter than 28 inches which has been adopted by a number of different gunmakers is the result of the competition to meet the demand of sportsmen for light weapons. Finality in barrel length, however, has not been reached ; and there is undoubtedly a considerable divergence of opinion as to the limit to which it is possible to go. But before we come down to the question of actual lengths there are two very important points which need consideration, namely velocity and recoil.

Both these have been dealt with in detail in Volume II and so it is only necessary to state again here that for all practical purposes of sport the velocity is not affected sufficiently to make any difference in penetration, even at long ranges.

Similarly, it has been shown that the reduction in barrel length has no appreciable effect on recoil provided the weight of the gun is kept constant. It had been thought possible that the drop in muzzle velocity due to shortening a barrel from 30 to 25 inches might cause a helpful reduction in the recoil developed, even though it was too slight to make any practical difference in striking velocities at long range. If this were the case short barrels would create a kind of automatic compensation which would mean that a 25-inch barrelled gun could be made lighter than one with 30-inch barrels without

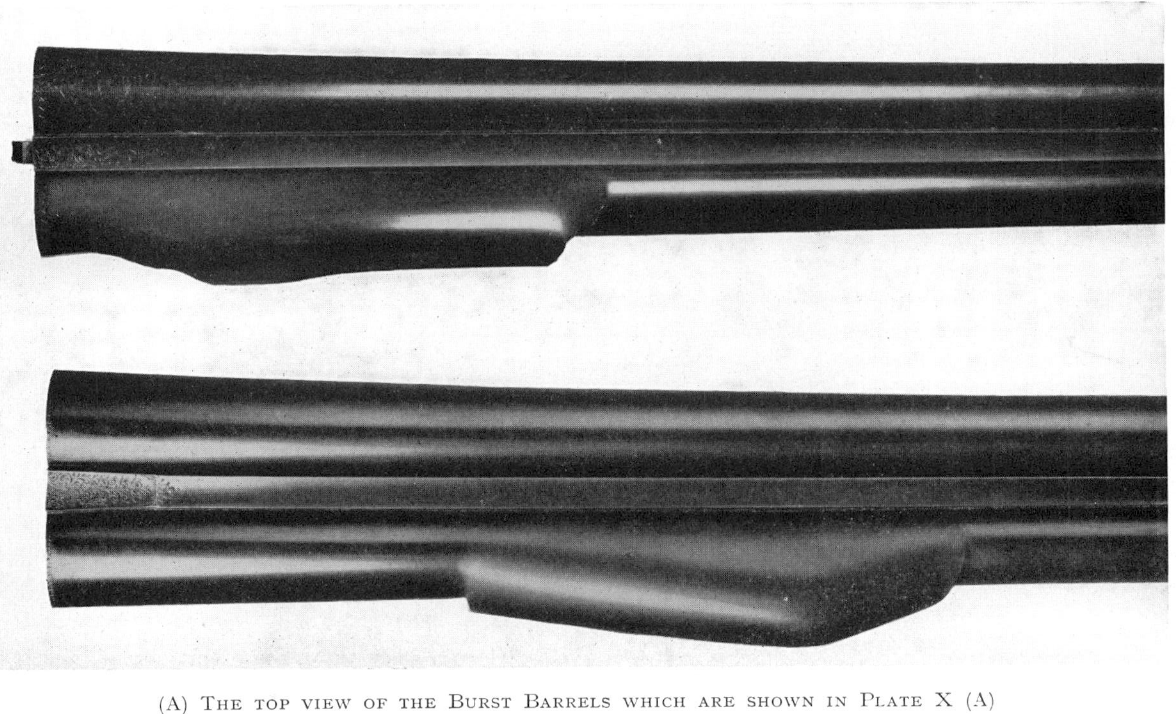

(A) The top view of the Burst Barrels which are shown in Plate X (A)
(B) The top view of the Burst Barrels which are shown in Plate X (B)

The similarity of these two bursts is again pronounced; they have no resemblance to the typical obstructional burst, such as is shown in Plate VI. In both cases the top rib is straight, and there is no suspicion of a "ring bulge." These two photographs should be compared with that given in Plate VI (A), when the difference in the general type of burst will be obvious

increasing the recoil. Unfortunately, however, this perfectly reasonable theory did not prove correct, and the reduction in recoil accompanying the shortening of a barrel is negligible provided the total weight of the gun is kept constant.

So we come down to the fact that for all practical purposes the penetration and recoil is the same in guns of the same weight irrespective of their length of barrels.

The final weight of a gun must be governed by recoil, but in spite of this obvious truth all sorts of arguments are constantly being put forward to show that weight for weight short barrelled guns give less recoil than those fitted with longer barrels. It is stated, for instance, that the recoil which is actually felt by the shooter cannot be measured instrumentally. Now it is perfectly true that recoil can be rendered much more noticeable by an ill-fitting gun. But that is beside the point. And although it may be impossible to measure instrumentally the actual sensations which any individual feels as the result of recoil, there can be no getting away from the fact that instrumental measurements which indicate a high recoil in one gun and a low recoil in another will always be borne out by practical experience when the guns are fired from the shoulder, provided both fit equally well.

Individuals will always vary in their powers of resistance to recoil, and those who are more immune than others will be able to use lighter guns. But even so there must always be a limit to the weight of the gun, and in nine cases out of ten this limit will be placed by recoil rather than the actual safety of the weapon, especially if many shots are fired in rapid succession.

But the actual length of barrels can be influenced by other factors which are quite independent of weight and recoil, the two most important ones being barrel flip and the inertia of the forward portion of the barrels.

The question of barrel flip was dealt with at length in Volume I (pages 223–7), where it was pointed out that short barrels gave a different flip from longer ones, which difference, as a rule, tends to make a gun fitted with short barrels shoot higher than long barrelled guns. The degree to which any particular gun tends to shoot high or low is always counteracted in actual practice by the bend in the stock. Consequently a 25-inch barrelled gun will almost certainly require more bend in the stock than a gun with 30-inch barrels. For this reason a shooter should never have the stock of a new gun with short barrels built to the same measurements of his old guns with long barrels, as if this were done he would shoot over the top of his birds almost all the time. Similarly, it is a mistake to fit a new pair of short barrels to the stock of a gun which was originally used with long barrels, and there can be no doubt that many disappointments with short barrels have been caused by failure to appreciate this fact.[1]

[1] Mr. E. P. Bernard has pointed out in an article in *Game and Gun* (November, 1931) that a shooter's eye will never be in exact prolongation with the top rib of his gun when " aiming " at a bird, but will always be slightly above it. He will, therefore, obtain a foreshortened view of the top rib. Mr. Bernard consequently suggested that a short barrelled gun will always appear to shoot higher than a long barrelled one because an extra degree of elevation must be imparted to the former in order to make both lengths of barrel appear to be the same foreshortened length.

This will be understood by referring to Fig. 27 (p. 243). If the gun represented by AB is fitted with shorter barrels, B will occupy a position in the line ET nearer to E; in which case AB will have extra elevation, and C will be further above T than the actual position shown in the diagram.

This is undoubtedly true, but in practice the increase in elevation due to this cause is too small to account for the differences which are actually obtained. If the angle of elevation given to the 30-inch barrels is θ, then the angle must be $\theta \times \frac{30}{25}$ with 25-inch barrels. If θ is 30 minutes, then it will become 36 minutes when 25-inch barrels are used; and this would mean that the latter gun would only shoot $2\frac{1}{2}$ inches higher at 40 yards.

There is no doubt that this explanation of Mr. Bernard's does account for a proportion of the increase in elevation resulting from the change to short barrels from long; but only a small proportion of the whole change. Further, it does not explain why a similar change is produced when over and under guns are used irrespective

This natural tendency of short barrelled guns to shoot higher than longer barrelled ones is frequently quoted as a great advantage, but it is difficult to understand how it can be either an advantage or a disadvantage. It is perfectly true that the majority of misses at crossing birds are probably low; but this fault will not be corrected by the length of barrel, as the gunmaker should, and does, always fit his customer in the first instance so that the latter places his charge centrally irrespective of the barrel length.

It is towards the end of the day, when one is tired, that one is inclined to shoot low; and if one shoots correctly at the beginning of the day this tendency can become equally evident with any length of barrel. It is, however, a fact that the lighter the gun the less tired one becomes; and consequently the longer the tendency to shoot low is delayed. This, however, is due to the *weight* of the gun rather than the length of barrels, although it is true that short barrels do help to reduce the weight. But in the case of guns of the same weight and different barrel length it is extremely doubtful whether the shorter barrels will be found to make any noticeable difference in shooting high or low to a tired shooter, provided he can normally control both lengths of barrel with equal ease.

For it is this question of the control of the barrels which is, to my mind, the real crux of the whole problem and which is dependent entirely on the inertia of the forward portion of the barrels. When one swings one has to overcome the forward inertia of the barrels, as was explained in Volume I (pages 132 and 133). Some men may find the reduction in the forward inertia of the barrels an advantage, as they are then enabled to swing more quickly and with less effort; but others find it a distinct disadvantage because they miss the steadying influence imparted by that inertia, and they cannot control their

of their barrel length. There can be no question about the differences in flip produced by the adoption of short barrels, or over and under barrels; and flip is the only cause which appears to explain the whole difference in every case.

swing properly and cannot bring the gun up with certainty time after time on the same fixed spot.

It is for this reason, I think, that unanimity has not been reached as to the best length for short barrels. Some makers do not recommend their customers to go below 27 inches ; others go to 26½ inches ; others to 26 inches ; and yet others to 25 inches. The very fact that there is this divergence of opinion emphasises the importance of trying different lengths ; also the truth of the statement made at the beginning of this section, namely that the best length of barrel for any individual to adopt is the length with which he finds he can shoot best.

So the shooter who wants a light gun will be well advised to try different lengths of short barrels at a shooting school or schools. If he is disappointed at the results obtained with 25 inches he should not necessarily condemn all short barrels and declare in favour of 28 or 30 inches, but should try lengths of 26 or 27 inches. Personally I do not like barrels as short as 25 inches because I find I miss the steadying influence of the forward inertia. The simile may seem somewhat far-fetched, yet a 25-inch barrelled gun always seems to convey a similar impression to that derived from riding a horse with a straight shoulder and no rein. I like to feel something more in front. But 27 inches I find a very different matter, and were I to buy a new gun for general rough shooting I would be inclined to select this length. Yet just as some men find the loss of the forward inertia caused by reducing the barrel length to 25 inches to be a handicap, so others can find it a positive advantage. This just shows how unwise it is to dogmatise, and how wise it is for a shooter to try guns with various lengths of barrels for himself.

A very good guide to the general consensus of opinion among practical shooting men is to be found in the relative market values of guns with different lengths of barrels. Not many years ago I was discussing the question with the man who does most of the buying for the firm which is probably the biggest dealer in high-grade second-hand guns of British manufacture in the world.

I asked him : " If you were offered guns of exactly the same quality and condition, all by the same maker, but fitted with barrels of 30, 29, 28, 27, 26 and 25 inches, which would you buy first as being the most readily saleable ? "

The answer came at once without any hesitation : " Twenty-eight inches."

But whatever length of barrel has been selected as being the most helpful and suitable after a thorough trial of different lengths, it is essential that the would-be purchaser should give a gun of the same weight and barrel length a further trial by firing a considerable number of shots with the actual cartridges to be used in the shooting field. This is most important as it is a common practice for gunmakers to load cartridges to be used on a shooting ground with light loads so as to reduce the recoil and thus render the practice more pleasant. This is an advantage when many shots are fired in quick succession at clay targets. It can, however, be misleading, as it gives a false impression of the behaviour of the gun ; and a test to be complete should be made with cartridges which are loaded with the full charge. If the recoil is then found to be too severe the remedy is to increase the weight of the gun by an ounce or two, or else to use a lighter load. For the axiom, and it really is an axiom, must never be forgotten : *a light gun needs a light load.*

There now remain but four comparatively minor points which need consideration in order to complete our survey of the problem of barrel length.

The first of these is the question of forward allowance with short barrelled guns. It has been claimed by their advocates that the forward allowance on a crossing bird is less with 25-inch barrels than longer ones, so it may be of interest to see exactly to what this claim amounts. This can be done best with the help of the diagram in Fig. 25.

In this diagram S is the shooter ; B the bird, and P the point at which aim must be taken in order to hit the bird which is flying in the direction BP at 40 miles an hour. If the range (i.e. SB) is 40 yards, the forward allowance (BP) can be taken as being 8 feet.

SC and SD represent guns fitted with barrels of 25 and 30 inches respectively, in which case the total lengths of SC and SD can be assumed without material error to be 42 and 47 inches.

The apparent forward allowance with the short barrelled gun will be CM, and that with the long barrelled one DN. With the data assumed these distances will be 2·8 and 3·1 inches respectively, so the difference will be but 0·3 of an inch. And in the case of birds which are not crossing exactly at right angles, and which are nearer than 40 yards, the difference will be considerably less, and seldom more than 0·1 of an inch.

FIG. 25.—Diagram to illustrate the theoretical effect of barrel length on forward allowance.

S, the Shooter; B, the Bird; BP the necessary forward allowance; ND the swing with 30-inch barrels; and MC the swing with 25-inch barrels.

So it will be clear that for all practical purposes this difference is negligible.

But the real fallacy in this theoretical advantage lies in the fact that the forward allowance depends on the *angle* through which the gun has to be swung in order to give the necessary forward allowance on the bird; and this angle is the same irrespective of the length of the barrels, as can be seen in the diagram.

The truth is that in actual practice it is impossible to estimate any given number of feet in front of a moving bird. Niceties of $\frac{1}{10}$—or even $\frac{1}{3}$—of an inch in the distance travelled by the muzzle of the gun during the swing may be present in both theory and actual fact; but they cannot possibly be detected by the shooter.

The next point is in connection with a theoretical advantage of long barrels.

It was pointed out in the *Badminton Library* chapter

devoted to guns that if it were possible to wield a gun with barrels so long that the muzzle could actually be made to touch the bird the shooter would never miss. And from this it was argued that although such a length was obviously absurd it was better to go as far as possible in that direction in order to render shooting more easy, and barrels of 30 inches were consequently recommended.

Now theoretically I suppose this argument is incontrovertible. It is based on similar foundations to those on which are built up the arguments in support of a long sight base for rifles. In practice, however, rifles and shotguns are not altogether analogous, for they are used in different methods. A gun should never be aimed in the sense that a rifle is aimed but the direction of discharge is really controlled by the forward arm being pointed in the proper direction. The result of this difference in usage is to nullify in a gun any advantage conferred on a rifle by having the sights set as far apart as possible.

Further, the practical conditions of sport frequently demand a compromise between extreme accuracy and ease in use. A rifle fitted with a 36-inch barrel will certainly be wonderfully accurate on account of the great length of sight base which it is possible to obtain ; but such a weapon would be too unwieldy for rapid snap shots in thick jungle.

So the truth probably is that for all practical purposes of sport in ordinary shooting no noticeable advantage is conferred in actual aiming—if such a word can properly be used in connection with a shotgun—by long barrels.

The third point is also theoretical, although it probably has more practical importance than the two previous ones. It is that a high-velocity load of 36 grains of powder and 1 ounce of shot cannot be used to full advantage in very short barrels.

The series of experiments made by the late Mr. W. D. Borland to determine the effects of different lengths of barrel on velocity and recoil which were recorded in detail in Appendix IV to Volume II showed among other things that the greatest differences in velocity resulting from a reduction in barrel length from 30 to 25 inches occurred with the high-velocity load, because the heavier powder charge of 36 grains was not utilised with such comparative effectiveness in the short barrel as the standard charge of 33 grains. Now it is true that even the maximum difference in velocity recorded by Mr. Borland was not sufficient to cause any practical difference in penetration at sporting ranges. But it must also be remembered that the whole purpose of the high-velocity load is to obtain an admittedly slight increase in velocity. It is, therefore, waste of effort to use a load in any barrel which cannot be utilised to its full effect on account of the length of that barrel. There is absolutely no possible advantage to be gained, while there are two accompanying disadvantages.

The first of these is that recoil is increased, as has already been seen, without any corresponding gain in velocity. And since guns are usually fitted with short barrels with a view to reducing weight, the recoil may easily exceed the limit of comfort. In any case the recoil developed by a high-velocity load will be disproportionally severe.

The second disadvantage is the tendency to increased muzzle blast due to the higher muzzle pressure caused by the combustion of an abnormally heavy powder charge in an abnormally short barrel. This tendency to increased muzzle blast will be almost inseparable from the use of a high-velocity load of 36 grains of powder and an ounce of shot in a 25-inch barrel, and cannot but tend to produce irregular patterns.

To go to the opposite extreme, it would certainly appear that the low-velocity load is especially suited to short barrelled guns, as the best value in the way of velocity is obtained when this load is used for the payment that has to be made in recoil.

The fourth point is the question of the relative suitability of different barrel lengths for different bores.

Hitherto the actual lengths which have been quoted are all those usually fitted to ordinary 12-bores. But everything that applies to this size of gun applies equally to all other sizes, nevertheless some allowance should probably be made for the different weights of powder charge which are used in the different bores. For this reason, for instance, barrels of 25 inches should certainly be avoided in a 12-bore chambered for 3-inch cases, as the full benefit of the combustion of the heavy powder charge would not be obtained; and the same applies to all magnum guns, which means that these cannot be fitted with such short barrels as guns of the same calibre taking standard lengths of cartridge.

Similarly, very large bores will need a greater minimum length of barrels than very small. As a general rule it can be taken that 10-, 8- and 4-bores need average lengths of barrels which are 2, 4 and 6 inches longer respectively than the corresponding average length for an ordinary 12-bore. On the other hand, smaller sizes than twelve can be fitted with barrels which are, on the average, slightly shorter. For example, neither a 16- nor a 20-bore should ever be fitted with barrels longer than 28 inches. But on the other hand, the barrels of these sizes should never be less than 25 inches long. In fact I would be inclined to place this length as the limit of shortness even for a boy's ·410, partly because of the question of the inertia of the forward portion of the barrels, and partly because shorter barrels than 25 inches can become more dangerous owing to the ease with which they can be turned about, and in this respect almost approach a pistol or revolver, which are the most dangerous weapons of all for the inexperienced to handle.

Finally, I cannot help thinking that if the shooter finds he has no very definite preference for any particular barrel length after trying various lengths at shooting schools, he cannot do better than use the length of his stock as a guide to the length of his barrels. A long stock is balanced better, both in handling and appearance, by fairly long barrels of from 28 to 30 inches. Similarly, a very short stock is better suited by shorter barrels of 27 or 28 inches. One friend of mine who was 6 feet 5 inches used 25-inch barrels for thirty years. But his guns, fitted as they were with stocks 15½ inches in length, always reminded me of a highwayman's blunderbuss rather than a modern game gun. So if the shooter has no pronounced views on the matter let him ask his gunmaker to match the length of his stock by that of his barrels, when he will obtain a gun or guns which are as beautifully proportioned to the eye as I hope they will be as great a joy in the actual shooting field.

CHAPTER XII

FITTING A GUN

WHEN a decision has been made as to the type of action and length of barrels for the new gun, or guns, the next question which arises is that of fitting the gun. In order to fit a gun properly to any individual the gunmaker must fulfil three conditions.

(1) The stock must be so shaped that when the shooter brings the gun up to his shoulder and fires it the centre of the pattern should cover the mark it was desired to hit at a range of from 20 to 30 yards. And this result should be obtained without the shooter having to make any conscious correction for alignment.

(2) The stock must also be so shaped that the shooter should be able to fire an indefinite number of shots without being bruised in one particular place more than another.

(3) The general lines of the gun and stock should be kept as graceful as possible.

Let us take these three conditions in turn.

In order to fit a gun properly for alignment the correct degree of elevation must be obtained so that the shot charge is placed neither too high nor too low. Similarly, the charge must be centred correctly for direction : that is, it must not be placed too much to the right nor too much to the left. Fitting for elevation and fitting for direction are two distinct branches of the art and are dependent on different factors. One thing, however, is common to both ; namely, the correct fitting for the length of the stock. It is, accordingly, only proper to consider first this part of the work of fitting a gun.

FITTING FOR "LENGTH"

If the stock is too long the end of the butt catches on the shoulder when the gun is mounted and so interferes with quick shooting; while if it is too short the arms must be bent unduly at the elbows for ease and comfort, and the recoil will probably appear more severe on account of the gun not being held firmly against the shoulder.

It will be quite obvious that a tall man will need a longer stock than a short one; but before we come to the question of measuring for length it may be as well first to consider how the measurements for the length are actually made on the stock. This question was

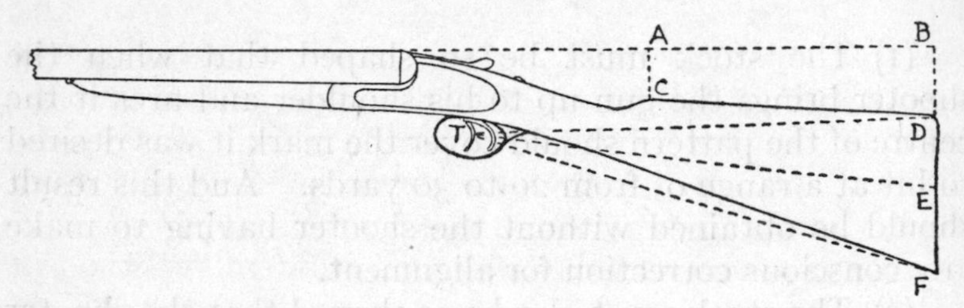

FIG. 26.—Outline sketch of the stock of a gun, showing how measurements are made for "Length" and "Bend."

C, the Comb; CD, the Face; DF, the Butt; D, the Heel; F, the Toe; E, the Middle of the Butt; T, the Front Trigger.

"Length" is measured by the distance of T to E, but the distances TD and TF are also necessary in order to obtain the correct angle between the Butt and the Face.

"Bend" is given by the measurements of AC and BD.

dealt with in Volume I, but for the sake of convenience a brief recapitulation will be made here.

Fig. 26 is an outline sketch of the stock of a gun, which really explains itself. The measurements denoting the length of the stock are made from the middle of the front trigger to the heel, centre and toe of the butt. All these three measurements are of equal importance, but the one which really controls the other two is the measurement from the trigger to the middle of butt, and it is this measurement which is always quoted when describing the length of a stock. Provided the angle of the butt is constant the other two measurements will follow the one from trigger to middle. And in the great majority of cases the butt does make a constant angle with the upper edge, or face, of the stock.

We can now return to the question of fitting for length.

The best method of all is by actual trial. An experienced gun-fitter can suit a new customer in the matter of length to within a fraction of an inch, and his judgment can be confirmed by an invention known as a "Try Gun." This is really nothing more than an ordinary gun fitted with a stock which can be adjusted to any length or shape, and which is an invaluable adjunct in gun-fitting.

It is frequently stated that the length of the stock is dependent on the length of the shooter's forearm, and that the correct length can be obtained by laying the stock of the gun flat against the inside of the forearm with the middle of the butt exactly in the hollow of the elbow. The top joint of the first finger should than exactly reach to the front trigger.

I cannot help thinking, however, that this method of measuring is extremely unreliable, for it is possible to accommodate one's arm almost to any length of stock, and it is difficult to say which length is the correct one. As an example of the error possible from this cause I can quote from my own personal experience. Many years ago I was thus measured for length by one of the leading gunmakers in the country and was finally given a stock which proved very nearly an inch too long for me ; and although I protested at the time I was assured that I must be mistaken. Subsequently I was measured by both Messrs. Holland and Messrs. Purdey and given stocks of exactly the same length, which was shorter by $\frac{7}{8}$ of an inch than the stock which I had previously been told was correct.

Apart from a shooter's build the length must also be controlled in part by his individual style of shooting. For instance, the man who holds his left hand well ahead of the fore-end will probably need a shorter stock than the man of the same height and length of arm who holds his gun with his left hand only just in front of the trigger guard.

These are exceptional cases, however, as it is probable that the great majority of shots hold their guns with their forward hands at a spot just about level with the front of the fore-end.

Stocks ususally vary in length from 14¼ inches for a short man of about 5 feet 4 inches to 14¾ inches for a tall man of about 6 feet, while exceptionally short or tall men will want correspondingly shorter and longer stocks.

The angle of the butt is, as has already been stated, an almost constant quantity, and very sloping butts or those that almost make a right angle with the face should only be required by shooters who have some peculiarity in build or else in their style of shooting. The appearance of these abnormal butts is certainly against them, perhaps because of their difference from the shape to which we are accustomed. The two butts shown in Plate VIII of Volume I are of a shape which is both normal and ideal for over 90 per cent. of shooters.

FITTING FOR ELEVATION

If the barrels and stock of a gun were in one straight line, and the gun was shaped like a billiard cue, the shooter would always miss by firing above the mark which it was desired to hit. This is because it is impossible to bring the eye right down to the line of a cue or walking-stick when either is raised to the shoulder like a gun.

Fig. 27 shows this fact diagrammatically. The straight stick is represented by AB ; E is the eye which is above the level of the butt end of the stick and T is the target. When aim is taken quickly the eye aligns the front end of the stick, B, on T, and in such a position the path of the shot would be ABC, that is in the direction in which the stick is pointing.

In order to enable the shooter to place his shot correctly for elevation the line of the stock must be bent down from that of the barrels.

The necessity for this downward bend of the stock may seem so obvious and elementary that I hope I will be forgiven for inserting this brief explanation. The principle, however, is so important both in fitting for elevation and for direction that I feel that it cannot be passed over.

The actual degree of bend which it is necessary to give to a stock must naturally be dependent chiefly on the physical peculiarity of the shooter, as well as on his style in shooting. Some men, for example, can get their heads much closer down to their stocks than others, and such will not require so much bend.

But bend also depends on what may be termed the physical peculiarity of the gun, that is on the Flip. This was dealt with fully in Volume I, and so it will now

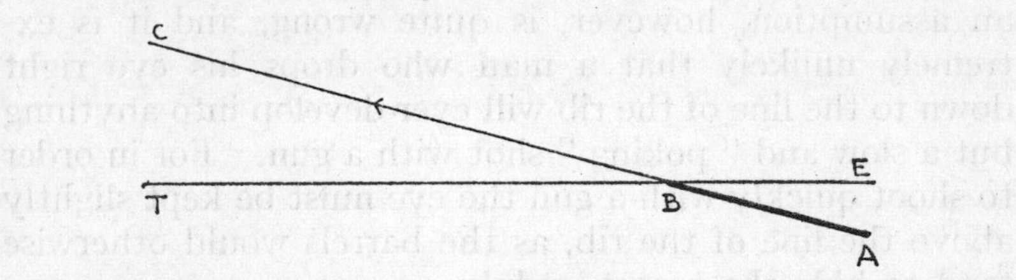

FIG. 27.—Diagram to illustrate the necessity for "Bend" in a gun stock.

only be necessary to emphasise again the fact that guns with great stiffness of barrel such as is conferred by the barrels being placed one above the other, as in Over and Under guns, or by the barrels being shorter than usual, will need more bend than guns in which the barrels give a more pronounced downward flip.

This fact is now generally appreciated by those gun-makers who specialise in short barrels and it will explain why so many sportsmen found their shooting suffer after having a pair of short barrels fitted to the stock of a gun which originally had longer barrels, or after having a new short barrelled gun built to the same measurements as their old long barrelled one.

For this reason any system of fitting for bend which does not include actual tests of shooting must be regarded as being unreliable.

Bend is actually measured by the two distances AC and BD in Fig. 26, which explain themselves, being the vertical distances of the comb and the heel below the line of the barrels.

It is sometimes stated that to be correct the bend should be such as to bring the shooter's eye into line with the top rib when the gun is brought to the shoulder. And some gunmakers make specially shaped ribs with a view to helping rapid alignment. Theoretically it may be best so to combine the degree of bend and the shape of the rib that the shot is centred on the spot at which aim is taken along the line of the rib. This theory, however, is based on the assumption that a shotgun is used in the same general way as a rifle, that is by actual aiming along the rib just as one aims with the sights of a rifle. Such an assumption, however, is quite wrong, and it is extremely unlikely that a man who drops his eye right down to the line of the rib will ever develop into anything but a slow and " poking " shot with a gun. For in order to shoot quickly with a gun the eye must be kept slightly above the line of the rib, as the barrels would otherwise tend to hide the target unduly.

It is always difficult to say exactly how one should shoot with a gun, and many of the best shots cannot say just what they do. Some sort of alignment must obviously be necessary, and it is probable that the great majority of men only see the muzzle end of their barrels when shooting. Specially shaped and raised ribs may help a few ; but they will certainly not help the majority ; while some guns are made without any ribs at all and are not found to make shooting any more difficult.

In gun-fitting, practice is of more value than theory ; and practice has shown that in the vast majority of cases the bend should be such that the shooter's eye will naturally drop into position slightly above the line of the rib, and so enable him to see the bird and the muzzle of the gun.

The best—in fact the only—way to find the correct bend is to fire quickly at some fixed mark, just as one would shoot at a flying bird, and to decide on the bend which results in the shot being properly placed for elevation.

FITTING FOR DIRECTION

The great majority of shooters bring their guns up to their right shoulders when firing, and since it is difficult to bring the controlling line of vision into the same vertical plane as the gun when it is held against the right shoulder, the stock must be bent laterally as well as vertically and for exactly the same reason. This lateral bend is known as " Cast," and when the stock is so cast that the vertical plane containing the barrels lies to the left of a parallel vertical plane through the heel of the butt, the stock is said to be " Cast Off."

In the case of a man who shoots from his *left* shoulder, however, the vertical plane of the barrels must clearly be situated to the right of a parallel vertical plane through the heel of the butt, and such guns are said to be "Cast On."

At the present, however, let us confine ourselves to the consideration of a man who shoots from his right shoulder.

The amount of Cast which he will require must naturally depend partly on his width of chest and shoulders. But the problem is rendered more complicated by the fact that we have two eyes, both of which should be used when shooting with a shotgun. If the left eye were always closed, the right eye only being used, the problem of Cast would become much simpler. The use of two eyes, however, greatly helps speed and judging distance ; so both eyes must be taken into consideration when determining the degree of Cast that is necessary.

Since both eyes are kept open they must, in a measure, share the task of aligning the gun on the target. The task, however, will only very rarely be shared equally ; for in the vast majority of human beings one eye is stronger than the other and exercises more control. In common parlance the stronger eye is known as the "master eye."

Anyone can test themselves for their master eye as follows.

Select any vertical straight line at least 10 feet away. The edge of a door or cupboard; the angle of the walls in the corner of a room; the edge of any building; in fact any vertical line.

Next, *keeping both eyes open*, point with the right arm and first finger extended and place the tip of the finger on the selected vertical line.

Now shut the left eye, keeping the right eye open only, and note whether the tip of the finger is still exactly on the vertical line. If it appears to have moved, note the approximate degree of movement.

Then shut the right eye, keeping the left open, and again note whether the tip of the finger has strayed away from the vertical line, and if so, by how much.

If the right eye is the master eye it will exercise the greater control when the finger is pointed with both eyes open, and consequently the apparent position of the finger in relation to the vertical line will be more nearly the same when the right eye only is open to that of the finger when both eyes are open.

But if the right eye is closed, the weaker left eye will take up sole control and will want to make the finger point in the vertical plane containing the left eye and the selected aiming line. In other words, the finger will point in the line of vision of the left eye when the left eye only is open; and in the line of vision of the right eye when the right eye only is open. But when both eyes are open the right eye, being the master, will have more say in the alignment and the finger will point more nearly in the line of vision of the right eye than of the left.

In my own case my right eye is very markedly the master, and there is no difference in the alignment of my finger when I point it with both eyes open or with my right eye open alone. But if I close my right eye the apparent position of my finger is changed completely to a spot well to the right of the vertical aiming line.

This will easily be understood with the help of the diagram in Fig. 28, which shows the lines of vision in plan.

R is the right eye and L the left, while M is the aiming mark. When the right eye is markedly the master and the finger is pointed with both eyes open it is placed in the line of vision of the right eye in the position F_1. If the right eye is then closed the finger will appear to the left eye to be pointing at the spot M_1 which is to the right of M.

Similarly, if the left eye is markedly the master and

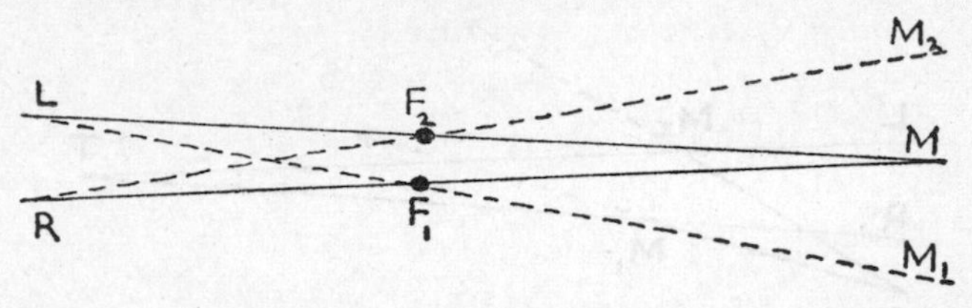

FIG. 28.—Diagram to illustrate the effects of either the right or left eye being markedly the master eye.

the finger is pointed when both eyes are open it will be placed in the line of vision of the left eye in the position F_2; and when the left eye is closed the finger will appear to the right eye to be pointing at the spot M_2.

When shooting with a shotgun the eyes only take the muzzle part of the barrels into consideration when making the the necessary alignment, and since the butt is bedded against the right shoulder some manipulation is necessary to bring the barrels into alignment with the line of vision. If the gun were quite straight, and the body placed perfectly square to the line of fire, the barrels would point to the left of the mark, since the eye would be making the alignment with the muzzle and it is not possible to bend the head over sideways to the right in order to bring the line of vision into the same vertical plane as the gun.

This can be seen from the diagram in Fig. 29, which

has not, of course, been drawn to scale. Here R is the right eye, L the left, T the target, and G the butt of the gun in position against the right shoulder. When the right eye is markedly the master the muzzle of the gun would be placed in the line of vision of that eye in the position M_1; and the line of fire would be to the left of the target as shown by the dotted line.

The most obvious remedy in this case is for the shooter to stand with his body making a distinct angle with the correct line of fire, and with his left shoulder in advance of his right. Such a stance will enable some men to bring their right eye into the same vertical plane as the gun, and in their case no cast to the stock may be

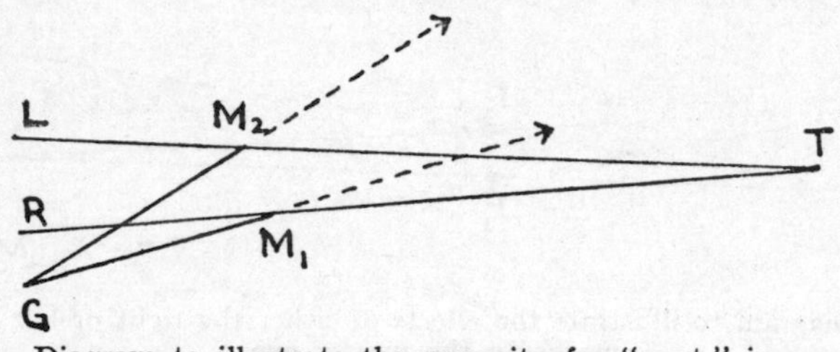

FIG. 29.—Diagram to illustrate the necessity for "cast" in a gun stock.

necessary. But by no means all shooters are so built as to be able to bring their right eye over the gun in comfort. A great deal depends on the length of neck, size and shape of jaw, width of chest and general looseness of build. For this reason the majority of men will find it more comfortable if a certain amount of cast is given to the stock of the gun; the amount of cast being dependent on individual physical build.

But if the left eye is markedly the master the muzzle of the gun would be placed at M_2 in Fig. 29, and the line of fire would be a long way to the left of the target.

In this case it is impossible to adopt any stance in which the left eye can be brought into the same vertical plane as the gun, and the only remedy is to give cast to the stock of the gun.

It may have been noticed that I have stated that in my own case my right eye is "markedly" the master, and I have used this same qualification in subsequent examples. This has been done purposely because it quite frequently happens that neither eye is sufficiently master to assume *complete* control when the finger is pointed with both eyes open. In such cases the finger will appear to move away from the vertical line when either eye is closed, but the movement is less when the master eye is kept open, showing that it was this eye which exercised the *greater* influence in the alignment.

In such cases the actual line of fire would fall between the two extreme limits shown in Fig. 29, and it becomes essential to give some cast to the stock of the gun.

It will thus be realised that if the right eye is only partially the master the gun will have to be given more cast than would be necessary were the whole control of alignment taken over by the right eye, instead of only the greater part of it.

The greatest amount of cast will clearly be necessary when the left eye is markedly the master, and in such cases the gun is fitted with what is termed a " fully cast-off " stock, or a " cross-eyed " stock.

A completely cast-off stock is not a very sightly object, and although I know a good many men who shoot with them successfully, I know of others who find them uncomfortable and awkward to handle on account of the recoil not being taken in a comparatively direct line. It is not surprising, therefore, that other devices have been invented for overcoming this difficulty of the left eye being the master.

The principle underlying all such devices is to prevent the left eye from seeing the muzzle end of the barrels when the gun is in position at the shoulder, and different gunmakers fix opaque discs to the breech end of the barrels or to the action, which protrude between the left eye and the muzzle of the gun.

These discs are at the best clumsy and spoil the appearance of the gun, and far and away the best device of this nature is the Cogswell and Harrison special Hand-Guard.

This invention is as ingenious as it is simple and merely consists of an ordinary leather covered steel hand-guard which slips on to the barrels over the muzzle and protects the left hand from very hot barrels. One side of this special hand-guard, however, is lengthened so as to extend well towards the breech end of the barrels and this end is turned outwards so as to form a disc which protrudes from the barrel in between the left eye and the muzzle, thus preventing the left eye from seeing the muzzle and controlling the alignment.

But there are other methods for overcoming this difficulty of shooting from the right shoulder when the left eye is the master.

The first of these is to close the left eye altogether. This is certainly efficacious, but is a great handicap in quick shooting. Judging distance is not so difficult, because the left eye need not be closed until the gun is brought to the shoulder. There are many cases on record of shooters adopting this plan with success.

Perhaps a modification of this method is better in which the left eye is only partially closed during the act of firing. The shooter "winks at the birds," so to say, and the winking dims the vision of his left eye and this allows the right to take control.

Another plan which I have known adopted with success is to wear a cap or hat with the peak or brim placed well down over the left eye, so as partially to eclipse the angle of vision, or to fix a disc protruding downwards from the brim of the hat. And yet another is to hold the barrels with the left hand turned round in such a way that the knuckles and base of the thumb obliterate the muzzle from the line of vision of the left eye. But I have always thought that this method of holding the gun might tend to tilting the barrels.

Another plan, which can easily be adopted by those shooters who wear spectacles, is to have a small removable disc attached to the rim of the left lens. This disc is shaped rather like a segment of a circle and looks like an abnormal thickening of the rim at one part. It is a simple

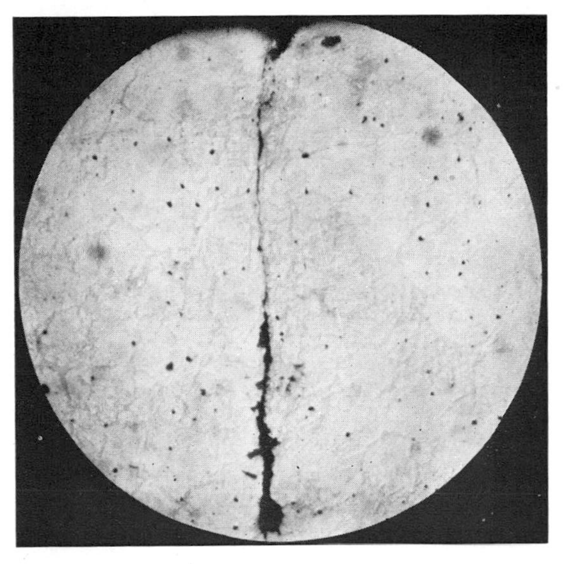

(A) A Photo-micrograph of the Fissure in the Barrel shown in Plate X (A) taken at the point 3

At this point the fissure is relatively very deep and a low magnification of 100 diameters was used in this photograph in order to include the whole of the fissure in the field of view of the microscope

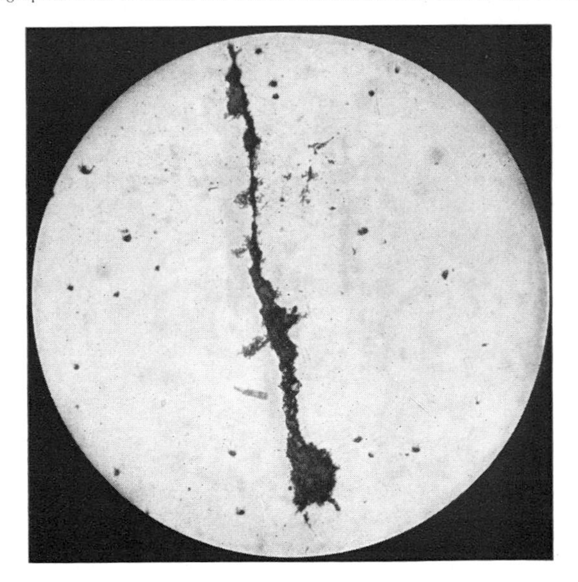

(B) This Photo-micrograph was taken with a magnification of 250 diameters and shows only the bottom end of the Fissure shown in Plate XII (A)

matter to test whether it excludes the muzzle from the vision of the left eye when the gun is at the shoulder. Once the correct placing for the disc has been found it can either be made a permanent fixture, or put back into the correct position when the occasion arises.

This type of disc is too small to interfere in any way with normal vision, and is thus no handicap in judging distance. This plan is undoubtedly the best for those who wear spectacles ; while even those who do not could easily wear a plain frame without any lenses, with the disc attached to the frame of the left eye.

I have no doubt that any optician could fit a suitable disc, but I was first shown the idea by Mr. Mallard, of Messrs. Mallard and Spence, opticians, Walm Lane, Willesden Green, N.W.2, and 19 Brent Street, Hendon.

Incidentally the fact that success can be obtained by preventing the left eye from seeing the muzzle proves the contention that it is only the muzzle end of the barrels which are used for aligning the gun, at any rate by the great majority of shots.

But the best way of all for overcoming the difficulty of the left eye being the master is to shoot from the left shoulder. This is an absolute cure and puts the left-eyed man on exactly the same footing as the right-eyed one. It is no more difficult to shoot from the left shoulder than from the right : in fact it is easier for the left-eyed man. It is possible that some men who have shot for years from the right shoulder might find it hard to make the change in middle age. But that is only because of long habit. When a boy first begins to shoot he should be tested for his master eye in the way which has already been described, and if his left eye is the master he should begin shooting from his left shoulder and never shoot from his right with a gun and only on special occasions with a rifle.

The only possible argument which can be advanced against shooting from the left shoulder is that it is more difficult to manipulate the bolt action of a rifle when the rifle is at the left shoulder than when it is at the right.

But this is hardly relevant to shotguns, and I know of at least one man who shoots from his left shoulder and who can use a bolt actioned rifle as well as any right-shouldered marksman, and better than most. In big-game shooting it is often a great advantage to be able to shoot from either shoulder, as not infrequently one has to take a shot from some cramped position, and personally I always used to practise shooting from both shoulders with my sporting rifles. It is really not at all difficult.

Gun-fitting is now much more generally understood by gunmakers and its importance appreciated by sportsmen than was the case forty years ago. I remember in India before 1914, that I came across quite a few cases of men who were very keen on shooting, but who shot with distressingly poor success, who, on making the simple test already suggested, found that their left eyes were the master although they had been quite unconscious of the fact. A useful, although admittedly not infallible or scientific, test is to note which eye a person uses when looking through a telescope or microscope. As a general rule, the stronger eye will be applied to the instrument instinctively.

If any shooter who has never been properly fitted for a gun should suddenly find that his left eye is the master, I would suggest that he should seriously consider shooting from his left shoulder. Let him practise bringing a gun up indoors ; and I shall be surprised if after a fortnight he does not find it as easy as bringing it up to the right shoulder.

For a boy who is beginning shooting I do not think there can be two opinions. The left-eyed boy should learn to shoot from his left shoulder just as the right-eyed boy does from his right.

Probably the most difficult shooter to fit is the one whose eyes are very nearly of equal strength. Some gunmakers recommend a stock which is half-way between the normal and a full cast off, but I am inclined to think that this is not the best plan to adopt. An eye can suffer from the effects of undue temporary strain or of some temporary injury. Some years ago a hot cinder, emitted from the funnel of a road engine, was driven into my right eye with such force that it became partially embedded in the cornea, and had to be removed by an ophthalmic surgeon with a knife. My eye was put out of action for some time, and when I began shooting again I found that I seemed to be missing even more than usual. A test showed that although my right eye was still the master it was not so markedly so as it had been ; and this fact was confirmed by a visit to the opthalmic surgeon. So for the next two months I adopted the plan of " winking at the birds " and found that it helped me considerably. And by the end of that time my right eye had sufficiently recovered to regain its former mastery.

When the two eyes are normally of approximately equal strength it seems likely that the actual mastery might quite easily change from one to the other and back again according to circumstances. And in such cases any gun which was a compromise in the matter of cast would be of little help.

So it seems likely that the best way out of the difficulty for a shooter with eyes of approximately equal strength is to shoot from whichever shoulder he finds the easier with a gun of normal cast for that shoulder, and to " wink at the birds " with the opposite eye.

Cases are sometimes quoted in which the shooter has lost the sight of the right eye and yet continues to shoot with success from his right shoulder. But these are very rare. I have only come across one myself, and that was an elderly cousin of mine. He told me that he always used to try to shoot well clear to the right of a bird instead of at it, and he also confessed that although he could hit birds crossing from right to left with comparative frequency, he was not nearly so successful with birds going from left to right. Curiously enough the thought of shooting from his left shoulder had never entered his head.

I had always regarded the doctrine of the " master eye " more in the light of an established and incontrovertible fact rather than a theory. So I was more than ordinarily disconcerted to see in the *Lancet* of November 29th, 1930, that this is apparently not the case. This issue contanied a verbatim report of the Bradshaw Lecture delivered before the Royal College of Surgeons of England on November 13th, 1930, by Mr. J. Herbert Fisher, Consulting Ophthalmic Surgeon to St. Thomas's Hospital. In the course of his lecture Mr. Fisher said:

"The idea of the master eye is, I believe, a fallacy, but one found very useful by the gunsmith. A man who has been shooting badly is asked by his gunmaker to point a gun at a certain mark some yards away; when he has done this the tradesman, looking along the barrel, finds that it is directed, say, to the left of the mark, and informs him that his left eye is his master eye; the gun is, of course, actually being pointed too much in the line of vision of the right eye and too little of that of the left; a cast-off gun is recommended, made and sold, and with it its owner makes better shooting. He is, of course, sighting the new gun no more and no less than he was the old one, but bringing it to his shoulder, guided by proprioceptive impulses, exactly as he did the former weapon, the 'cast-off' results in his charge of shot being thrown more to the right and better results are obtained. If he did, as a matter of fact, sight his new gun he would be looking along a barrel straight from breech to muzzle, and as far as vision is concerned the fact that the barrel was set at an angle to the stock could make no difference at all. What had gone wrong with the man was that he had gradually and imperceptibly to himself lost accuracy in co-ordinating his upper limb movements when bringing his gun to his shoulder, so that he was not, subconsciously, pointing it to the position upon which both his eyes were fixed, and to which he believed himself to be directing it. Master eyes are not invoked to explain bad billiards, and except in Gilbertian opera a cast-off cue is not suggested as an advantage to anyone playing the game and then only if it be in the hands of his opponent."

Now Mr. Fisher's opinion will naturally be treated with the respect which it deserves, yet there are one or two points in this extract from his lecture which do not seem to be quite correct. For example, no comparison is possible between billiards and shooting. In shooting the gun becomes almost an integral part of the body, and the position of the head cannot be moved relatively to that of the gun. In billiards the cue is held by the hands alone and the head and whole of the upper part of the body can be, and are, moved relatively to the cue. The billiard player moves his head until the controlling line of his vision is brought into the same vertical plane as that containing the cue. If his eyesight is such that his right eye is what I have termed "markedly the master," it will be his right eye that is brought into the vertical plane of the cue. But if his left eye is "markedly the master," this eye can be brought into the same vertical plane with equal ease. The whole point is that the head is free to move relatively to the cue, while in shooting the head is not free to move relatively to the gun.

Hitherto the remedy has been to move the gun, and Mr. Fisher himself admits that this method is successful. In view of this success I think the majority of shooters will be wise to have their guns fitted with the appropriate normal cast off or cast on for shooting from the right or left shoulder rather than trying to acquire "accuracy in co-ordinating their upper limb movements."

The theory of the master eye may be fallacious, but it undoubtedly enables the shooter to be fitted with a gun as well as to ascertain whether he should shoot from his right shoulder or his left.

Newton's Theory of Gravitation is, perhaps, superseded by Einstein's Theory of Relativity. But the Laws of Gravitation enable us to find correct solutions for all problems connected with the movements of bodies on the earth ; and so it is unlikely that they will be discarded.

Similarly, testing for the master eye will probably be continued by shooters and gunmakers until the surgical profession have evolved a method of gun-fitting which is both simpler and more efficacious.

FITTING FOR COMFORT

We now come to the second of the three conditions which were given at the beginning of this chapter as being essential in a well-fitted gun, namely, that the shooter should be able to fire an almost indefinite number of shots with ordinary loads without being bruised in one particular place more than another. A gun which is fitted perfectly for length, bend and cast may quite easily bruise the shooter unduly, and in such circumstances Fitting for Comfort becomes an equally important branch in the art of fitting the gun.

One of the most common of minor discomforts caused by recoil is a bruised second finger. I call this "minor" because the remedy is so simple. The second finger is bruised by the trigger guard, and in the majority of cases a bruised second finger is due to the stock being too short, but a badly shaped trigger guard is a common cause. The rear end of the trigger guard should be made with a distinct slope, as if the guard is nearly at right angles to the line of the stock a bruised finger will be almost inevitable. The trigger guard in the Frontispiece to Volume I is sloped at a very nice angle, and a guard which makes a sharper angle with the stock should be avoided.

Another cause is the position of the comb. If this is placed too far forward there may be insufficient room left for the hand on the "grip" or "small" of the stock, when a bruised finger will probably be the result of cramped holding. The correct position for the comb in relation to the trigger guard is well shown in the Frontispiece of Volume I.

It is also true that abnormally loose holding on the part of the shooter may result in a bruised finger, and in this case the best remedy is to learn to hold the gun more tightly.

But whatever the cause, a remedy which is both simple and effective is to remove the screw which holds the rear part of the trigger guard to the stock and then to slip an ordinary india-rubber umbrella ring over the end of the guard until it rests in the angle of the guard, after which the guard can be screwed to the stock again. The umbrella ring makes a perfect cushion and protects the finger completely.

But in a really well shaped and fitted stock the necessity for such a protection should not arise.

Another place which is not infrequently bruised is

the cheek, and in the majority of cases such bruising is due to the shooter having a jaw which is rather more square, or a cheek bone which is rather more prominent, than usual.

Such bruising can be most painful, but can generally be prevented by a little hollowing out of the face of the stock. And it is really extraordinary what relief can be given by the removal of a very little wood.

Sometimes, however, this remedy is not sufficient and the only effective preventative is the insertion of a rubber pad into the face of the stock, or else padding it with some soft leather, or rubber covered with leather.

Such padding rather detracts from the look of the gun, and so should not be added until all else has failed. I am inclined to think that this bruising of the cheek may sometimes be due to the shooter actually hitting his cheek with the gun when he puts it to his shoulder and is not caused by the recoil at all. Such a habit is very difficult to eradicate, and for this reason boys beginning to shoot should always be impressed that they must bring the gun up to the face, and not the face down to the gun.

Fitting for comfort cannot be tested with a try gun, but must depend entirely on the gunmaker's knowledge, skill and experience.

FITTING FOR APPEARANCE

And finally we come to Fitting for Appearance. I do not regard this as unimportant, for there is a vast difference between the beautiful and graceful lines of a best-grade gun and the harsher outline of a cheap one. Beauty is not a thing to be pushed on one side as of no account, and it is a joy to see how a really skilful gunmaker can so modify the curves of the stock that even a gun with a full cast off does not appear as anything very extraordinary; while a gun made to the same dimensions by a less cunning craftsman will look a veritable caricature of a weapon.

The making of an exceptional gun which appears

ordinary is the hall-mark of the skilful stocker and fitter. For this reason I am always inclined to be suspicious of a gunmaker's ability to fit really well when I see a gun of some very abnormal shape. It *may* be necessary; yet it is very rarely that such abnormalities are seen amongst the guns built and fitted by the very best makers.

Sometimes the shooters themselves are to blame and will insist on some peculiarity in the shape of the stock. But the idea was probably suggested to them in the first place by some gun-fitter, and it is quite possible that the idea remedied the fault. But even so the most expert fitters would probably have arrived at the same end without employing such objectionable means.

It must be remembered that the perfectly fitted gun will always have graceful lines, just as the brilliant tennis player always seems to make the most difficult shots look so easy: it is the second-class player who makes them look difficult, which indeed they are. And it is the same with gunmakers and guns.

HOW TO MEASURE A STOCK

A sportsman abroad may sometimes wish to send a gunmaker measurements from a gun which fits him well in order to have another and similar gun made. In such circumstances he should send measurements for length, bend and cast.

Length is given by the measurements TD, TE and TF in Fig. 26.

Bend by AC and BD, which can be obtained by placing a long and perfectly straight rod on the rib of the barrels so as to protrude backwards over the stock, when the two measurements required can be taken.

Cast is difficult for an amateur to measure correctly, and possibly the best course to adopt is to give the gunmaker details of height, build, chest measurement and span of the outstretched arms. If an actual measurement is required the gun should be placed triggers upwards on a flat table in such a position that the centre of the rib coincides exactly with a straight line drawn on the table. Then the distance between the straight line and the foot of a perpendicular dropped to the table from the heel of the butt gives the cast. And it should be made clear whether the gun is " Cast Off " for shooting from the right shoulder, or " Cast On " for shooting from the left, as would be necessary for the left-eyed shot who shoots from his left shoulder.

CHAPTER XIII

THE COST OF GUNS, SPECIAL GUNS AND SECOND-HAND GUNS

THE matter of cost has already been dealt with at some length in Volume I, and I can but repeat here that even in 1939 over 60 per cent. of the actual selling price of a best gun represented the cost of labour, both in the actual manufacture and the regulating for pattern. Now this percentage is much higher. And when the cost of raw materials and overhead charges which are inseparable from a gunmaker's business are remembered—insurance for men engaged in the handling of explosives is higher than ordinary rates, for example—it will be realised that the margin of profit is comparatively small. It is in fact literally true, as was stated in Volume I, that the actual percentage profit is less in the case of a best gun than in that of a cheap one. In fact I am quite certain that if value for money is the main consideration, a best gun is the cheapest article which can be bought for the price demanded.

And this brings us to another question with which the purchaser of a gun is faced, namely, as to what constitutes a really "best" gun.

The only possible answer to this question is that a really "best" gun is the highest grade of weapon made by one of the leading gunmakers. Which reply is often met by the response, "Oh, I am not going to pay a fancy price just for a fashionable name."

I have heard this remark again and again, but the sportsman should remember that when he buys a gun from a leading maker he is not paying a fancy price for a fashionable name. He is paying for the most highly skilled labour which it is possible to obtain in that particular line; labour which is not reckoned by time expended, but only by perfection of results; and he is also paying for the satisfaction—and it should be a real satisfaction—in the knowledge that the materials used throughout are of the very highest quality.

Comparisons are proverbially odious, and I have no intention of referring to any particular firms of gunmakers by name. Naturally many of us have our favourite gunmakers, and in many cases such feelings are the outcome of what is really a family friendship extending through two, three or more generations. But if any sportsman has no such tie, and is anxious to get the very best work, he should remember that the most delicate barometer is to be found in the second-hand market. These prices are not the outcome of mere fashion, for fashion alone will never maintain any gunmaker at the top rung of the ladder once the quality of his work has begun to fall away: these prices are a very sure guide as to the status of any firm.

One last point before I leave this question of cost. I have not infrequently heard the remark passed by some shooting man that a small bore gun, such as a 20-bore, should be cheaper to build than a 12-bore. There could be no greater fallacy. As has been explained fully in Volume I, the cost of a gun is really the cost of labour; and there is just as much labour in building a 20-bore as a larger gun. Every part is duplicated in both, and a 20-bore has to withstand a higher pressure. If anything a small bore should really be more expensive than the usual size, because the number made is not so great and consequently it is not possible to cut out so many of the parts at a time in a rough state and thus reduce overhead costs.

SPECIAL GUNS

It not infrequently happens that the sportsman who is buying a gun wants one for some particular form of shooting which is best served by a special weapon. Consequently what may be termed Special Guns deserve a little notice.

Almost all these Special Guns are "special" only in the matter of size or boring: their actions are in every way identical to the actions used in ordinary game guns. So consideration will only be paid to their special features.

Guns for Clay Target Shooting. A clay target is a small object at the best of times, while the area which it offers when viewed exactly end on is so small that it is surprising that they are broken as often as they are. Since there is no question of life and death the principles which were laid down in Chapter VII as to the importance of maintaining both pattern and penetration need not be followed so rigidly, and pattern becomes of more importance than penetration.

It is difficult to say definitely what is the minimum number of pellets necessary to ensure a clay target being broken. Frequently a single pellet will suffice; while at other times a target may be picked up which was apparently not touched but which had been perforated by 3 or 4 pellets. There can be no rule, but it would not appear unreasonable to regard at least 2 hits as being necessary to make fairly certain of a break.

The area of a clay target when seen from underneath is 13·9 square inches, which would mean a necessary minimum pattern of 102 in the 30-inch circle, or 112 if we add on the 10 per cent. for loss due to stringing. Such a pattern is easily obtained, but when we come to look at a clay target end-on the problem assumes a very different complexion. For the area of a target end-on is but 3·3 square inches which would require a necessary minimum pattern of 428 without making any allowance for stringing.

Now it is only possible to obtain a pattern of about this density at 30 yards—an average long shot at a clay target—by using a full choke and 1¼ ounces of No. 7 shot. And even then the pattern should be helped by a moderate velocity and "soft" pressure, while a crimp turnover would also be an invaluable advantage. Such a charge cannot be handled to full advantage in any gun smaller than a 12-bore 2¾-inch, and so this would certainly seem to be the ideal gun for clay target shooting pure and simple. A larger gun would be too clumsy and heavy for firing many shots on end. But the gun selected should be of full weight, that is 7½ lb., as recoil becomes a dominant factor when firing long series of shots in rapid succession.

If the conditions of the competition lay down that no gun larger than an ordinary 12-bore game gun chambered for the 2½-inch case may be used, the best that a competitor can do is to use a full choke and as heavy a charge of No. 7 shot as possible. Since penetration is not so important as pattern, it would be well to reduce the powder charge to 32 or 31 grains of a 33-grain powder and use 1⅛ ounce of No. 7 shot.

The chief points to remember are that pattern is of first importance and that recoil comes next.

GUNS FOR PIGEON SHOOTING. When shooting at living blue-rock pigeons the relationship between penetration and pattern which was suggested in Chapter VII should be maintained. Since the object is to kill the bird dead at the first possible moment a heavier shot charge than the ordinary standard 12-bore game charge is generally regarded as necessary, and for this reason a full-choked 12-bore 2¾-inch is the most popular gun.

GUNS FOR WOOD-PIGEON SHOOTING. Pigeon shooting as practised at Monte Carlo and elsewhere on the Continent is forbidden by law in England. I have no intention of discussing the ethics of this form of shooting, but it cannot by any stretch of imagination be regarded as a sport, since one of the first essentials in any true sport is the hunting of a wild animal.

Wood-pigeon shooting is, therefore, in a very different category, for there is no bird more wary or more difficult to approach. Wood-pigeon are invariably credited with great vitality, and they certainly do seem to carry off an abnormal amount of shot at times. I am, however, inclined to think that some—although by no means all—of their reputation for toughness is due to the fact that they are much smaller birds than they look, and that in consequence they need a dense pattern to ensure a pellet striking a vital spot, as can be seen from the Table on page 96. Owing to the reputation for toughness which these birds enjoy, sportsmen frequently use large shot sizes, thereby reducing the densities of their patterns.

If any shooter has sufficient opportunities for shooting wood-pigeon to make it worth his while to get a special gun, there can be no doubt that a full-choke 12-bore $2\frac{3}{4}$-inch would be a wonderfully effective weapon. Yet even so I am inclined to think that an ordinary 12-bore $2\frac{1}{2}$-inch would be very nearly as good if it were fitted with an extra pair of barrels both of which were full choke. With Maximum cartridges it would be just as effective as the larger gun. It is a distinct disadvantage to a good many shots to use guns of different weights. One gets accustomed to a particular weight of gun and a change in weight can upset one's swing. So, on the whole, I would recommend an extra pair of barrels, both full choke, being fitted to an ordinary game gun in preference to the purchase of a long-chambered pigeon gun, as the 12-bore $2\frac{3}{4}$-inch is commonly called.

GUNS FOR WILDFOWLING

The pursuit of wildfowl often entails shots having to be taken at very long ranges at trips of fowl rather than at individual birds. Large shot is essential in order to maintain penetration at the long ranges, and a heavy shot charge is equally necessary to keep the pattern up to the necessary minimum density. The combination of a heavy shot charge and large size of shot means a large gun, and not so very many years ago 4-bores and 8-bores were by no means rare, while 10-bores were common. None of these large bores call for special mention, and the most suitable size was decided best by the shooter's physique. It gradually came to be realised, however, that no man was really strong enough to tramp over miles of foreshore carrying a very heavy large bore gun and use it to full advantage. For this reason the 4-bores and 8-bores gradually became relegated to professional fowlers or else to be used in flight shooting only, and the 10-bore came into general favour. But as time passed this size, too, was found to be beyond the ordinary man's strength and now the 12-bore 3-inch is unquestionably the most popular gun, although it is quite possible that a *light* 10-bore would handle the 12-bore magnum charge to greater advantage ballistically.

CHAMBERLESS GUNS. It is possible, however, that for wildfowl shooting a useful type of gun is the Chamberless Gun, a type which owed its development to the late Dr. C. J. Heath.

The term "chamberless" is not strictly accurate, as all guns must have chambers to receive the cartridges, but in these special guns, the diameter of the bore is the same as that of the chamber, and they are chamberless in that they have no chamber of larger diameter than the bore. Thin brass cases can only be used in such guns, for if ordinary paper cases were used the wads would be too small to seal the bore during the passage of the shot charge down the barrel. Owing to the absence of any form of chamber cone, brass cases of different lengths can be used with equal efficiency, and consequently different loads can be fired effectively from the same barrel.

Dr. Heath was for many years a strong advocate of the low velocity principle for wildfowl loads, and by its adoption used shot charges of $1\frac{3}{4}$ ounces of BB in a gun weighing but $7\frac{1}{4}$ lb. without any excessive recoil, while the patterns are excellent. This apparent absence of recoil has been at various times attributed to the absence of the chamber cones. But this explanation is, of course, quite incorrect, the true explanation being the low muzzle velocity with which these heavy shot charges are propelled. These heavy shot charges require 3-inch brass cases, and Dr. Heath found that a felt wad of but $\frac{1}{4}$ inch thickness was sufficient because the absence of a chamber cone permits of effective obturation of the bore from the very moment that the felt wad emerges from the mouth of the cartridge-case.

For snipe one ounce of No. 8 can be used in a short case with a normal powder charge.

The very fact that thin brass cases must be used must prevent such guns from ever coming into general use for ordinary shooting, but in wildfowling the brass cases are an advantage and for this form of sport these chamberless guns are undoubtedly excellent.

Although Dr. Heath's chamberless guns were the result of his own initiative, all guns which are specially chambered for thin brass cases are really chamberless in that the diameters of the bore and the chamber are practically identical. But the ordinary guns chambered for thin brass cases are made up to the full weight, while Dr. Heath's chamberless guns were designed and evolved specially for the low velocity principle of loading, and it is this fact which was so much in their favour since they were much lighter than the standard types of guns chambered for similar thin brass cases.

PUNT GUNS. Punt Guns or Stanchion Guns hardly come within the category of shotguns, and so only the briefest description of them will be given, especially as full particulars of these guns, their ammunition, appliances and the methods of using them are given in *Letters to Young Shooters* (*Series III*), by the late Sir Ralph Payne-Gallwey. This admirable book is out of print, but copies can still be obtained in the second-hand market ; and although it was published as long ago as 1896 the particulars about punt guns are just as accurate now as they were then. For punt guns have changed little in the last hundred years, and the majority of punt guns in existence and use at the present time are muzzle-loaders. Breech-loaders have undoubted advantages for this form of shooting, but these advantages are not in any way comparable to the advantages possessed by the breech-loading game gun, while muzzle-loaders are less liable to suffer damage should it be necessary to heave the gun overboard in bad weather and leave a mooring buoy to mark its position.

Punt guns vary in diameter of bore from 1¼ to 2 inches, and fire shot charges of from 12 oz. to 2 lb.

The propellant is always black powder, as suitable smokeless propellants give little or no advantage, and cannot be used in muzzle-loaders.

The areas within which sport with punt guns is to be obtained are unhappily gradually decreasing in size, and it is probable that at the present time there are more punt guns in existence than can be used. The number of breech-loading punt guns which have been made is comparatively small, and it is doubtful if many new ones have been built since 1914. It is always possible to pick up a punt gun second-hand, while the cost of building a new breech-loader would be so terrific as to frighten the majority of amateur punt-gunners.

The late Mr. H. Leyborne Popham, who probably had as much experience of punting after wildfowl as any amateur in the present century and far more than most, told me that he always used a special double 4-bore wildfowling gun by Bland mounted with a rope to take the recoil which was passed through a hole in the stock, instead of a punt gun proper.

BALL AND SHOT GUNS

The light weight and general handiness of a shot gun are so pronounced in comparison to a rifle that there have always been big-game hunters who advocated the use of spherical ball in a shotgun for close-quarter work against heavy game in thick jungle, or from the back of an elephant. And there is the additional advantage in using a weapon with which the shooter must be more familiar than he can usually hope to be with a heavy rifle. The presence of choke, however, has always been a difficulty. If the spherical ball fitted the bore, a bulge or burst would be inevitable when the barrel was choked even to the lightest degree. And if the ball was of sufficiently small diameter to permit its passage of the choke "windage" would occur. That is, the gases would escape past the ball during its passage up the bore, which would cause loss in velocity and accuracy.

There were two methods of overcoming this difficulty, both of which were popular in India sixty years ago. The first was to use a gun fitted with absolutely true-cylinder barrels; and the second was to wrap the under-sized ball in a patch of soft leather which would help to effect obturation while being sufficiently compressible to allow the ball to pass the choke without causing damage.

Then came the invention of the "Paradox" gun by the late Colonel Fosberry, V.C. In this type of gun the choked portion of the bore was rifled with deep grooves, while the rest of the bore was smooth. The bullet was conical and was given a spin by the rifling at the muzzle which was sufficient to ensure accurate and stable flight. Ordinary shot charges could also be used and very fair patterns be obtained.

The advantages of the Paradox were great, and in its early days it was frequently made in 8-bore and 10-bore sizes, as these guns were considerably lighter than rifles of the same gauge and gave nearly the same power. These large bore Paradox guns, however, were not seriously intended for use as shotguns, being merely heavy big-game rifles, and they were superseded by the medium bore "high velocity" rifle on the introduction of smokeless rifle powders.

The 12-bore Paradox, however, still remained popular for jungle shooting and was made in smaller sizes as well for use against lighter game in thick cover, while those who preferred a somewhat heavier weapon could have a Magnum Paradox, which was a 12-bore chambered for 2¾-inch cases.

The popularity of the original Paradox led to the manufacture of other guns of the same type. Some of these were made with "invisible" rifling the whole way up the bore, that is with very shallow grooves which were just sufficient to spin the conical bullet yet not enough to spoil the shot patterns unduly.

But at the very best these guns were not very good *shotguns* although they were effective *rifles*. In the first place they were all heavy—7¼ lb. was a normal weight for an average 12-bore: and the patterns were never so good as those obtained with an ordinary gun. If the boring was so made that patterns were improved the accuracy of the weapon as a rifle deteriorated; and since most men wanted these weapons as rifles in the first place and shotguns in the second, pattern was made to give pride of place to grouping power.

The next advance was the invention of the "Lethal" bullet. This was a spherical bullet made with three narrow flanges of lead round its circumference. It was of small enough diameter for passage even down a full choke; but the flanges were thick enough to seal the widest part of the bore effectively and thus prevent windage, yet they were soft enough to allow the bullet to pass the choke without strain. Another improvement was the insertion in the centre of the bullet of two circular steel discs set at right angles to one another which helped the bullet to expand on impact against an animal.

The Lethal bullet was introduced early in the present century and rapidly became very popular in India as it enabled a sportsman to turn his ordinary shotgun into quite an efficient rifle for close-quarter work in the jungle.

In 1921 the "Contractile" bullet was placed on the market. In principle this bullet is very similar to the Lethal. It consists of a spherical ball of smaller diameter than the muzzle end of a full-choke barrel, which is contained in a thin "skin" of soft metal. There is a space between the skin and the core which is filled with wax, and the skin is held in position by a few projections which protrude from its inside surface and touch the core. There are also holes in the skin through which the wax is forced when the bullet is compressed, thus causing lubrication. Expansion on impact is produced by the presence inside the core of a capsule of heavy amalgam.

The diameter of the skin is sufficient to seal the bore, but the space between the skin and the core permits of easy contraction during the passage of the choke, and this contraction forces the wax out through the holes in the skin.

I do not think that there is anything to choose in efficiency between the Lethal and Contractile bullets. Both are quite excellent. I carried out tests of the Contractile bullet which were reported in the *Field* of May 14th, 1921. The cartridges used in these tests were loaded with 35 grains of Smokeless Diamond. In a full-choke pressure barrel the average 1-inch pressure was but 1·51 tons and the average 6-inch pressure 1·35 tons, while the mean observed velocity over 20 yards was 1,113 f.s., which would give a corresponding muzzle velocity of about 1,200 f.s.

It should be realised that a spherical bullet offers much less resistance than a shot charge, and it is for this reason that the pressures and velocity are lower than those developed by an ordinary shot cartridge.

My tests included trials for accuracy which were made in a single-barrelled experimental gun fitted with interchangeable barrels bored true cylinder, improved cylinder, half choke and full choke.

I fired groups of five shots at 50 yards, and it was interesting to notice how the size of the group increased with the degree of choke. With a true cylinder I obtained a 4¼-inch group: that is the centres of all the shots were contained in a circle of 4¼ inches in diameter. An improved cylinder gave a 5-inch group; a half-choke one of 7 inches; and a full-choke one of 10 inches.

It must be remembered that these groups were all obtained in a single-barrelled gun, as the object of the tests was to try to ascertain the probable degree of accuracy of which the *bullet* was capable rather than the gun. It would not follow necessarily that the two barrels of an ordinary game gun would "shoot together" and give such good grouping as a single barrel. This could only be determined by testing an individual gun, as it is doubtful whether any two guns would behave quite alike.

But 50 yards is a long range for the type of shooting in which spherical ball can be most useful, and it is fairly safe to assume that the accuracy of any ordinary game

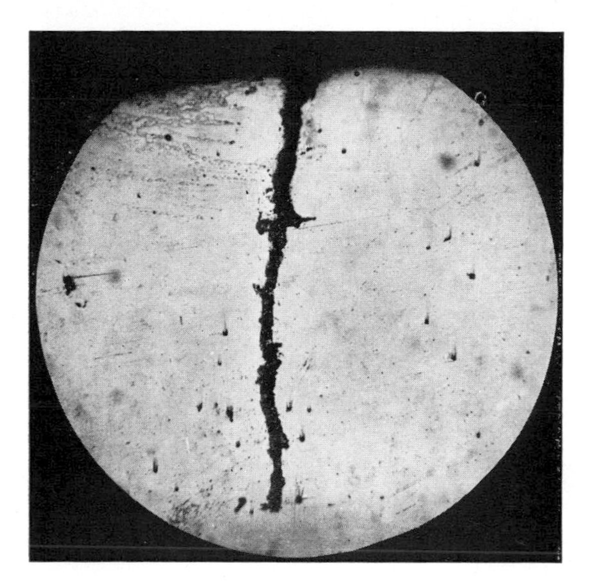

(A) A Photo-micrograph of the Fissure in the Barrel shown in Plate X (A) taken at the point 4 with a magnification of 250 diameters
The fissure is here shallower and wider than it was at point 3

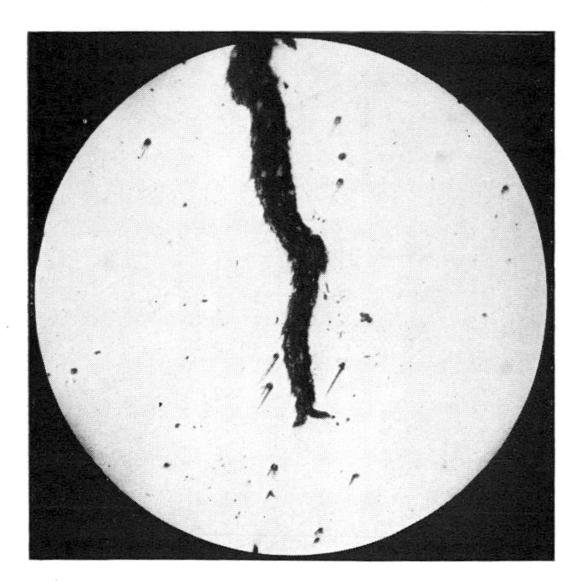

(B) A Photo-micrograph of the same Fissure taken at the point 5 in Plate X (A) with a magnification of 250 diameters
Here the fissure is still wider but less deep

gun when used with these bullets is sufficient for the distances at which shots are generally taken.

Sportsmen will naturally ask, "Is it really safe to use Lethal or Contractile bullets in my gun; or will I damage the choke?"

My own *belief* is that these bullets can be used even in a full choke with absolute safety. Nevertheless, in order to be absolutely on the safe side, I think it might be better to place a half choke as the limit in which to use them, especially if the gun is a good one. In improved cylinder and quarter choke they can be used with absolute confidence.

A third and more recent type of round ball for use in choked guns is the "Destructor" bullet which consists of 16 lead pellets of about the size of SSG shot in a spherical lead case, the outside of which is flanged so as to permit its passage through a choke.

The advent of Lethal and Contractile bullets has had a very marked effect on the number of true Ball and Shot guns made and sold, and these weapons are not nearly so popular as they used to be.

There is another type of bullet designed for use in choked guns known as the "Rotax." This bullet consists of a hollow cylinder of smaller external diameter than the choke, windage being prevented by flanges as in the Lethal. The inside portion of the cylinder is fitted with large helical flanges which make the bullet spin during its passage through the air, and thus maintain accuracy. I have had no personal experience of this bullet and so am not in a position to offer an opinion. It would seem, however, that the penetrative powers of the bullet must be less than those of the Lethal or Contractile, while it could be more easily deflected by twigs than a spherical bullet.

Another bullet designed on the same basic principle as the Rotax was the German "Brenneke" which had a pointed nose, while the outside of the cylindrical part of the bullet was engraved with helical ridges which helped to impart a spin. Another feature was a felt wad which was screwed to the base. This bullet was sometimes imitated, but those imitations which I have seen were very clumsy and gave exceedingly poor results. But I doubt if even the genuine Brenneke could ever have competed with the Lethal or Contractile for all-round practical utility.

The Winchester " Rifled Slug " is yet another bullet designed on the same principle as the Brenneke, with helical grooves on the outside of the cylindrical part of the bullet.

SHOT PISTOLS

Shot pistols can be very useful on occasions to others beside poachers. A pistol is light and very easily carried, so can become a constant companion when a gun would be an impossible nuisance, and one thus becomes able to keep down destructive vermin when fishing or taking a walk. For the big game hunter, too, they can be very handy and useful weapons.

I am inclined to regard a double-barrelled pistol as a mistake : it is too heavy and clumsy to be easily portable, which is the first essential. It is also almost impossible to use two triggers effectively in a pistol owing to the difficulty of slipping one's trigger finger from the front trigger to the rear one without changing the grip on the butt. For this reason if a double-barrelled pistol is regarded as essential it would be better to have a single trigger mechanism, which would add to the cost.

One of the most important parts of any pistol is the butt. The photograph in Plate III shows the wooden butt of a muzzle-loading holster pistol by Joe Manton. In order to avoid any possibility of confusing the lines the lock was removed from the pistol when the photograph was taken. This butt is an almost ideal shape for a pistol, and it would be impossible to do better than follow its lines.

The best length of barrel is from 10 to 11 inches, while the action can be of any type according to the price which the sportsman is prepared to pay.

It is frequently possible to pick up old single-barrelled shotguns at a very small cost, and such actions will make excellent pistol actions. A hammerless action is preferable to a hammer one as there is no projecting hammer to catch in the pocket or bag in which the pistol is carried.

The question of bore is not so easily decided and must largely be a matter of individual opinion. A ·410 is rather on the small side for serious work, and a 20-bore gives a somewhat heavy recoil. Probably a 28-bore is the best compromise, as it is distinctly more powerful than the ·410, lighter and more pleasant to fire than a 20-bore, and the cartridges are sufficiently small not to take up too much space when portability is an important factor.

The boring will probably have to be decided by actual experiment. Theoretically a certain degree of choke should be an advantage, but I have seen quite excellent patterns given by a true cylinder 20-bore pistol with an 11-inch barrel. This particular barrel, however, was bored very "wide," which certainly helped matters.

Pressures near the muzzle, and muzzle blast, must always be difficulties in a shot pistol, and for this reason the powder charge should be kept on the low side, and best results will certainly be obtained by low-velocity loading.

The 20-bore pistol which I have just mentioned belongs to my friend, Rear-Admiral Sir Patrick Macnamara, K.B.E., C.B., R.N., and we tried some experimental loads together when we found that the best patterns were given by a combination of 20 grains of Smokeless Diamond and $\frac{7}{8}$ ounce of No. 6 shot. At 20 yards the average pattern was 169, and at 30 yards 118 ; while with the standard load the average patterns at these distances were but 150 and 82. The observed velocity from an 11-inch barrel was naturally low, being but 750 f.s. with the low-velocity load and 823 f.s. with the standard load. This would mean that penetration would be sufficient up to about 35 yards with the low-velocity load and 40 yards with the standard. Since 30 yards would be the absolute limit of range at which a shot should be taken with a pistol the low-velocity load is appreciably the better of the two.

In order to show what can be done with a pistol it is interesting to record that Admiral Macnamara once killed a cock pheasant, a snipe, a duck and a woodcock in four consecutive shots with this 20-bore pistol. And since then he has killed four snipe with five cartridges.

Finally, the novice in pistol shooting cannot be reminded too forcibly that a pistol is the most dangerous of all firearms on account of the ease with which its short barrel can be turned about. On this account even extra care should be exercised, if that were possible, when handling a pistol than when handling a gun or any other lethal weapon.

BUYING SECOND-HAND GUNS

Most shooters will probably be faced at some time or other with the problem of buying a second-hand gun, either for themselves, friends or keepers. So a few notes on this subject may not be out of place.

The qualities of actual design which go to make a good second-hand gun are exactly the same as those which go to make a good new one, and so no further references will be made to actions, length of barrel, size of gun, etc., as all these points have been dealt with fully.

There cannot be the same choice in the matter of boring in a second-hand gun as in a new one, yet it is always as well to ascertain, if possible, the exact degree of choke in either barrel. If the vendor is a gunmaker or a dealer who specialises in second-hand weapons he will be certain to have a proper gauge at hand with which he can measure the actual amount of constriction made in the choke. This information should give some idea of the patterns which are likely to be made, but if possible it is always better to see the gun actually shot for pattern, especially if a high price is being paid.

If this is not possible the number of the gun should be

noted and enquiries made of the original maker concerning its date of manufacture, original boring, and any other information which can be given. The maker will invariably be glad to help with such information because the owner of a gun of his make, even if it were purchased second-hand, is always a potential customer.

When a gun is being bought second-hand from a gun-maker or dealer with a reputation to maintain, its general "soundness" ought to be above suspicion. But sometimes a gun may be bought under conditions in which there cannot be any such implied warranty. In such cases the buyer must trust to his own judgment and he will then be well advised to test and examine the gun in the following manner.

First test the gun to see whether the action has worn loose in any way. The simplest way of doing this is to hold the closed gun with the barrels uppermost in a horizontal position, grasping the barrels and stock firmly with the left hand just in front of the trigger guard, and then to hit the heel of the butt sharply with the fist of the right hand. If the action is at all loose, a distinct rattle will be felt in the left hand every time the butt is struck.

If the gun is felt to rattle appreciably, the purchase should not be made without first consulting a competent gunmaker.

This test is very useful, but it is not infallible. In some types of action, the Purdey action for example, the mainsprings are exerting an upward pressure against the barrels which is sufficient to prevent any rattle being felt. So if there is any doubt about the type of action the locks had better be removed and the test repeated. Sometimes a gun may seem quite tight with the locks on which will rattle badly when they are off. It is a sound plan, therefore, to make this test with the locks removed in any type of self-opening gun.

If the barrels are badly "off the face of the action," that is if the breech ends no longer fit tightly against the action face, it is sometimes possible to see daylight between the breech end of the barrels and the action when the gun is closed and held up against the light.

The next test should be to see whether the barrels are sound and free from cracks. Such a thing is admittedly unlikely, but it is not impossible, and it is as well to be on the safe side.

All that is necessary to do is to suspend the barrels by a loop of string passed round the hook of the forward lump, and then to tap the right and left barrels in turn to make sure that they give out a clear metallic ring and not a dead sound.

The inside of the bore should be examined carefully for pitting and dents. Perhaps the easiest way of detecting a dent is to examine the outside of the barrel rather than the inside. To do this remove the barrels from the stock and hold them out just below the eye in a similar manner to that in which they would be held when looking down the bore. Now move the barrels about until some dark mass —the top edge of a window is excellent for the purpose— casts a shadow-like reflection on the barrels. It will be found that this reflection takes the form of a thin dark line running longitudinally along the uppermost part of the surface of the top barrel. If this line is foreshortened any dent which may happen to lie on it will immediately show as a break. If there is no such break, there is no dent on that particular longitudinal line. The barrels should then be revolved in turn until the dark line has been thrown on every portion of both barrels, when any dent which may exist will be noticed.

Sometimes the muzzle of a barrel is bulged all round ahead of the choke, and this is known as the "choke being lifted." Such lifting of the choke can be noticed at once by foreshortening a thin shadow in the manner which has just been described.

In order to see dents from the inside, look down the bore while holding the gun against the light and gradually manipulate the barrels by describing small circles with the hand which is holding them out. If there is a dent it will throw a shadow, which will appear as a dark spot, when the barrels are held in a suitable position in regard to the light and the eye.

Just as the barrels should be examined for pitting, so should the action be examined for corrosion. But if the only visible damage consists of pitting round the striker holes, and the gun is in otherwise good condition, this pitting can be safely assumed to be due to erosion caused by gas escapes, as was explained in Volume II, and can be ignored.

A very good guide as to the amount of use which a gun has had is the state of the chequering. If this has worn almost smooth it is a sure sign that the gun has seen a great deal of service, and the price should be correspondingly low.

It is, of course, possible for a gun to be re-chequered ; but this is not very likely to have been done unless the vendor is deliberately trying to " fake " the gun.

The Proof Marks should be examined carefully, and it is a safe rule not on any account to buy a gun which has not been Nitro Proved. Any dealer who knowingly sells a gun which has not been Nitro Proved and who fails to point this fact out to the purchaser is stepping over the border-line of honest dealing. So this is a point to which the purchaser should make a point of paying special attention. The whole matter of Proof Marks will be dealt with in Chapter XV, so I will say no more about them here beyond stating that they also indicate whether a barrel is true cylinder or has any degree of choke at the muzzle.

If the gun seems in every way satisfactory the only point that remains is the fit, and this can be tested roughly by putting the gun up to the shoulder and aiming at some mark. If the fit does not seem very far out the purchase can be made with confidence, and any alterations in fit which may be necessary can be carried out afterwards either by the original maker of the gun, or by any other competent fitter.

One final word of warning. There are many cases recorded of names of the leading makers being " forged."

That is, inferior guns have been spuriously engraved with names of famous makers who had nothing to do with the guns in question. And there have also been instances of ribs taken off old pairs of barrels by leading makers which have been put on the barrels of very cheap guns. The ribs carry the name of the maker of the original gun, and such a procedure can only be regarded as a deliberate forgery. The possibility of such things occurring emphasises the importance of consulting the alleged original maker if there is the slightest reason for suspicion.

CHAPTER XIV

CLEANING AND CARE OF GUNS

BY this time the reader will have been through every stage of choosing, buying and using his guns and cartridges ; and there only remains the problem of cleaning the guns after use. Although it takes but little time to clean a gun thoroughly this work is all too often neglected or else left to some servant who is, through no fault of his own, ignorant of what should be done.

In order to clean a gun properly a suitable outfit of appliances is essential. The cleaning outfits generally included in the cases of even the very highest grade guns are usually too crude for words. This is because gunmakers do not seem to have studied the question from the point of view of the shooter : the methods which gunmakers use themselves are very efficient but quite inapplicable to private life. Consequently the appliances usually sold show no advance of knowledge over that which prevailed in the early days of breech-loaders. In this respect the Americans are far ahead of us. The average American shooter takes more interest in the purely mechanical side of his guns and rifles than his " opposite number " in Great Britain, and American retailers cater for this interest. To the best of my belief the only firm in Great Britain which has specialised in the more scientific appliances for cleaning both shotguns and rifles is Messrs. Parker-Hale, Ltd., Bisley Works, Birmingham. If I am maligning other firms I can but apologise : but I have not seen the varicty of up-to-date appliances which Messrs. Parker-Hale invariably have in stock in either the shops or catalogues of any other firm.

Let us now see what appliances should be included in a proper outfit for cleaning shotguns.

CLEANING ROD. First comes the cleaning rod. The

ordinary wooden rods are quite satisfactory, but it is essential that the female screw at the end into which the various brushes, etc., screw should be of standard size. This is most important, as few things can be a greater nuisance than the inability to transfer any standard brush or other appliance to any particular rod. A shooter may be abroad and unable to get any brush except those with standard sized screws. It is, therefore, a great mistake to get any rod except one with a universal screw fitting.

A type of rod which is to my mind altogether superior is made by Messrs. Parker-Hale on the lines of a rifle cleaning rod. It is steel covered with celluloid, jointed in the middle. This joint is of very good design and better than the usual type of joint. These rods are not so bulky as wooden rods, stronger, and altogether neater to use.

It is wise not to economise in the number of rods, as it is a great convenience to have a different rod for every type of brush, etc., which is used and thus avoid the bother of unscrewing and screwing on different appliances to one rod. For this reason two rods should always be included in every gun case—there is seldom space for more—while half a dozen is not too many to have ready for use in the gun-cupboard. The initial cost is not heavy ; the rods will last for an almost indefinite number of years, and the convenience is great.

WIRE BRUSHES. I regard a wire brush as essential. It is sometimes argued that it scratches the bore. Theoretically I suppose it does ; but in practice it does not, provided a brass wire brush is used, which is much softer than the steel of the barrels. Theoretically again, brass is not a very suitable substance for a brush for cleaning firearms, because, during use, small particles of the brass will almost inevitably adhere to the bore : and this close contact between brass and steel is likely to set up electrolytic action which is conducive to the formation of rust. But in this matter I do not think we must be too pedantic in binding ourselves to theory, as there is no doubt that brass brushes have been used in innumerable firearms without causing any harm. Personally I have used brass brushes in my shotguns for years and I intend to continue their use.

The most common pattern is that known as the "Turk's Head" type, but a better kind is the "Payne-Gallwey" which consists of a number of flat circular brushes, the bristles of each radiating outwards from the centre, all fixed on one common stem, making a cylindrical brush about 2 inches in length.

Another excellent kind is an American invention, the "Marble" Cleaner. In this the circular brushes are mounted on a flexible stem which can be bent so as to bring extra pressure to bear on one side or another, which is a useful dodge when the brush begins to get worn.

LEATHER POLISHER. I believe this was first designed by the late Sir Ralph Payne-Gallwey. It is a most excellent device and corresponds to a leather lap for cleaning rifles, consisting of a number of circular leather discs fixed one in front of each other on a common stem.

JAG. This is a very important item as it carries the principal cleaning material. The form of jag depends on the material to be used. Gunmakers invariably use tow and this is well suited for the purpose as it is cheap and absorbent. It is, however, by no means easy to twist exactly the right amount of tow on to the jag. If there is too little the gun is not cleaned, and if there is too much there is risk of damaging the barrel. I fancy most shooters have seen some keeper cleaning a gun with tow and banging the end of the cleaning rod on the ground in order to push a lump of tow through the barrel which is really too big for the purpose. A shotgun barrel is a thin tube, and this is one of the easiest methods of bulging a barrel, and thus spoiling its shooting, that exists.

Consequently I would never advise the use of tow outside a gunmaker's shop. Flannel patches, similar to those used for cleaning rifles, are better for the actual cleaning, and much easier to manipulate.

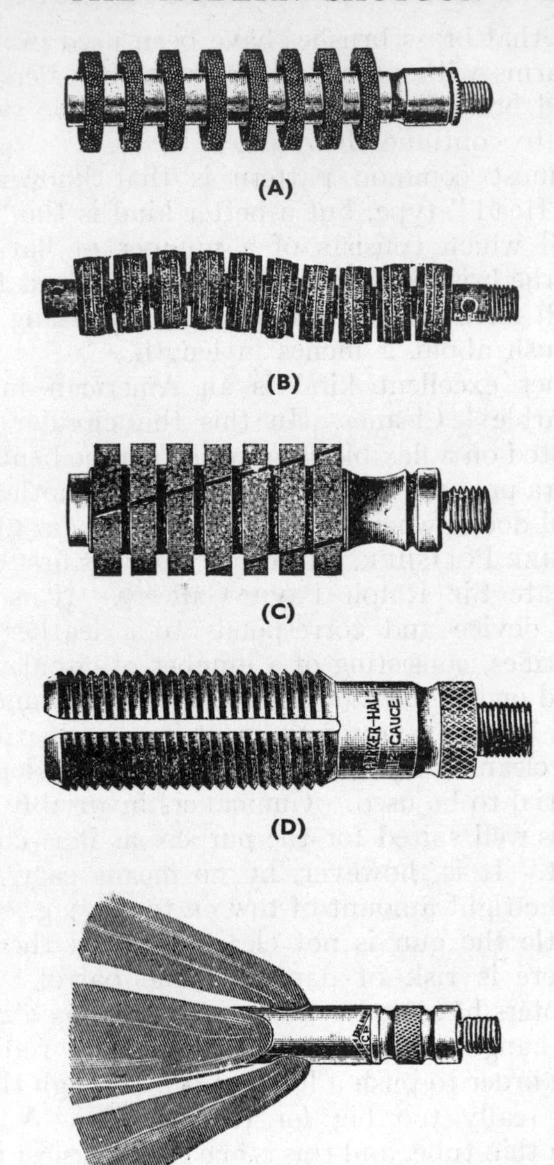

FIG. 30.—Cleaning appliances for Shotguns.

(A) "Payne-Gallwey" Brass Wire Brush. (B) Marble's Patent Cleaner. (C) "Payne-Gallwey" Leather Polisher. (D) Parker-Hale Jag for flannel Patches. (E) Loop Cleaner.

A jag of some sort is, however, necessary to carry the flannel patch, and the best type I know is Messrs. Parker-Hale's which is shown in Fig. 30 (D). One end of the flannel patch is inserted in the slot and the rest of the patch is than wrapped round the jag, thus making a perfectly cylindrical, resilient and absorbent surface which exactly fits the bore. The original jag of this type was made of brass, but later horn was substituted for brass, and this was a great improvement, as it is lighter than brass and cannot possibly injure the inside of the bore.

Messrs. Parker-Hale sell flannel patches of the right size for different bores; but it is much cheaper and just as good to make up one's own. The actual size of the patch must depend on the thickness of the flannel or flannelette. This latter material can be bought by the yard very cheaply, or one can cut up old flannel trousers, pyjamas, etc. Once the correct size has been found by experiment, a large number of patches can be cut up very quickly.

The patch should make a nice tight fit in the bore when wound round the jag, but should not be so tight as to require undue force in pushing it through.

At least two of these jags should be included in the outfit, and three or four are not too many, as it is useful to have spare jags at hand for using oily or dry patches as the occasion demands as well as to have one for carrying a patch covered with some abrasive paste.

Another useful type of jag is that shown in Fig. 30 (E), which is known as a "Loop Cleaner." The illustration explains the method of use, two long thin patches replacing the single patch wrapped round the Parker-Hale jag. This Loop Cleaner is a useful tool for drying out a barrel, or for smearing the inside of the bore with oil; but for general purposes the Parker-Hale jag is preferable.

A worn Payne-Gallwey wire brush makes a very useful jag, as quite a small flannel patch can be used wrapped round it.

BRISTLE BRUSH. A bristle brush of similar design to the Payne-Gallwey wire brush is a useful adjunct, but not an essential one. It is particularly handy for smearing the inside of the bore with thin oil.

MOP. The ordinary wool mop which is almost always included in the outfit supplied by a gunmaker is also useful but not essential. It can be used like the bristle brush for smearing thin oil inside the bore.

CHAMBER BRUSH. The chamber is of larger diameter than the bore and so requires a larger brush. One of the type shown in Fig. 31 is as good as any and is particularly useful for cleaning the rear ends of the chamber cones.

TOOTHBRUSHES. A couple of old toothbrushes should be carried in every gun case as they are invaluable for cleaning the outsides of the barrels, fore-end and action.

RAGS. At least two rags, one oily and one com-

FIG. 31.—Chamber Brush with Protector.

paratively clean and dry, should be carried in every gun case for wiping the gun over and drying it when wet. In course of time a dry rag will develop automatically into an oily one, but special oiled rags can be bought. These, however, are rather expensive, and it is quite easy to make a rag oily oneself. It is astonishing to see the amount of oil which a rag can absorb without becoming impregnated all over ; but if the rag is first moistened in petrol and a comparatively little oil is poured on the middle when the rag is spread out, the oil will be dissolved by the petrol and this oily solution become spread evenly all over the rag. If it is now left to dry the petrol will evaporate and leave the rag oily all over, but not dripping.

OILS. Cleaning oils are most important. In the days of black powder Rangoon oil was used universally, but chemistry has made advances since then. Generally speaking, two main types of oil are needed for cleaning guns: a very fine oil, and a very heavy one which can really be a grease.

A thin oil is essential for ordinary cleaning as a thick oil will not percolate right into the action and spread itself over smooth surfaces. But if a thin oil is left in the bores and the gun is kept standing in a cupboard for some time the oil will all drain downwards and leave the upper parts of the bores exposed. So for protection from the atmosphere a thick oil or grease is necessary.

In Volume II it was explained that the presence of an alkaline residue prevented the formation of rust, so it will be clear that an *alkaline* oil should be used if possible. Unfortunately it is not easy to procure a thin oil which is markedly alkaline, as chemically it is difficult to dissolve an alkali in an "oil." For this reason different samples of the same oil will frequently vary in their degree of alkalinity, and so it is not possible to say definitely that any particular oil is more alkaline than another. The only three oils which I know to be alkaline are B.S.A. "Kleenwell," Young's "·303 Cleaner" and Cogswell and Harrison's "Coswell." I think that there is little to choose between these three oils, and one or the other should certainly be selected.

All three of these are thin oils, but Wakefield's "Oilit" and the American "Three in One" are probably finer, and so a small tin of one of these last-mentioned two oils should also be included in the outfit, as a very fine oil is useful for the locks and action. Neither of these oils is alkaline, both giving neutral reactions.

There are various thick oils or greases between which there is little to choose. Young's "·303 Semi-Liquid Cleaner" and "Coswell" jelly are the only greases which, to my knowledge, are alkaline. Ordinary mineral jelly is excellent, and a good mixture can be made by melting some mineral jelly and adding either Young's or Kleenwell thin oil to the resulting fluid. This mixture should be well stirred and then left to cool, when a thick oil will be formed which has a slight alkaline tendency.

In India and neighbouring countries coco-nut oil can

be bought very cheap in the bazaars, and is an excellent preservative for firearms, as it solidifies at a very high temperature.

There are other kinds of preservatives for firearms sold, but I am inclined to pin my faith to those which have been mentioned. Some of these preservatives have a great affinity for water, being in reality nothing more than soft soap. Such substances must obviously be a danger in a damp climate, and so it is safer to use one of the greases suggested instead of anything of a soapy nature, which may be most useful for washing the hands but not quite so suitable for preserving a valuable gun.

ABRASIVE CLEANING PASTE. Some kind of abrasive paste is an essential item in any cleaning outfit since it provides the best, quickest and easiest means for removing metallic fouling (leading) from the bore.

At a pinch almost any comparatively mild abrasive will do. Powdered pumice, Monkey Brand soap, "Brasso," "Soldier's Friend": these will all answer the purpose. Their regular use, however, is not to be recommended, as from their very nature they have a pronounced polishing action which will in time wear away the steel of the barrel. For this reason powdered emery should never be used by amateurs.

There are three special abrasive pastes made for the very purpose of removing metallic fouling from rifles. These are "Motti" Paste, B.S.A. "Cunirid" and "Coswell" abrasive. Motti is the most active abrasive of the three; and Cunirid or "Coswell" is, therefore, the safer. These pastes are so mild that it is impossible to make any measurable effect on steel by their use.

The B.S.A. and Cogswell and Harrison also sell a much more potent abrasive known as "Polishing Paste." Confusion between it and Cunirid should be avoided as it is much more violent, being similar to jeweller's rouge. By its use it is quite possible to enlarge the bore of a gun or rifle in a very short time. It is of great value, in the hands of an expert, for polishing rifle barrels and making the bores absolutely parallel; or for purposely enlarging them slightly at a particular point. But the ordinary shooter will be wise to avoid it and pin his faith to Cunirid or the "Coswell" abrasive.

MAXWAX. And finally I think that some preparation is needed for maintaining the appearance of the stock. Linseed oil is useful, while any of the oils I have mentioned can be rubbed into the wood with varying advantage. But the best preparation I know is "Maxwax," which is sold in small tubes. It cannot be regarded as an essential, but its use does help to maintain the appearance of the stock and fore-end.

ORDINARY CLEANING AFTER USE

Having acquired a full complement of cleaning implements and appliances the shooter's next step is to use them.

Let us assume first of all that the gun has been used on a fine day when no complications have been produced by wet working its way into the mechanism.

On taking the gun to bits the first part which needs attention is the barrels, and in order to hold them more comfortably the fore-end should be snapped on.

The first step is to remove the powder residue which has been deposited more or less loosely in the bore. It is a pity to dirty a clean flannel patch unnecessarily and it is similarly a mistake to use a brush as the residue clings to the brush and makes it dirty. What would seem to be the best plan of all was suggested by a correspondent to the *Field* many years ago, and I would like to take this opportunity of expressing to him my gratitude for one of the most useful and practical tips I have ever been given.

This tip is to use bits of old newspaper. The paper can be torn up into pieces of a suitable size, which can very soon be found out by actual trial. One of these pieces of paper is then rolled up into a ball and merely pushed through the barrel, for which purpose a horn jag screwed to the end of a cleaning rod is best, as there is then no risk of scratching the bore. It does not matter in the least whether the paper is covered with print or not ; in fact the more print the better, as the ink acts as a mild lubricant. About three pieces will usually be enough for each barrel, after which all loose residue will have been removed.

Then scrub each barrel out well with a brass brush dipped in Young's or Kleenwell oil, and then wipe the barrel out dry with a flannel patch. The barrels should now be inspected. Quite possibly they will be quite clean, in which case they should be given a coating of oil by passing a bristle brush or flannel patch up and down each which has been well saturated with Young's, Kleenwell, or Coswell oil.

But if any signs of leading are seen further treatment is necessary. Leading always appears as longitudinal streaks in the bore, and the most usual places are just in front of the chamber cones and in the choke. It can sometimes be seen better from the muzzle end than the breech, so an inspection should be made from both ends of the barrel.

The best way of removing leading is by the use of Cunirid or Coswell mild abrasive paste. Some of this paste should be squeezed over the leather cleaner and the barrel well rubbed out with this. The paste in the bore must then be wiped out with a slightly oily patch and another examination made. If there are still some signs of leading left, the same treatment must be repeated. But one good scouring with Cunirid should remove all ordinary leading. After a time the leather cleaner will become so impregnated with Cunirid that fresh paste need only be smeared on very sparingly at comparatively rare intervals. If this cleaner is kept simply for this purpose its somewhat dirty appearance will not matter in the least.

Now remove all the Cunirid with a slightly oily patch, and then leave the barrels in oil as before.

If the process of cleaning is carried out in a study, or other living room, as it not infrequently is, a small cork bath mat should be kept handy on which to rest the muzzle end of the barrels when using a cleaning rod. This will protect both the barrels and the carpet.

Should the barrels be placed in a vice for cleaning they must be well padded with rag, and great care exercised to avoid denting them by clamping the vice too tightly.

The next step is to remove the fore-end from the barrels again, and brush it all over with a toothbrush dipped in Young's, Kleenwell, or Coswell oil, after which a few drops of either oil can be squirted into the slots in the rear end when the fore-end should be placed standing up, pointed end downwards, so as to allow this oil to percolate down into the ejector mechanism.

While the fore-end is so left attention can be paid to the action and stock. The face of the action should be well scrubbed with a toothbrush dipped in Young's, Kleenwell, or Coswell oil, and the rest of the action wiped over with an oily rag, special attention being paid to the knuckle and front ends of the cocking levers. A few drops of the same oil can be squirted into the action through the slots in the knuckle, past the action bolt, and past the triggers.

The outside of the barrels can now be given a wipe over with an oily rag, and a toothbrush dipped in oil run down along both sides of the upper and lower ribs. The extractors should be pulled out and a little oil squirted under the heads, after which the gun can either be put away in its case, or else assembled and placed in the rack in a cupboard.

Water Treatment. Provided British powders are used, all of which give an alkaline residue on combustion, the treatment which has been described is sufficient. But if a foreign powder is used it is advisable to pour some hot water down each barrel in order to dissolve the potassium chloride deposited by the cap and so prevent "after rusting." Cold water is just as efficacious, but hot water dries out more readily and so is more convenient. If this water treatment is adopted the use of paper for removing the worst of the fouling can be omitted, as the water will wash it away.

After water treatment the barrels should be dried out carefully with flannel patches.

In all other respects the procedure is the same as before.

If " Non-Rusting " caps are used this water treatment is unnecessary. And here it may be as well to issue a warning.

Because of the wonderful protection against all rusting provided by the best type of modern ·22 rim-fire rifle and pistol ammunition which have completely done away with any necessity for cleaning apart from that of removing leading in the barrel when it may have accumulated to too great an extent after several thousand rounds, there is a common belief that central fire cartridges with non-rusting caps afford a similar protection and that cleaning is unnecessary.

There can be no greater mistake. In a ·22 rim-fire cartridge the cap composition comprises about 33 per cent. of the total explosive charge. In a central-fire cartridge the cap composition comprises only about 1 per cent. of the total explosive charge. Consequently its influence is relatively slight compared to that exercised by the cap composition in a ·22 rim-fire cartridge. It will doubtless be suggested that the total explosive charge in a shotgun cartridge is much bigger than that in the ·22 and so the actual weights of cap composition do not differ so greatly. This is true up to a point. But the bore of a shotgun has a much larger area than that of a ·22 rifle, and for the same length of barrel the area of the surface of the bore is eleven times greater in the case of a 12-bore than in that of a ·22. All that the central-fire non-rusting cap does, or can do, is to remove the danger of " after rusting." It affords no protection against ordinary rusting to which all ordinary iron and low chrome steels are liable. And unless the bore of a barrel is properly cleaned and protected against ordinary atmospheric rusting that barrel will run grave risk of suffering irreparable damage sooner or later.

CLEANING AFTER A WET DAY

Cleaning after shooting in heavy rain calls for extra care and special precautions, as wet has a wonderful way of working right into the action.

One of the principal places of entry is the knuckle. Rain runs down the barrels and percolates between the fore-end and the barrels and thence down through the slots in the knuckle into the action. Theoretically the fore-end should fit so tightly to the barrels that no moisture can get past. But in practice a certain amount of play is inevitable, as it is absolutely necessary for the fore-end to be taken off and put on with ease, and this prevents a completely water-tight fit.

But wet also works into the action through the slots in the bar and past the action bolt every time the gun is opened for loading or unloading. And another means of entry is past the triggers.

Thus it happens that the following precautions should be adopted in cleaning *in addition* to the procedure which has already been described.

Let us begin with the action.

The first step should be to shake out as much moisture as possible through the slots in the knuckle. This can be done by holding the stock and jerking the action downwards : and it is surprising to see the amount of wet which can sometimes be shaken out by this means.

The next step is to remove the locks. If the gun is fitted with Hand Detachable Locks this is easy, and it is really almost as simple in the case of side locks. I have dealt with the removal of locks in Volume I, and so will but state now that if any sportsman doubts his ability to remove the locks he had certainly better not try. But it is really a most simple proceeding, the only training necessary being ability to use a turn-screw without burring the slots in the heads of the screws.

If the locks are removed they should be carefully wiped over and placed in some warm spot to dry.

As much of the action as can be reached should now

K*

be wiped and then the whole stock should be placed with the locks in a warm spot. But the spot should not be too warm—inside a hot cupboard for example—or there is risk of warping the wood.

The fore-end should next be treated in a similar manner, that is, well shaken to get rid of all movable wet, and then wiped over and put with the locks and stock to dry.

The most important places to which attention must be paid in the barrels are the ribs and extractors. Wet can be most easily removed from the crevices on each side of the ribs by running an edge of blotting-paper along them. They should then be well brushed from breech to muzzle with a toothbrush which will carry any remaining drops of moisture along with it.

The extractors should certainly be removed. This is very simple, all that is necessary being the removal of the stop-pin which will be found in the bottom of the forward lump, as has been explained in Volume I. When the stop-pin has been unscrewed the extractors can be taken out. They should be wiped all over, and then the barrels and the loose extractors and the stop-pin should be placed with the stock, locks and fore-end to dry out. The stop-pin and the pins which hold the locks had better all be put together in the lid of a tin, or in some small tray or saucer, as there is risk of losing them otherwise.

The next morning every part of the gun and mechanism should be well oiled, and the locks treated with a little Oilit or Three in One, after which the whole gun can be reassembled, and the stock and fore-end well rubbed with Maxwax.

It should be realised that it is really of great importance to give the different parts of the mechanism every chance to dry out, and that they will get a much better chance if left separately all night in some warm corner, than they would were the gun put together or even put away in its case.

Even if the locks are not removed the stock should

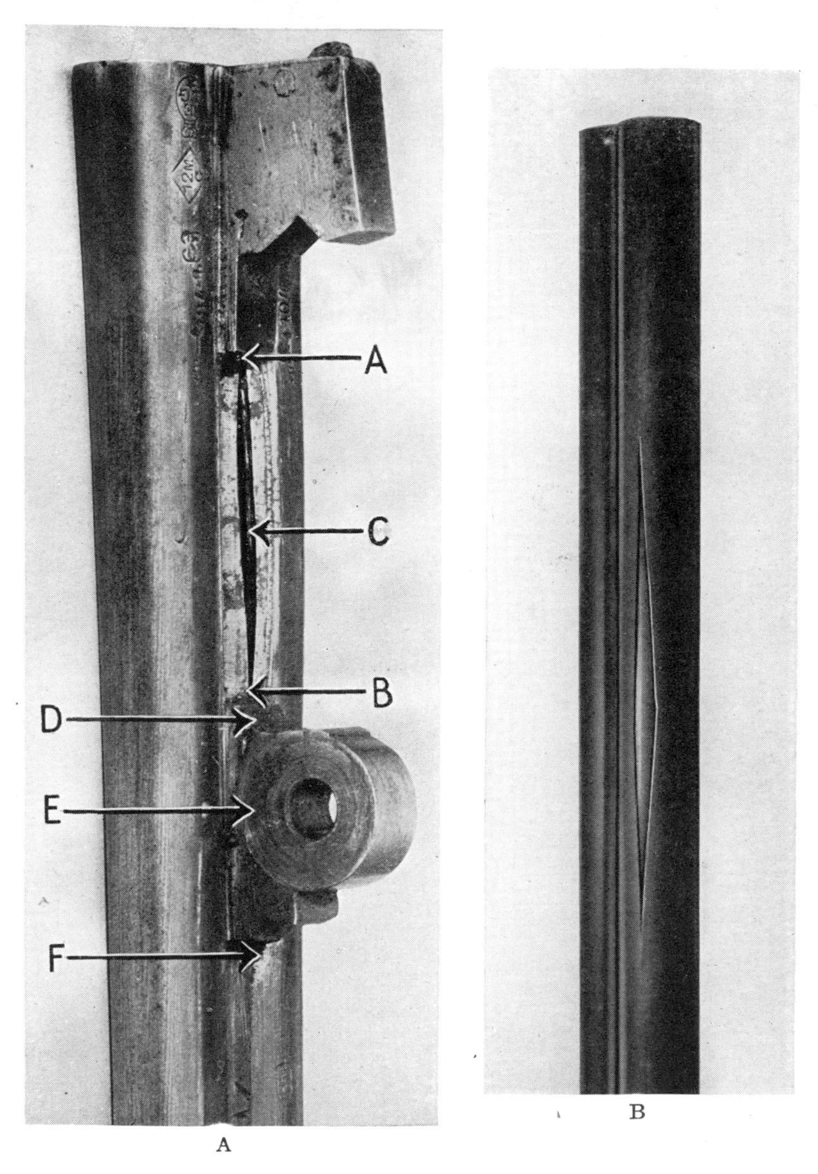

(A) A .410-bore Gun which burst owing to a flaw in the Right Barrel

(B) A 12-bore Gun which burst owing to a flaw in the Right Barrel

be left to dry all night, as the moisture will then have a chance to evaporate out through the slots in the knuckle.

It is for this reason that I am inclined not to regard a solid knuckle as such an unqualified advantage. It is true that less moisture gets into the action of a gun in which the knuckle is solid. But moisture will always work in past the action bolt, the triggers, and under the lever; and the slots in the knuckle help it to get *out* again by evaporation, especially if the locks are not removed.

By the exercise of a little care an action can be rendered much more than normally waterproof. If the weather looks threatening the upper part of the fore-end which comes into contact with the barrels should be smeared generously with mineral jelly, vaseline, or Young's Semi-Liquid Cleaner before starting out. Dollops of the same grease should be put into the slots in the knuckle, and as much grease as possible put on the lumps of the barrels. When the gun is closed this grease will be forced past the action bolt, and will help to make a waterproof barrier.

The outside of the gun should then be carefully wiped over to remove any superfluous grease or oil. A little petrol on a dry rag is a great help in getting the outside of the gun, including the stock, absolutely free from oil, which is important as an oily gun marks one's clothes.

PUTTING A GUN AWAY FOR THE SEASON

Cleaning a gun before putting it away at the end of a season, or for any period of more than a couple of months, presents a slightly different problem from cleaning it when it is to be used again in the course of a few days. In the latter case a thin oil is all that is necessary; but in the former a thick oil or grease is preferable because it is not prone to drain downwards and leave the upper surfaces on which it was applied exposed to the air. But in addition to smearing the inside of the bores with one of the greases mentioned either by means of a bristle brush or a flannel patch, the outsides of all metal parts—barrels, action and fore-end—should be smeared with a toothbrush dipped in the same thick oil or grease which was used for the bores.

There is, however, one precaution which I think is sound. This is, to clean out both barrels inside with hot water first. When using powders which leave an alkaline deposit or cartridges with "Non-Rusting" caps this step is probably unnecessary. Nevertheless, it is so little extra trouble that I would strongly advise all sportsmen to take it, as the water will remove any trace of potassium chloride deposit and there will then be no risk whatever of "after rusting," a risk which may always be present if a gun is left indefinitely in a damp climate without periodic inspections.

It is a good plan to let the barrels dry out all night after the water treatment before applying the grease, although it is really quite easy to dry them with flannel patches.

If the gun is put away in its case wrap the action in a greasy rag.

I do not believe in baize covered barrel rods. They get damp very easily, and many a barrel has been rusted by their use.

COMPRESSION OF ACTION SPRINGS

Many sportsmen make a great point of snapping off the locks of their guns so as to release the mainsprings; but they usually forget all about the ejector springs, which are left in a permanent state of compression. The truth of the matter is that it is really no more necessary to release the main or ejector springs of a gun than it is to release the springs of a watch. The loss in strength owing to compression is negligible, even after many years.

But if any shooter feels happier when his springs are released there is no reason why he should not ease the ejector springs as well as the mainsprings.

The mainsprings can be released by pressing the triggers. If the gun is in pieces it is better to hold the face of the action against a block of wood, or an old book, when snapping off, so as to give the strikers something fairly hard on which to fall. If the gun is assembled snap caps, or dummy cartridges, had better be employed.

The ejector springs present a more difficult problem. In the great majority of actions the simplest way of releasing them is to remove the fore-end while the gun is still in the open position after the snap caps have been ejected. The barrels can then be taken from the stock in the ordinary way. It must be remembered, however, that if this is done the ejector tumblers must be re-cocked before the gun can be put together again. To do this the fore-end should be slipped into position on the barrels alone, when it will be found that the extractor heads are protruding beyond the breech end of the barrels because they are held in their extreme rearward position by the ejector tumblers, which are now in the " fired," or " uncocked," position. The barrels should now be gripped firmly in both hands and the extractor heads pressed down on some wooden surface, such as a table, until a click is heard which denotes the cocking of the ejector tumblers. The extractor heads will then lie flush with the breech of the barrels, and if the fore-end is removed the gun can be put together in the usual way.

Should it ever be necessary to perform this operation in the actual shooting field in order to remove a cartridge-case which has overridden the extractor, the extractor heads can be pressed against the side of the heel of one's boot. Incidentally a turn-screw to fit the stop-pin should always be available, either as an implement in a shooting knife or else carried in the cartridge bag. It may never be wanted, but there is no harm in having one handy.

If the ejector springs are released the gun obviously cannot be put away assembled, but must be kept in its case. Nor will it be possible to keep the fore-end in position on the barrels, since the ejector heads will be protruding. So the fore-end should be wrapped in an oily rag and put in its proper compartment.

PERIODIC OVERHAULS

Of all the precautions which should be adopted for the care and preservation of guns the most important is to send them back to some competent gunsmith, preferably the maker, for periodic overhauls. It is impossible to emphasise this too strongly. The frequency with which such overhauls ought to be carried out cannot be definitely stated, as so much must depend on the care with which guns are treated by their owners. It is a safe rule to make a point of sending one's guns back to the makers at the end of every shooting season, when they will be stripped, examined for any signs of incipient rusting, and thoroughly cleaned up. After a wet season especially this complete stripping is most important, as corrosion, or rust, *can* be set up in the actions of the best-cared-for guns. If, however, it is taken in time no harm will be done: but once it has become established it is very likely to recur even after cleaning because the original polished surface of the metal will have become roughened by the corrosion; and corrosion will start again more readily on a slightly rough surface than on one which is perfectly smooth.

Some years ago I saw a best grade gun in which the right lock had become so clogged with rust that the strength of the striker blow was seriously impaired. This had produced faulty ignition which in its turn had resulted in failure of the gases produced by the incomplete combustion of the powder to expel the shot charge from the barrel; and when the next round was fired the barrel burst—happily without damaging the shooter. This was a clear case of cause and effect, and although admittedly an extreme one, it does help to indicate the importance of keeping the mechanism free from rust. It is true that if the locks had been taken off periodically as I have suggested this rusting would not have occurred, at any rate to the same extent. Nevertheless, if the owner of the gun had sent it up to the makers periodically for overhauling the rust could not have become so deep rooted.

Another, and even more insidious, place where rust can, and does, set in is under the ribs. As was explained in Volume I, the ribs are soldered to the barrels. It not infrequently happens in course of time that a particle of solder becomes detached and drops off, leaving a tiny hole. Moisture gets into this hole and rusting sets in all unsuspected. I have seen a gun, which had otherwise been carefully looked after, in which the wall of one barrel was so weakened by rust that it burst. So the danger is real.

A gunmaker can detect the presence of any moisture under the rib quite easily, first by rubbing the outside of the barrels with a little water which is all dried off, and then by warming the barrels gently in the flame of a bunsen burner. If any wet has got in under the rib it will be seen to issue from the entry hole as steam.

This test should on no account be undertaken by an amateur in spite of its seeming simplicity, as it is easy to overheat the barrels and make the solder run.

If any hole in the jointing of the ribs is detected both ribs should be taken off, and the barrels cleaned out underneath, after which the ribs can be re-soldered in position.

In this connection it can be mentioned that it is quite possible to get "Ribless" guns, that is guns in which the top and bottom ribs are omitted altogether. At first sight such guns look rather peculiar, but that is probably because one is not accustomed to their appearance. The barrels are held together by the usual packings which were described in Volume I, and so a rag can easily be passed between them and they can thus be dried very easily. Although ribless guns have been made for very many years, they have never become generally popular, in spite of certain quite definite advantages ; and to the best of my belief Messrs. Alexander Martin are now the only firm that make such guns as a regular feature.

Another, and very common, injury to barrels is through dents. The wall of a shotgun barrel is very thin, and is dented easily by a tap against any hard substance.

Shooting-sticks probably cause more dents in a single year than everything else put together: but there are other causes: a knock against the door of a car when getting in or out; the clinking together of two pairs of barrels when the guns are carried over shoulders—how often one of two men turns suddenly round and the two guns touch; a fall owing to the gun being left leaning up against a wall. These are all everyday causes of dents.

Once I left my gun carefully in a car with some others during lunch, and on my return to the car I noticed that my gun was not in the position in which I had left it. I concluded that some keepers or beaters had been examining the guns, and at once looked along the barrels. Sure enough I spotted a brand-new dent.

After this experience I have always been careful to keep my gun in sight during lunch, or else to put it in some place where it cannot be interfered with—lying on the floor or ground if possible, as it cannot then fall down.

Whenever I handle a friend's gun I always make a point of looking for dents, and if the season is well advanced I usually find a dent or dents in almost one out of every three guns I examine. And these dents are invariably quite unsuspected by the owners of the guns.

The easiest way of detecting dents has already been explained in the last chapter, and so I will now only urge the importance of getting them removed with the least possible delay.

A dent in the outside of a barrel means a small lump sticking up on the inside; and every shot that is fired helps to wear this lump down. This makes the barrel thinner at the site of the dent and thus weakens the barrel. This weakening is probably very slight: its extent must depend on the depth of the dent and the number of shots that are fired between the dent being formed and removed. Even so, any unnecessary weakening is a pity, not to say a mistake. Besides, a dent can spoil the patterns. So from every point of view the fewer shots that are fired after a dent has been detected the better, while the workman who actually raises the dent will have a better chance of making a perfect job.

Dents are raised by inserting a tapered plug down the barrel until its further movement is stopped by the dent pressing on the taper. The workman then taps just round the dent very gently with a small hammer, and gradually eases the plug farther along the bore, tapping all the time, until the dent is finally raised completely.

The barrels are not the only part of a gun which can be dented as the wood of the stock can suffer in the same way. And although such bruises in no way affect the shooting they mar the appearance of a nice gun. One of the commonest causes of dents in stocks is carrying the gun under the arm with a cartridge bag hanging on the same side as the gun is carried. The buckles on the cartridge bag dent the stocks. For this reason one friend of mine always has the buckles of his cartridge bags covered with deer skin, and this precaution has reduced the damage to his gun stocks to a surprising extent.

The cost of an overhaul of a pair of guns in which attention is paid to the points I have mentioned is comparatively trifling, and is money well laid out. Personally I always regard the cost of an annual overhaul as a kind of insurance premium against worse calamities. And as explained in Volume I it is a good plan to have the side plates re-varnished every other year as the varnish helps to keep the beautiful blue mottling of the case hardening, which wears away in course of time.

A more costly attention is a general re-blueing ; but this should not be needed very often, and most guns will last from five to ten years before this is necessary.

A very important repair which will inevitably become necessary in course of time if a gun is used a lot is the tightening up of the action. It is always better to take this in time, as looseness begets looseness, and a gun which is " off the face " can be a real source of danger as will be seen in Chapter XVI.

A gun with a separate action pin, or cross-pin as it is also termed, can be tightened up and the barrels brought right back on to the face quite easily by the insertion of a somewhat thicker cross-pin. But in guns with a solid action the work is much more difficult. A method commonly adopted is to dovetail a new hook into the forward lump, but probably a better method is to weld a small lining to the hook by electric welding. But neither of these two methods is as good as the insertion of a new cross-pin.

GUN COVERS AND CASES

A canvas gun cover is a most useful protection to a gun when one is carried in a car, and one such cover should be allotted to every gun. Plain canvas cases which have no leather piping or muzzle caps are the best, as they can be turned inside out to dry after being out in the wet.

The gun case itself is a very important item in the whole outfit. It should be strong enough to protect the gun, or guns, from any blow or fall during a journey, and for this reason I myself am strongly in favour of the old-fashioned solid leather-covered oak case, especially if the owner is likely to go abroad. These cases are admittedly heavy, and somewhat bulky ; but they are very strong. The most modern cases are much smaller, neater in appearance, lighter and altogether more compact. They are delightful for carrying guns by car, and in this respect are superior in every way to the old Leg of Mutton leather cases. But they lack the solid rigidity and capacity for protection afforded by the leather and oak case, as well as the space inside for an adequate cleaning outfit. The ideal arrangement would seem to be a small modern case for travelling by car, and a solid old-fashioned one for serious journeys.

But I am indebted to Lieut.-General Sir Philip Neame for a most economical alternative. This is to have for normal use a light and compact leather case without any wooden foundation ; and for railway journeys, etc., an outer wood case which can be made of ply-wood for lightness. This is strong enough; and as the initial cost is but 20s. to 30s. it can be renewed both cheaply and easily if damaged.

HOW TO PUT A GUN TOGETHER

It is a common sight to see a sportsman struggling to put a gun together, especially if it be a weapon to which he is not accustomed. Undue force is frequently used, and burred, or otherwise damaged, lumps are often the result. Keepers are often bad offenders in this respect. It is not easy to advocate any exact method of procedure as being right, as ideal results can be obtained by slightly different means. It is, however, quite possible to quote definite faults which should be avoided. The most common of these are to hold the barrels too far down and to hold them at too acute an angle with the stock when trying to hook the forward lump on to the knuckle.

If the barrels are held too far down it is impossible to maintain full control over the breech end and so fit the lumps into position with certainty instead of by chance.

When the barrels are held nearly at right angles to the stock the hook will not fit into position.

The principles which should always be followed are first to grip the barrels well up by the breech end; secondly, to hold them so that they make a distinctly obtuse angle with the stock; and thirdly, once the hook is felt to engage, to try to pull the barrels apart from the stock. If the hook has not actually caught no harm is done, while if it has caught this movement automatically helps to close the gun.

It is also a good plan to press the action lever over while hooking on the barrels so as to give the lumps every chance to slip into the slots in the action. And the stock should be pressed against the right forearm (assuming it is held in the right hand) and thus steadied.

If the barrels are held too near the breech with the left hand the flesh can be pinched in a painful manner when the gun is closed. So it is as well to be careful in this respect. The photographs in Plate XXI show the wrong way to try to put a gun together, as well as one of the right ways.

CHAPTER XV

THE PROVING OF GUNS

THROUGHOUT all three volumes recurring references have been made to the Proving of Guns, Proof, and the Rules of Proof. It is now time, therefore, that this most important subject should be explained.

All sportsmen are probably aware that every firearm manufactured in Great Britain must be " proved " before it leaves the maker's hands. This is to ensure that the weapon should be capable of withstanding a considerably higher stress than any it would be likely to undergo in ordinary sporting use ; and the proving of arms thus provides that a weapon must be made with a margin of safety sufficient for all normal and practical requirements. Thus it will be realised that the proving of arms not only safeguards the user of the weapon, but also helps the manufacturer, as it satisfies him that the weapon he sells is as reliable as can humanly be expected.

But the proving of arms has another advantage, as it sets up a definite standard for strength which every weapon must withstand. Provided a weapon can pass this standard it can be regarded as being sufficiently strong, and consequently the makers are enabled to reduce the weights of the barrels more than would be possible were no definite standard established. In America, where there is no official proof, weapons are generally heavier and clumsier than British, bore for bore and charge for charge ; and this is possibly because the American manufacturers have no definite standard to which to work. In their own interests, therefore, they err on the side of safety.

In Great Britain weapons are all officially proved before being issued, and the manufacturers know that any gun or rifle which they make, and which has passed the severe test of proof, is sufficiently strong; so they are able to vary the weights of their arms without any misgivings as to safety in use.

The official proving of firearms dates back to the reign of Charles I. The Gunmakers' Company was founded in 1637, and the circumstances in which it had its origin may be gathered from the following extract from the Company's Charter, which states:

"That divers blacksmiths and others inexpert in the art of gunmaking had taken upon them to make, try, and prove guns after their unskilful way, whereby the trade was not only much damnified, but much harm and danger through such unskilfulness had happened to His Majesty's subjects."

It was for the reformation of these evils that the Charter in question was applied for and granted; and in this manner the official proving of arms was placed in the hands of the Gunmakers' Company, now an old Company of the City of London, which has carried it out ever since.

With the rise of Birmingham as an industrial centre the gunmakers of that city found it inconvenient always to have to send their weapons to London to be proved, so they petitioned the Government that they should be allowed to set up a Proof House of their own on the same lines as that conducted by the London gunmakers.

This petition was granted in 1813, and in that year the Birmingham Proof House came into being. As there was no City Company of Gunmakers in Birmingham similar to that which existed in London, the control of the Birmingham Proof House was made over to representatives of the City who were known as the Guardians of the Birmingham Proof House. These Guardians have always, and very rightly, included amongst their number members of the Birmingham gun trade; and it is also a fact that the Chairman of the Guardians is almost invariably a Birmingham gunmaker.

But although the names may be slightly different the methods are similar, because both the London and

Birmingham Proof Houses use the same Rules, Regulations and Scales of Proof. And the actual routine of each Proof House is under the supervision of an official known as the Proof Master, who is appointed and paid by the Gunmakers' Company and Guardians respectively.

One frequently hears claims to the effect that such and such a test has been carried out in the "Government Proof House." This description is quite inaccurate, as neither Proof House is a Government organisation in any way beyond the fact that it owes its existence to an Act of Parliament.

Incidentally no greater tribute can be paid to the Gun Trade than the very fact that for more than three centuries they have regulated and controlled the proving of arms which are made in this country so efficiently that the English Proof Marks have attained a high value in the minds of users of firearms, and are recognised with confidence all over the world.

For purposes of Proof all Small Arms are classified into ten classes as follows:

FIRST CLASS. Single-barrelled Muzzle-loading Arms of Smooth Bore.

SECOND CLASS. Double-barrelled Muzzle-loading Arms of Smooth Bore.

THIRD CLASS. Muzzle-loading Rifled Arms.

FOURTH CLASS. Breech-loading Arms of Smooth Bore.

FIFTH CLASS. Breech-loading Rifled Arms, including Express Rifles, declared for use with Black Powder only.

SIXTH CLASS. Breech-loading Rifles, declared for use with Nitro Powders, not being of the Seventh, Eighth and Tenth Classes.

SEVENTH CLASS. Breech-loading Rifled Arms chambered to take a Military Small Arm Cartridge, and not being of the Tenth Class.

EIGHTH CLASS. Breech-loading Rifled Arms specially constructed for use with Shot and Bullet, having the whole, or a portion only, of their bore rifled, and not being of the Fifth Class.

Ninth Class. Revolving Arms and Repeating and Automatic Pistols.

Tenth Class. Breech-loading Rifled Military Arms.

A study of these classifications will show that only two Classes affect us now, namely the Fourth Class, which includes all ordinary shotguns, and the Eighth Class, which includes Ball and Shot guns.

Both these types of guns are all submitted to two different kinds of Proof, but before we consider these it will be best to go back a few years. Previous to 1925 all ordinary sporting guns of British manufacture were submitted to three different types of Proof; namely, Provisional Proof, Definitive Proof and Nitro Proof; and it is interesting to see exactly what these different stages in the proving of guns mean.

Provisional Proof. This is the gunmaker's proof and is applied to the barrels of all weapons before any serious work is started, the object being to save the gunmaker from spending money and work on a faulty tube or barrel, as this Provisional Proof should detect any flaw in the material.

The barrel, or tube, is proved without being attached to any action. In order to render it possible to fire a charge in a tube the latter is fitted with a plug which screws into the breech end. In this plug there is a "touch hole" similar to those which used to be made in muzzle-loading cannon. The plug is screwed home, the proof charge inserted, and the touch hole primed with powder. The barrel is then laid on the ground, and the charge is fired by means of a trail of powder. For purposes of convenience a number of barrels are proved simultaneously, all being fired by the same trail.

If the barrel withstands the proof charge it is examined and, if passed as being satisfactory, a mark, known as a "Proof Mark," is then impressed on the barrel to show that this test has been made.

Definitive Proof. This Proof was applied to the finished arm. As a matter of fact guns are usually, as was explained in Volume I, sent up for Definitive Proof while still "in the white." From the point of view of safety, however, the gun is in its finished state. The Definitive Proof used to comprise, prior to 1925, testing both barrels of the gun in turn with a charge of special black powder known as T.P. (Tower Proof) powder, and if the test was passed the gun was viewed. Then, all being well, certain Proof Marks and View Marks were impressed on both barrels, while the View Mark was also impressed on the action. The presence of these various marks showed that the gun had passed satisfactorily the test which the two Proof Houses considered necessary before it could be used with safety.

NITRO PROOF. This test was introduced in 1896 and was an *optional* Proof in that it was not legally compulsory. This Proof put a somewhat greater breech strain on the gun than did the Definitive Proof, and its purpose was to test guns which were intended to be used with the then new nitro powders. This Nitro Proof was not compulsory, because in the early days of nitro powders many guns were sold which were not intended for use with these powders. By 1906, however, the use of nitro powders had become quite general, and consequently the majority of guns were declared for use with nitro powders, as the Rules of Proof laid down that they should be when submitted for Proof. So after this date almost all high-grade guns received Nitro Proof in addition to Definitive Proof, and their barrels were impressed with special Marks to indicate that this test had been carried out successfully.

It may seem that these two Proofs were hardly necessary; but it should be realised that they differed materially one from the other. For example, Definitive Proof for an ordinary 12-bore shotgun firing a 2½-inch cartridge was given by 178 grains of T.P. (Tower Proof) powder, which was a powder of about the same violence as Curtis and Harvey's No. 6 Black Powder. The Nitro Proof, on the other hand, was given by 116 grains of a powder known as T.S.2. This latter powder gave a higher *breech* pressure than did the T.P. powder; but the

T.P. powder, on account of its greater charge, gave a higher *barrel* pressure.

The reason for the two Proofs lay in the fact that the quicker a powder burns the greater the pressure at the breech, and many nitro powders were inclined to burn so quickly as to set up a high *breech pressure.* Some powders, especially those of the more progressive types, burn more slowly ; and these do not create such a high pressure at the breech or in the chamber, but *maintain a higher pressure farther up the barrel.* It was difficult to make one powder which developed maximum pressures both at the breech and well up the barrel, and consequently two different powders were used so that every barrel was tested for a considerable factor of safety both at the breech and all the whole way up its length by the combination of the Definitive and Nitro Proofs, while the *action* was tested more severely by the Nitro Proof.

In 1925, however, a very important change was made by combining these two Proofs into one. This was effected by using a new powder known as T.S.P., and now there are only two Proofs, namely Provisional and Definitive.

The present Provisional Proof is similar to that which was carried out prior to 1925, and the Proof Marks are the same. But the new Definitive Proof is a more severe test than either the old Definitive Proof or the optional Nitro Proof, because the new T.S.P. powder gives a higher breech pressure than the old T.S.2, and a slightly higher barrel pressure than the old T.P.

Since 1925 the Marks impressed on the barrels and action of a gun are really the combination of the old Definitive and Nitro Proof Marks, but in addition the bore *and the length of the cartridge-case* is also impressed on each barrel.

From this it will be realised that an examination of the Proof Marks on a barrel will show whether those barrels, and presumably the gun to which they belong, were made before or after 1925. The actual Proof Marks for Definitive Proof since 1925 are the same as the two sets of Proof Marks for both Definitive and Nitro Proof prior to 1925; but on a barrel made since 1925 the length of the cartridge-case is added as well. If the length of the cartridge-case is not included in the Proof Marks it can be concluded that that pair of barrels, and probably the gun to which they belong, were made before 1925.

PROOF MARKS

Let us now see what the various Proof and View Marks are.

PROVISIONAL PROOF. The Marks denoting Provisional Proof are:

London Proof House

The letters "G P" interlaced in a cypher surmounted by a Lion Rampant, thus:

On arms of English make. On arms of Foreign make.

Birmingham Proof House

The letters "B P" interlaced in a cypher surmounted by a Crown, thus:

On arms of English make. On arms of Foreign make.

DEFINITIVE PROOF. The Marks denoting Definitive Proof are:

London Proof House

The Proof Mark, being the letters "G P" interlaced in a cypher surmounted by a Crown, and the View

Mark, being the letter " V " surmounted by a Crown, thus:

On arms of English make. On arms of Foreign make.

The letters " N P " surmounted by an Arm Dexter in Armour, embowered, holding a Scimitar, thus:

On arms of English make. On arms of Foreign make.

Birmingham Proof House

The Proof Mark, being the letters " B P " surmounted by a Crown, and the View Mark, being the letters " B V " surmounted by a Crown, thus:

On arms of English make. On arms of Foreign make.

The letters " N P " surmounted by a Crown, thus:

On arms of English make.

On arms of Foreign make.

In addition to the Proof Marks shown above the following Marks are also impressed on the barrel by both Proof Houses:

The words " Nitro Proof " with the weight of the maximum Service Charge of shot to be used in conjunction with the standard powder charge, as, for example

NITRO PROOF $1\frac{1}{8}$

Also the nominal gauge and length of cartridge-case, as for example

OTHER PROOF MARKS. In the case of any barrel in which there is any construction at the muzzle the word " CHOKE " must be impressed on the breech end of the barrel.

It will be realised that when this word is seen among the Proof Marks on a barrel it means that the barrel is bored with some degree of choke, the actual amount is not in any way specified, as it might afterwards be altered.

It may be of interest to record here a brief history of how this " CHOKE " Proof Mark came into being. Following the invention of choke boring some new Rules of Proof were issued in October, 1875. In those days it was common practice for sportsmen abroad to use their shotguns, which, it must be remembered, were built appreciably heavier than guns of the present day, for close-quarter work on big game when they were loaded with spherical ball. In fact a mould for spherical ball was quite an ordinary implement in a standard outfit of tools sold with a gun. Naturally a 12-bore gun was accompanied by a 12-bore mould, and equally naturally it never entered any shooter's head to think of using any size of ball except one of the same gauge as his gun.

But the invention of choke changed this easy state of affairs, for no longer could a 12-bore ball be fired in a 12-bore gun. Accordingly, in the 1875 Rules of Proof it was laid down that any barrel which was choked to any degree at all was to be impressed with the words "NOT FOR BALL." In addition to this warning Marks were impressed indicating the *degree* of choke, thus:

12B { indicating that the bore was 12 gauge while
14M { the muzzle was but 14 gauge.

As time went on choke became almost universal, while the limitations of the use of ball which it imposed became generally understood. So when the next Rules of Proof were issued in December, 1887, the Marks indicating that a barrel was choked were changed. The figures giving the gauge at the muzzle end were omitted altogether, and so there was nothing to show the *degree* of choke, while the words "NOT FOR BALL" were replaced by the single word "CHOKE."

This was both simpler and more practical, since it permitted the degree of choke in a barrel to be changed without vitiating the meaning of the Proof Mark (unless, of course, the barrel was bored out to true cylinder—a very rare alteration) and has remained in force ever since.

Ball and Shot Guns. Barrels which are rifled through their full length are marked with the letters "S & B" signifying Shot and Bullet.

On barrels which are choke-bored with the choke rifled, the word "CHOKE" is preceded by the letter "R", signifying Rifled Choke, as for example "R CHOKE."

On barrels which have been proved for larger Service Charges of powder than those used in ordinary standard cases, the Service Charges are also impressed, in drams or grains, as may be considered most suitable, as for example

4 DR. OR 109 GR.

PLATE XV

(A) A photo-micrograph showing the flaw in the barrel shown in Plate XIV (A) taken at 100 diameters.

(B), (C) and (D) Photo-micrographs showing the grain in the steel of gun barrels taken at 100 diameters.

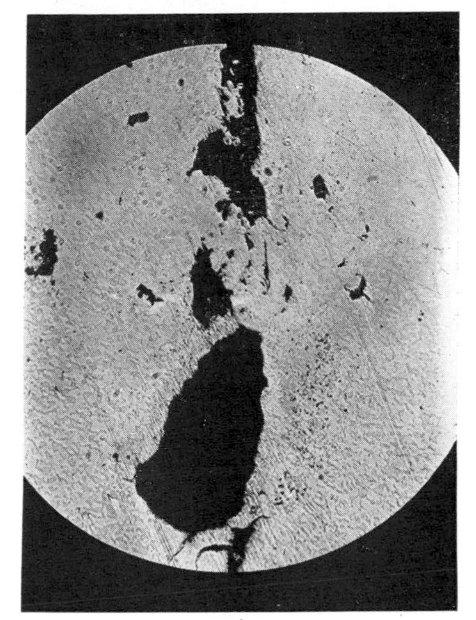

A

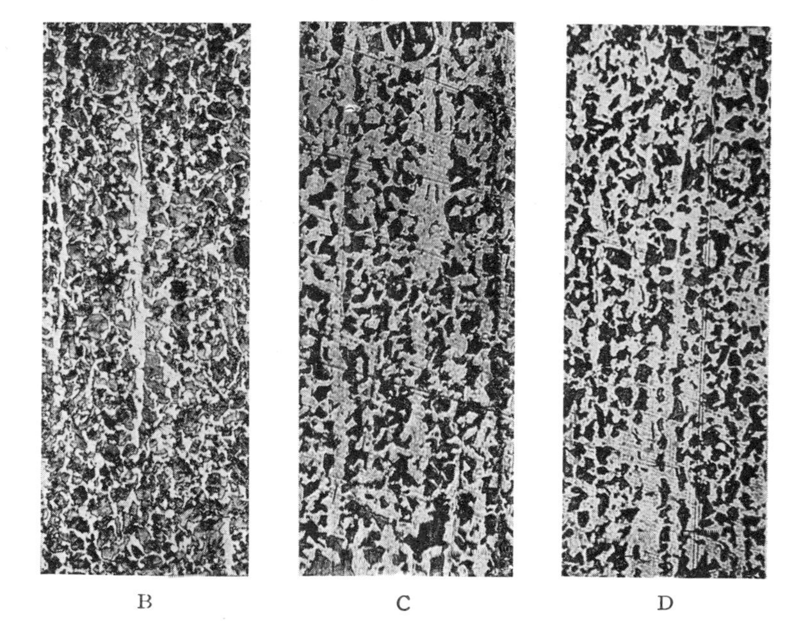

B C D

SIZE OF BORE, OR GAUGE. The Gauge Size of every barrel is also impressed with the other Proof Marks. From 4 to 10 Gauge inclusive the Gauges are divided into three parts, and the barrels are marked accordingly. Thus the divisions of 8 Gauge would be marked 8, $\frac{8}{1}$, or $\frac{8}{2}$, according to the size. From 11 to 17 Gauge inclusive the Gauges are divided into two parts, and so the divisions of 12 Gauge are 12 and $\frac{12}{1}$.

The Gauge division $\frac{12}{1}$ includes any bore of diameter from ·750 to ·740 inclusive; and the Gauge division 12 any bore of diameter from ·729 to ·739. If the diameter is ·751 the gun is not a 12-bore but its Gauge Size is 11, and the gun is proved as an 11-bore.

So if the nominal size of the bore of a barrel appears as the numerator of a vulgar fraction of which the denominator is 1 the sportsman will know that the barrel is bored rather on the "wide" side; while if the nominal size of the bore appears as a whole number he will know that the barrel is bored correctly. Similarly if the size of bore is indicated by a vulgar fraction in which the numerator is a number one less than the nominal gauge of the bore he will know that his gun has been bored rather "tight." For example, a barrel marked $\frac{13}{1}$ means that the actual gauge is slightly less than ·729 and may be anything between ·728 and ·719.

The Gauge Size of a barrel is always taken at a point 9 inches from the Breech end.

The following Table gives full particulars of the Gauge Sizes for all nominal sizes of cartridges, as well as the Proof Charges for Provisional and Definitive Proof and the usual Service Charges.

RE-PROOF. Sometimes a gun becomes so worn in the bore that it is of a larger gauge than that for which it was originally proved. For example, the diameter of the bore of both barrels of a gun may originally have been ·750 at points 9 inches from the breech, in which case the gun would have been proved as a $\frac{12}{1}$-bore. But in course of time the barrels may become so worn that their diameters are respectively ·753 and ·751. If the

TABLE XXIX

Proof and Service Charges for Different Gauges

Nominal Size of Cartridge.	Gauge as marked at Proof.	Diameter of Bore.	Provisional Proof. Powder, T.P. Grains.	Provisional Proof. Powder, T.P. Drs.	Provisional Proof. Shot. Grains.	Provisional Proof. Shot. Oz.	Nominal Length of Chamber.	Definitive Proof. Powder, T.S.P. Grains.	Definitive Proof. Powder, T.S.P. Drs.	Definitive Proof. Shot. Grains.	Definitive Proof. Shot. Oz.	Service Charge. Black Powder. Grains.	Service Charge. Black Powder. Drs.	Service Charge. Shot. Grains.	Service Charge. Shot. Oz.
	5/2	1·026													
	5/1	1·001	740	27			4″								
4	5	·976			1421	3¼	4¼″	492	18	2050	4 11/16	246	9	1530	3½
	6/2	·957													
	6/1	**·938**	649	23¾											
	6	·919													
	7/2	·903													
	7/1	·888	567	20¾			3¼″								
	7	·873						328	12	1367	3⅛	164	6	930	2⅛
	8/2	·860					3½″								
8	8/1	·847	492	18	984	2¼	3¾″	382	14	1613	3 11/16	191	7	1093	2½
	8	**·835**					4″								
	9/2	·824						436	16	1832	4 3/16	218	8	1203	2¾
	9/1	·813	417	15¼			4¼″								

10	10/2	·793					2 5/8″	218	8	936	2 1/8	95	3 1/2	60	1 3/8
	10/1	·784	348	12 3/4											
	10	**·775**			711	1 5/8	2 3/4″ 2 7/8″	232	8 1/2	984	2 1/4	109	4	656	1/2
	11/1	·763	294	10 3/4			3″ 3 1/4″	260	9 1/2	1094	2 1/2	123	4 1/2	765	1 3/4
	11	·751													
12	12/1	·740	266	9 3/4			2 1/2″ 2 5/8″	178	6 1/2	738	1 11/16	82	3	492	1 1/8
	12	**·729**													
	13/1	·719			547	1 1/4	2 3/4″ 2 7/8″	206	7 1/2	875	2	92	3 3/8	547	1 1/4
			260	9 1/2											
	13	·710					3″ 3 1/4″	226	8 1/4	957	2 3/16	102	3 3/4	656	1 1/2
14	14/1	·701	246	9											
	14	**·693**			492	1 1/8	2 1/2″	164	6	685	1 9/16	80	2 7/8	465	1 1/16
	15/1	·685	239	8 3/4											
	15	·677					2 3/4″	191	7	793	1 13/16	85	3 1/8	520	1 3/16
16	16/1	·669					2 1/2″	154	5 5/8	656	1 1/2	75	2 3/4	437	1
			226	8 1/4											
	16	**·662**													
	17/1	·655			437	1									
			218	8											
	17	·649					2 3/4″ 3″	178	6 1/2	738	1 11/16	82	3	492	1 1/8
	18	·637	211	7 3/4											
20	19	·626	205	7 1/2			2 1/2″	136	5	574	1 5/16	65	2 3/8	383	7/8
	20	**·615**			383	7/8									
	21	·605	198	7 1/4			2 3/4″ 3″	157	5 3/4	657	1 1/2	75	2 3/4	437	1
	22	·596													

TABLE XXIX—*continued*

Nominal Size of Cartridge.	Gauge as marked at Proof.	Diameter of Bore.	Provisional Proof. Powder, T.P. Grains.	Provisional Proof. Powder, T.P. Drs.	Provisional Proof. Shot. Grains.	Provisional Proof. Shot. Oz.	Nominal Length of Chamber.	Definitive Proof. Powder, T.S.P. Grains.	Definitive Proof. Powder, T.S.P. Drs.	Definitive Proof. Shot. Grains.	Definitive Proof. Shot. Oz.	Service Charge. Black Powder. Grains.	Service Charge. Black Powder. Drs.	Service Charge. Shot. Grains.	Service Charge. Shot. Oz.
24	23	·587	191	7	355	$\frac{13}{16}$									
	24	**·579**	184	$6\frac{3}{4}$			$2\frac{1}{2}''$	123	$4\frac{1}{2}$	520	$1\frac{3}{16}$	58	$2\frac{1}{8}$	328	$\frac{3}{4}$
	25	·571													
	26	·563	178	$6\frac{1}{2}$			$2\frac{3}{4}''$	140	$5\frac{1}{8}$	575	$1\frac{5}{16}$	65	$2\frac{3}{8}$	383	$\frac{7}{8}$
28	27	·556	171	$6\frac{1}{4}$	328	$\frac{3}{4}$	$2\frac{1}{2}''$	113	$4\frac{1}{8}$	465	$1\frac{1}{16}$	52	$1\frac{7}{8}$	273	$\frac{5}{8}$
	28	**·550**	164	6											
	29	·543	150	$5\frac{1}{2}$			$2\frac{3}{4}''$	130	$4\frac{3}{4}$	547	$1\frac{1}{4}$	58	$2\frac{1}{8}$	328	$\frac{3}{4}$
32	30	·537	144	$5\frac{1}{4}$	246	$\frac{9}{16}$									
	31	·531	137	5											
	32	·526													
	33	·520					$2\frac{1}{2}''$	95	$3\frac{1}{2}$	410	$\frac{15}{16}$	41	$1\frac{1}{2}$	246	$\frac{9}{16}$
	34	·515	130	$4\frac{3}{4}$			$2\frac{3}{4}''$	109	4	465	$1\frac{1}{16}$	48	$1\frac{3}{4}$	300	$\frac{11}{16}$
	35	·510													
	36	·506													
	37	**·501**	123	$4\frac{1}{2}$											
	38	·497													
·410	**·410** to ·415	**·410** to ·415	78	$2\frac{1}{2}$	219	$\frac{1}{2}$	$2''$	55	2	219	$\frac{1}{2}$	23	$\frac{7}{8}$	137	$\frac{5}{16}$
							$2\frac{1}{2}''$	65	$2\frac{3}{8}$	273	$\frac{5}{8}$	27	1	191	$\frac{7}{16}$
·360	**·360**	**·360**	41	$1\frac{1}{2}$	82	$\frac{3}{16}$	$1\frac{3}{4}''$	34	$1\frac{1}{4}$	137	$\frac{5}{16}$	$13\frac{1}{2}$	$\frac{1}{2}$	92	$\frac{3}{16}$

NOTE.—The Gauges and Diameters in Bold Type are those to which barrels are usually bored for Definitive Proof for use with the Cartridges belonging to the groups in which they are included.

gun were offered for sale, the person who so offered it would be legally responsible to see that it was re-proved as an 11-bore, since both the barrels would be 11 Gauge.

When this is done or the barrel is re-proved for any reason the following Marks would be impressed on the barrels :

London Proof House

The letter " R " surmounted by a Crown, thus :

Birmingham Proof House

The letter " R " surmounted by a Crown, thus :

And in addition the new Gauge Size would be impressed by both Proof Houses.

Special Proof. Any barrel which has been Definitively Proved, may, at the request in writing of the sender, receive a Voluntary Proof to cover any declared service load, pressure in tons inch, kilos per square centimetre, or atmospheres, with a proof charge which the London and Birmingham Proof Houses may jointly declare as being suitable. Such barrels are impressed with the following marks :

London Proof House

The letters " S P " surmounted by a Crown, thus :

Birmingham Proof House

The letters " S P " surmounted by a Crown, thus :

The declared load is marked in addition by both Proof Houses.

SAFETY OF GUNS NOT NITRO PROVED

A question which is frequently arising is whether an old gun which has never been nitro proved is safe to use with cartridges loaded with nitro powders.

In many cases it may be absolutely safe, but there is just the chance that the action may be too weak to withstand a rather lively pressure, and so it should be taken as a golden rule that all such guns should be submitted for re-proof with the new Definitive Proof which includes the old Nitro Proof. As a rule, old guns will pass this Proof without turning a hair, so to speak. But sometimes one does give way in the test, and such a gun could not have been a safe weapon to use, so it is as well to find out in time.

There is, however, another aspect to the matter. Should a gun burst through the use of some improperly loaded cartridge the owner of the gun would have a legal claim for damages against the vendor of those cartridges if his gun had been properly proved. But should the gun not have been nitro proved, and the cartridges have contained a nitro-powder, the owner of the gun might have no claim at all against the vendor of the cartridges even though those cartridges were proved to have been grossly overloaded and to have developed dangerous pressures.

Some years ago an incident came to my notice which provides an excellent example.

A sportsman bought some cartridges loaded with a

cheap foreign nitro powder which was nominally a bulk powder, but which had not been correctly standardised for bulk. The result was that instead of the powder charge being 33 grains by weight it was over 40 grains by weight, and the pressures generated were dangerous.

These cartridges were used in an old gun which had never been nitro proved. The gun burst and injured the owner. Yet this sportsman had no legal redress against the vendor of the cartridges in spite of the fact that their danger was established beyond any doubt.

Cases such as this are admittedly extremely rare. But when the question of re-proving old guns which have never been nitro proved is being considered it is essential that it should be viewed from all angles, and allowances must be made for what are admittedly exceptional cases.

So the sportsman should understand that if he uses such a gun *he does so entirely at his own risk*. The chances admittedly are that the gun may be perfectly safe and that the cartridges will be safe also. But should there ever be an accident the sportsman will have no claim to any redress.

So I do not think it can be impressed on all shooters too strongly that they should on no account use modern smokeless powders in any gun which has not been nitro proved.

FOREIGN PROOF MARKS

Occasionally in Great Britain, and more frequently abroad, the sportsman may consider the purchase of a second-hand gun of foreign manufacture. It will, therefore, be useful at times to know the meanings of various foreign Proof Marks, especially as such marks indicate the country of origin of the gun.

In America, as has already been explained, there is no official Proof, but the Proving of Arms is carried out in Belgium, France, Italy and Spain ; and was carried out in Austria and Germany up to 1945.

The Proof Marks of these different countries are as follows :

Belgian Proof Marks

THE LIÈGE PROOF HOUSE

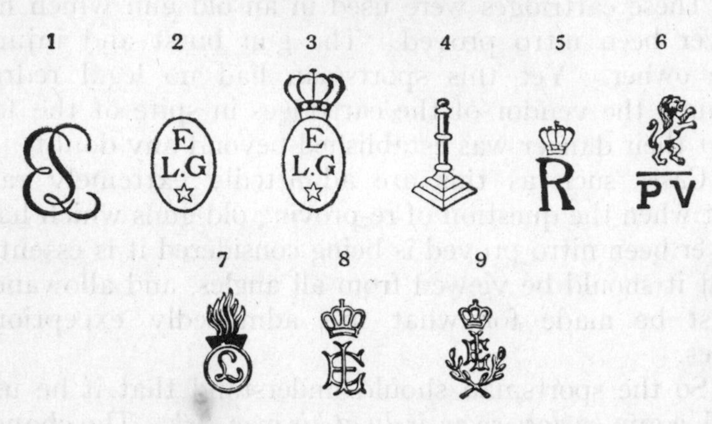

Single Muzzle-loading Shotguns must bear the marks 1, 2, and 4, or 1, 3, and 4 upon the barrel and 4 upon the breech.

Double Muzzle-loading Shotguns must bear the marks, 1, 2, and 4, or 1, 1, 3, and 4 upon the barrel and 4 upon the breech.

Single Breech-loading Shotguns must bear the marks 1 (or 8 or 9), 3, and 4 upon the barrel and 4 upon the action.

Double Breech-loading Shotguns must bear the marks 1 (or 8 or 9), 3, and 4 upon the barrel and 4 upon the action.

Choke-bored Guns must bear, near the gauge marks, the word " Choke," and if rifled in the choked part of the bore " Ch. B. Rayé."

Single and Double Rifles (except rifled choke) must bear the marks 1 (or 8 or 9), 3, 4, and 5 upon the barrel and 4 upon the action ; certain Express Rifles must bear in addition upon the barrel the word " Express " with the nominal calibre of the cartridge, etc.

Breech-loading Pistols must bear the marks 3 and

4 upon the barrel and 4 upon the breech or action, and if rifled 5, in addition, upon the barrel.

MUZZLE-LOADING PISTOLS must bear the marks 2 or 3 and 4 upon the barrels and 4 upon the breech.

REVOLVERS must bear the marks 3 upon the cylinder, and when rifled 5 upon the barrel. REPEATING PISTOLS must bear the marks 3 and 6 upon the barrel and 6 upon the action.

The exceptions to these rules are as follows :

SMALL BORE GUNS, RIFLES and PISTOLS (called " Carabines Floberts " and " Pistolets Floberts ") of the following bores, viz., ·22 in., 7 mm., 8 mm., 9 mm., must bear the marks 3 and 4, and if rifled 3, 4, and 5 upon the barrel and 4 upon the action ; and

MILITARY RIFLES of less than 8 mm. (·315) bore, in which nitro powder is used, must bear the marks 3, 4, and 6 upon the barrel and 4 upon the action.

BREECH-LOADING ARMS of any description PROVED FOR USE WITH NITRO POWDERS bear the mark 6 upon the barrel and action, in addition to any other marks applicable thereto.

On arms of foreign make the mark 7 is used in lieu of mark 3.

On barrels with solid lumps the mark 4 does not appear.

There are other marks used, but they are always in addition to the above-mentioned.

The most important of these are :

(1) A diamond enclosing a figure denoting the gauge of the gun, e.g. 12 or 16 for 12-gauge or 16-gauge.

(2) A horizontally elongated letter " C " inside which there is a figure indicating the length of the cartridge in millimetres for which the gun has been proved, e.g. 65 for 2½ inches ; 70 for 2¾ inches ; and 75 for 3 inches.

(3) A capital letter " D " followed by a fraction the numerator of which indicates the length of the case in millimetres and the denominator the diameter under the rim, also in millimetres.

(4) A fraction the numerator of which indicates the diameter of the bore at the muzzle and the denominator the diameter at the breech, both in millimetres and, of course, at the time of Proof, e.g. $\frac{174}{184}$. Here 174 millimetres is 0·685 inch and 184 millimetres is 0·725 inch. This means a constriction at the muzzle of 0·40 inch or 40 thousandths of an inch, which is full choke.

There is a reciprocal recognition of Proof Marks between the British and Belgian Governments which means that the Proof Marks of either country are legal currency in the other. The effect is that British weapons made and proved in Great Britain can be imported into Belgium without having to be submitted to Belgian Proof before being sold in that country, while weapons made and proved in Belgium have a similar free entry into Great Britain.

Austrian Proof Marks

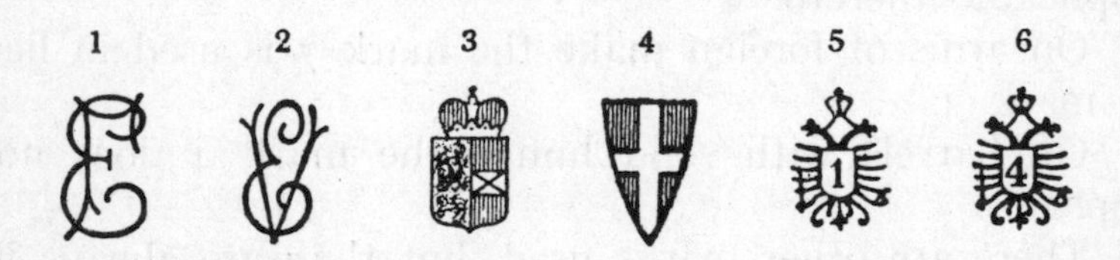

Single-Barrel Guns must bear the marks 1 (or 2) and 5 (or 6) in addition to the London or Birmingham marks for Definitive Proof as on pages 316 and 317.

Double-Barrel Guns must bear the marks 1 (or 2), 3 (or 4), and 5 (or 6) in addition to the London or Birmingham marks for Definitive Proof as on pages 309 and 310.

The agreement between the British and Austrian Governments was for partial recognition only, so all arms of Austrian manufacture were on arrival sent direct to either the London or Birmingham Proof Houses before being offered for sale.

German Proof Marks

1 2 3 4 5 6

B U S W

7 8 9 10 11 12

G SW E N R V

Muzzle-loading Shotguns must bear the marks 1, 1, 4, and 5 upon the barrel and 1 and 4 upon the breech, or 3 and 4 upon the barrel and breech.

Breech-loading Shotguns of cylinder bore must bear upon the barrel the marks 1, 1, 4, and 5; if choke-bored 1, 1, 4, and 6; if rifled in the choked portion of their bore 1, 1, 4, 6, and 8. The action must bear the marks 1 and 4.

Rifles must bear upon the barrel the marks 1, 1, 4, and 7, and if constructed for heavy charges (express rifles), the mark 9 in addition. The breech or action must bear the marks 1 and 4.

Under certain conditions, Shotguns (except such as are choke-bored) and Rifles may bear the marks 3 and 4 only upon the barrel, and the same upon the breech or action. Under the same conditions, Military Rifles, made according to Rifle Pattern No. 88, may bear the marks 2 and 10 only upon the barrel, and the same upon the action.

Revolvers must bear the marks 2 and 4 upon the barrel, revolving cylinder, and frame or body of the action. Repeating Pistols and Saloon Pistols must bear the marks 2 and 4 upon the barrel and action.

Arms which have already been proved and marked, but have subsequently undergone some alteration necessitating their being re-proved, are, upon re-proof, impressed with marks 11 and 3 upon the barrel and breech or action, in addition to the original marks.

Upon the passing of the German Proof Act of 1891,

arms which were then in stock were not subject to the provisions of the Act if they were, before being dealt with, stamped with mark 12 upon the barrel and breech or action.

There were other marks used, but they were always in addition to those already mentioned.

Neither Austrian or German Proof Marks have been recognised in Great Britain since September, 1939, and so any weapon imported into Great Britain subsequent to this date are legally unproved and it is an offence under the Proof Act to sell them without first having them proved at either the London or Birmingham Proof House.

Austrian Proof Marks were never completely recognised in Great Britain, but after the inclusion of Austria in the German Reich it is doubtful whether the Austrian Proof authorities had much chance of independent action.

French Proof Marks

THE PROOF HOUSE OF THE PARIS CHAMBER OF COMMERCE

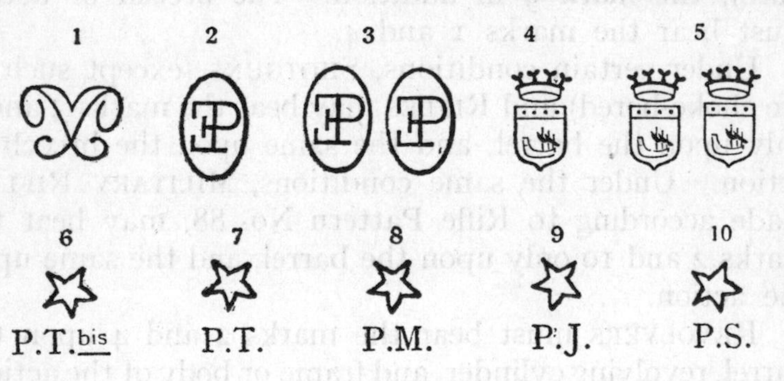

As the proof of small arms in France is optional the British Proof authorities do not consider a gun or rifle of French manufacture sufficiently proved unless it bear at least one of the marks 1, 2, 3 or 4, together with one of the marks 5, 6, 7, 8, 9 or 10 upon the barrel, and one of the marks 4, 5, 6, 7, 8, 9 or 10 upon the breech or action.

Saloon Guns, Saloon Rifles, Saloon Pistols and Stick Guns should bear mark 4 only for Paris, and 2

THE PROOF HOUSE OF THE SAINT-ÉTIENNE CHAMBER OF COMMERCE

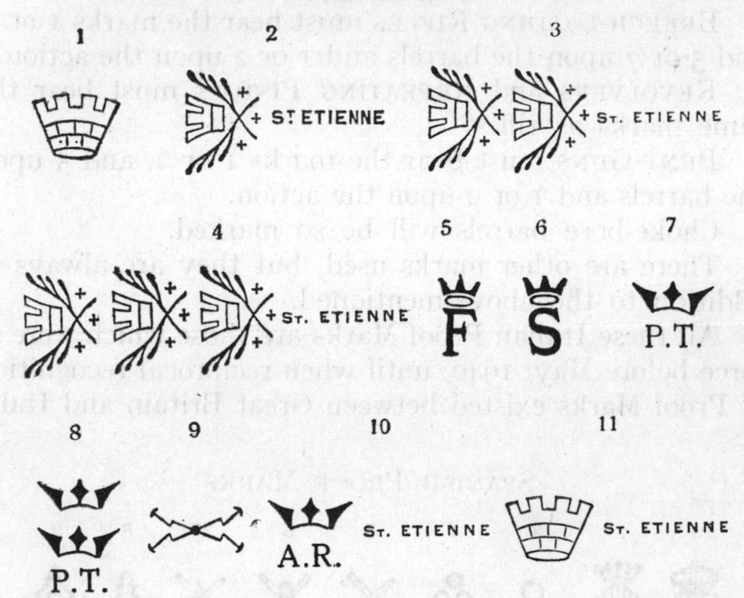

only for Saint-Étienne, upon the barrel and breech or action.

Revolvers, Pistols, etc., should bear the mark 11 for Saint-Étienne upon the barrel and revolving cylinder or action, and mark 4 for Paris.

Italian Proof Marks

Breech-loading Shotguns proved for black powder must bear the marks 1 or 2, and 3 or 4, and 5 or 6 upon the barrels and 1 or 2 upon the action.

Breech-loading Shotguns proved for nitro powder must bear the marks 7 or 8 in lieu of 5 or 6.

Breech-loading Rifles must bear the marks 1 or 2, and 5 or 7 upon the barrels and 1 or 2 upon the action.

Revolvers and Repeating Pistols must bear the same marks as rifles.

Punt Guns must bear the marks 1 or 2, and 5 upon the barrels and 1 or 2 upon the action.

Choke-bore barrels will be so marked.

There are other marks used, but they are always in addition to the above-mentioned.

All these Italian Proof Marks are those which were in force before May, 1940, until when reciprocal recognition of Proof Marks existed between Great Britain and Italy.

Spanish Proof Marks

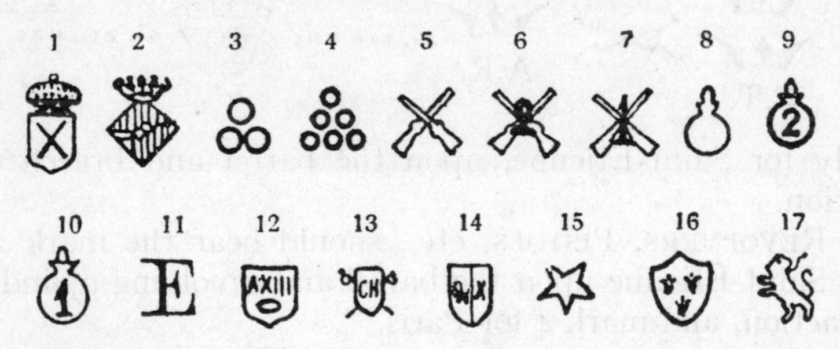

Single Muzzle-loading Shotguns must bear the marks 1 or 2 and 3 upon the barrel.

Double Muzzle-loading Shotguns must bear the marks 1 or 2 and 4 upon the barrels.

Single Breech-loading Shotguns proved for black powder must bear the marks 1 or 2, 5, and 6 (or 7 or 10), and if proved for smokeless powder the mark 12 or similar mark.

Double Breech-loading Shotguns proved for black powder must bear the marks 1 or 2, 5, and 6 (or 10), and if proved for smokeless powder the mark 12 or similar mark.

Breech-loading Rifles must bear the marks 1 (or 2), 8 and 9.

MILITARY RIFLES must bear the marks 1 or 2 and 14.

SALOON RIFLES must bear the marks 1 or 2 and 15.

PISTOLS must bear the marks 1 or 2 and 16.

REVOLVERS must bear the marks 1 or 2 and 17.

Marks 11 and 13 are used for special and supplementary proofs only.

There are other marks used, but they are always in addition to those already mentioned.

Reciprocal recognition of Proof Marks between Great Britain and Spain was established in 1927 and the Proof Marks of either country are legal currency in the other.

MAXIMUM CARTRIDGES AND LOW-VELOCITY LOADS AND PROOF

The question sometimes arises whether a Maximum cartridge or a Low-Velocity load can be used with safety since the weight of the shot charge is usually greater than the weight of the maximum Service Charge impressed on the barrels of a gun.

It must be realised that the whole object of Proof is to test guns for *pressure,* and the weight of the maximum Service Charge of shot which is impressed on the barrels is assumed to be used in conjunction with the maximum Service Charge of powder.

The pressure developed by a Maximum cartridge or a suitable low-velocity load is no higher than that developed by standard charges, and is frequently less. This is because in the case of the Maximum cartridge a special slow-burning powder is used while in the low-velocity load a powder charge appreciably lighter than the service charge is used with the heavier shot charge.

So long as this principle is maintained there can be no question of danger.

OFFENCES AGAINST THE PROOF ACT

There are certain Offences and Penalties imposed by the Gun Barrel Proof Act, 1868, of which all Sportsmen and Dealers in Firearms should be aware. And since ignorance of the law is no valid excuse, it may be as well to give details of some of the Offences and Penalties imposed by this Act.

Section 122 makes it an offence to import into England, Small Arms, the Barrels of which are not duly proved, and marked as proved, without giving notice in writing, within seven days next after their arrival, to the Proof Masters of the London and Birmingham Proof Houses, and, for every such offence, imposes a penalty, for every Barrel, not exceeding £20.

Section 122 also makes it an offence to omit sending such imported Arms, within twenty-eight days next after their arrival in England, to be proved at either of the Proof Houses of London or Birmingham, and for every such offence imposes a penalty, for every Barrel, not exceeding £20.

Sections 108 and 109 make it an offence to sell, exchange, expose or keep for sale, or export, or keep for exportation, or to attempt to sell, exchange, or export, or to pawn or pledge, or attempt to pawn or pledge, or to take in pawn or pledge, an Arm, the Barrel or Barrels of which are not duly proved, and marked as proved, and for every such offence Section 122 imposes a penalty, for every Barrel, not exceeding £20. And in this connection it should be realised that any firearm which may have been proved in a country with which Great Britain has no reciprocal recognition of Proof Marks is legally an unproved firearm.

Section 129 provides for the registration, at the Proof Houses of London and Birmingham, of the Proof Marks of a Foreign State, having a public Proof House established by Law.

Section 132 provides that Barrels bearing such duly registered Foreign Proof Marks shall be exempted from the provisions of this Act, but if any Barrel has on any part thereof, or on any part of the Arm into which it is made up, any mark, name, sign, or character, indicating, or purporting to indicate, that such Barrel or Arm respectively is of English manufacture, or shall bear the name of any English maker or Dealer, or of any Person, Partnership, or Company, carrying on in England the business of a maker or a Dealer in Arms or Barrels, such Barrel is to be deemed an unproved Barrel of English manufacture, rendering the person dealing with it liable to a penalty not exceeding £20.

The word "Barrel" in the Act includes the Breech and Action, or any part of the Arm through which it would be fired.

It should also be noted that when certain alterations or conversions are made in guns they call for the gun being submitted to re-proof before being sold, or sent back to the sportsman at whose request the conversion was made.

The most usual of such alterations is the converting of non-ejectors to ejectors. At first sight it may seem unnecessary for a gun to be re-proved after such an apparently simple change. But in reality it is a very essential precaution, since there is usually less spare metal left at the breech end of a non-ejector gun than there is in an ejector, because the solid leg of the extractor of a non-ejector is smaller in diameter than the split double leg of the extractors of an ejector, the reason being that the solid leg is stronger than the split, and so need not be so stout.

When the gun is converted the hole in the breech which receives the long leg of the extractor must be enlarged in order to provide accommodation for the split leg ; and this enlargement may reduce the walls of the barrel unduly if there is not much metal to spare between the two chambers. On this account there is always a potential source of risk when such a conversion is made, and so the need for re-proof will be obvious.

When a non-ejector has been converted to an ejector by a gunmaker who was not the original maker of the gun the fact should be engraved on the rib, and after the original maker's name should be added "Converted to ejector by ——."

Another conversion which is sometimes carried out

is the lengthening of the chambers of a gun. If this is done the thickness of the wall of the barrel at the head of the chamber will be reduced. So it is merely reasonable that a gun should be re-proved after such a conversion has been effected.

Sometimes rook rifles are re-bored and converted to ·410 shotguns. Such guns should, of course, be re-proved, while the name of the gunmaker who carried out the conversion should also be engraved on the barrel unless he was the original maker of the weapon.

SAFETY PROVIDED BY PROOF

There now only remains the question as to whether Proof is an absolute safeguard against an unreliable gun being placed on the market. Flaws in metal are known to exist, and sportsmen may wonder whether the fact that a gun has passed all the Proofs demanded by law can be taken as a guarantee that the gun is absolutely sound. This is a difficult question to answer, and any attempt at doing so had better be delayed until Chapter XVIII.

NOTE.—Since 1948 a new type of American cartridge has been developed which is sold extensively overseas and which is really a 2½-inch cartridge externally but carrying a 2¾-inch load. It is closed with the crimp turnover and in the 12-bore size contains a powder charge of up to what corresponds to 3¼ drachms of black powder and shot charges of 1⅛ and 1¼ ounce. The pressures are similar to those developed by British 2¾-inch cartridges and appreciably higher than those for which 2½-inch 12-bore guns are normally proved. It cannot, therefore, be stressed too strongly that such cartridges are not safe to use in ordinary 2½-inch guns.

The only practical solution for this difficulty is to prove guns which are likely to be used with these cartridges with what may be termed the " 2¾-inch Proof," and this must mean a tendency to heavier guns.

Any sportsman who uses these heavily loaded cartridges in a gun which has not been suitably proved is running a grave risk as the existing " 2½-inch Proof " was never intended to cover the use of cartridges which really contain " 2¾-inch loads."

CHAPTER XVI

BURSTS

WE now come to a question which happily seldom arises, namely that of bursts. When one remembers the vast number of guns which are in constant use ; the regularity and frequency with which these guns are fired ; the almost habitual neglect with which a considerable proportion of them are treated ; and the diversity of ammunition which is used in different parts of the world ; when one remembers all these facts there can only remain a feeling of wonder that the record of accidents due to guns bursting is so small. It is more than probable that the great majority of men who shoot regularly never see a gun burst in the whole of their lives. This fortunate rarity of accidents due to bursts bears high testimony to the quality of British guns, as well as to the reliability of cartridges which are in general use. But it has also two other effects : the suspicions of shooters are lulled, so that there is little appreciation of what are necessary precautions ; and the whole subject of burst guns is little understood, either by sportsmen or gunmakers.

This last point is not altogether surprising, as a proper understanding of the subject demands a certain amount of knowledge of the properties of steel as well as familiarity with the science of Internal Ballistics.

Since, however, when a burst does occur its true cause can become a matter of considerable moment a study of the subject is well worth while, especially as such a study will impress upon shooters the importance of adopting certain simple precautions which may easily result in the avoidance of accidents, many of which are due to ignorance or carelessness.

Since a burst must always be caused by the pressure exerted by the expanding powder gases it must entail rupture either of the barrel or the action. When an action ruptures, or breaks, the fracture invariably occurs across the bar in prolongation with the face of the action, as has been explained in Volume I (pages 50, 51, 87). The rupture of a barrel may occur at any point in its length according to circumstances.

Usually the expression "burst" is confined to a rupture of a barrel, the cracking of an action being termed a "break" or a "smash." These distinctions are really obvious, but for the sake of convenience in this chapter I will include "breaks" or "smashes" in the term "burst."

All bursts can be divided into three classes.

(1) Bursts caused by excessive pressure generated in the cartridge-case.

(2) Bursts caused by the presence of some obstruction in the bore.

(3) Bursts due to some abnormal weakness of the metal of the barrels or action.

But before we come to consider these three entirely distinct classes of bursts we must first turn our attention to a brief study of certain properties of steel.

Steel is an elastic substance. That is, when pressure is applied to any structure of steel that structure will yield to a certain extent under the influence of that pressure, but when the pressure is removed it will recover its original form. There is, however, a limit to this elasticity, and if this limit is exceeded the steel will no longer resume its original form; while if it is exceeded much the steel will break. This can be understood best with the help of the diagram given in Fig. 32 which represents the action of a piece of steel in response to a steadily increasing tensile stress. In practical tests a sample piece of steel is taken and submitted to a pull, or tensile stress, which is gradually but steadily increased. Under the influence of this tension the piece of steel is gradually stretched until it breaks. The diagram shows the manner in which the steel is elongated by the increasing tension until the final rupture occurs.

The point O in the diagram indicates the original length of the piece of steel under test, as can be seen. As the tension is applied this test piece is stretched, and the degree of elongation produced by any particular stress is shown on the graph. For example, under a tensile

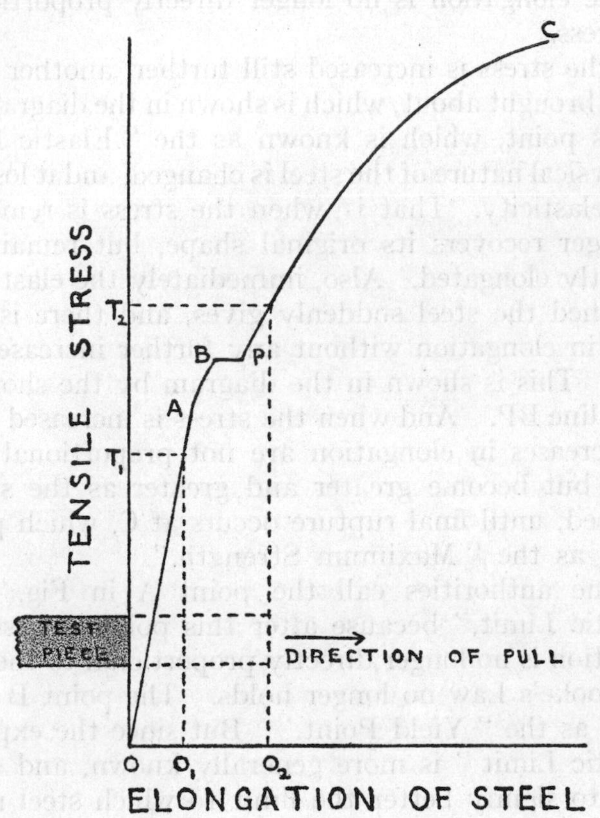

FIG. 32.—Diagram to illustrate how a piece of steel is elongated under the influence of an increasing tensile stress. B is the Elastic Limit ; and C the Maximum Strength.

stress of T_1 the test piece will stretch to O_1 ; and under a stress of T_2 it will stretch to O_2, as shown by the dotted lines.

At first the elongation produced is directly proportional to the stress ; that is, the amount of elongation is doubled when the stress is doubled, and so on proportionally. This experimental law is known as "Hooke's

Law," and is the foundation of the Mathematical Theory of Elasticity.

But if the stress is increased beyond a certain point a change occurs. This point is shown at A in the diagram, and when it is passed the behaviour of the steel alters and the elongation is no longer directly proportional to the stress.

If the stress is increased still further, another change is soon brought about, which is shown in the diagram at B. At this point, which is known as the "Elastic Limit," the physical nature of the steel is changed, and it loses part of its elasticity. That is, when the stress is removed it no longer recovers its original shape, but remains permanently elongated. Also, immediately the elastic limit is reached the steel suddenly gives, and there is an increase in elongation without any further increase in the stress. This is shown in the diagram by the short horizontal line BP. And when the stress is increased further the increases in elongation are not proportional to the stress, but become greater and greater as the stress is increased, until final rupture occurs at C, which point is known as the "Maximum Strength."

Some authorities call the point A in Fig. 32 the "Elastic Limit," because after this point is passed the elongation is no longer directly proportional to the stress, and Hooke's Law no longer holds. The point B is then known as the "Yield Point." But since the expression "Elastic Limit" is more generally known, and since it seems to signify better the limit to which steel may be stressed before losing all of its elasticity, I propose to use it to describe the point B. In doing so I am following a very common metallurgic custom, but the reader should remember that in these chapters the expression "Elastic Limit" is synonymous with "Yield Point."

When the powder gases expand very rapidly in the chamber and bore of a shotgun barrel they produce pressure; and this pressure, as has been explained in Volume II, acts equally in every direction. Its forward effect propels the wadding and shot charge, while its

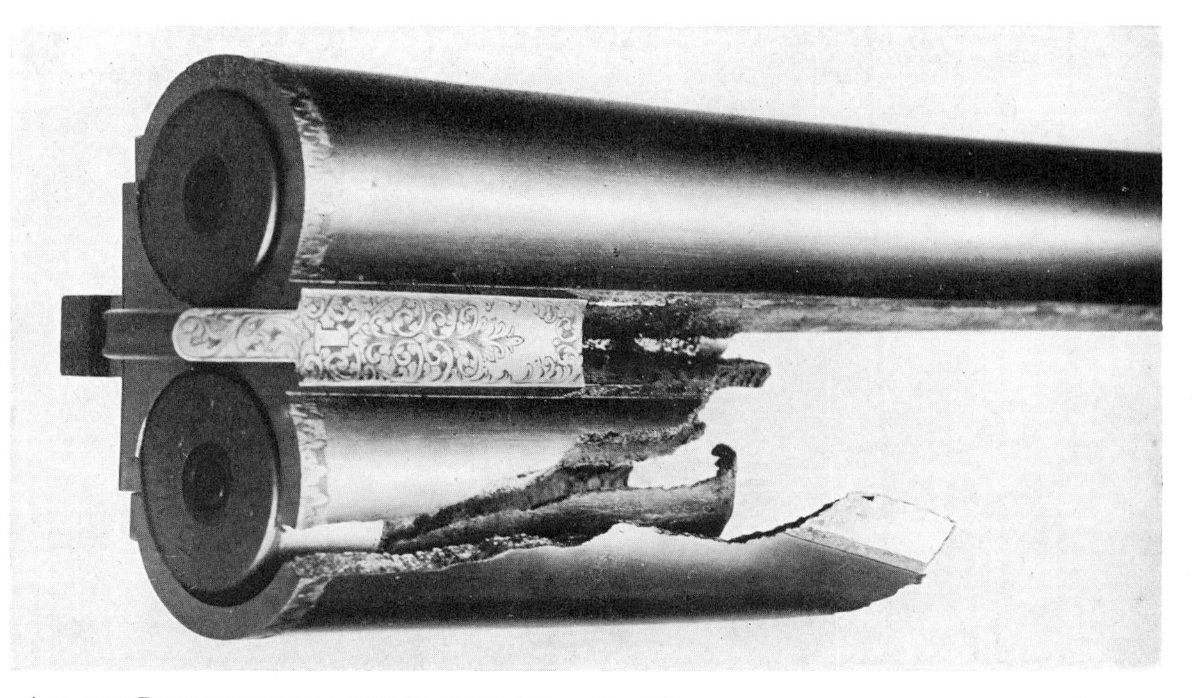

A 12-bore Barrel burst by a very excessive pressure caused by the accidental insertion of a 16-bore cartridge immediately in front of the 12-bore cartridge

The fact that the gun was fitted with an efficient top extension probably saved the action from being distressed

backward effect is felt in recoil. The lateral, or radial, effects are not felt by the shooter since they are checked by the walls of the barrel. But the walls of the barrel cannot check the pressure without some effort, and this effort comprises the overcoming of the internal stress in the steel which composes the walls. This stress is the direct outcome of the pressure and tends to pull apart the particles of steel in the walls of the barrel. In other words, the pressure generated by the expanding powder gases causes a tensile stress in the walls of the barrel, and the greater the pressure the greater will be this stress.

The intensity of the stress which the walls of the barrel have to overcome, however, depends on their thickness. This should be readily understood, since the thicker the walls are the greater the area over which the effort of overcoming the stress is spread, and consequently the effort is much less intense in any layer when the barrel is thick than when it is thin.

It may seem that I am labouring an obvious fact, namely that the thicker the barrel the stronger it is. But it is extremely important that the reader should understand that there is a definite relation between the gas pressure, the tensile stress in the steel of the barrel, and the thickness of the walls of the barrel.

This relation is given by a formula known as the "Gunmakers' Formula," which is:

$$P = t \times \frac{R^2 - r^2}{R^2 + r^2}$$

where P is the Gas Pressure in the barrel in tons per square inch.

t is the Tensile Stress on the internal layer of the barrel in tons per square inch of the metal.[1]

[1] It will be noticed that the Tensile Stress is quoted as acting on the "internal layer" of the barrel. When considering stresses in barrels the walls of the barrel must be regarded as being made up of a very large number of very thin layers, as if a number of tubes were fitted over one another. The maximum stress naturally occurs in the innermost layer, because this layer would have to give way before any stress would be felt by the next layer, and so on.

R^2 is the External Diameter of the barrel in inches.

r^2 is the Internal Diameter of the barrel in inches.

This formula is given in the Government Text Books on Ordnance and Small Arms, and it can be regarded as being quite sufficiently accurate for all practical requirements when applied to ordinary shotgun barrels. Its importance and value will readily be appreciated, for if the Elastic Limit and Maximum Strength of any particular type of steel are ascertained by actual test, the values of these stresses can be substitued in the formula which will then supply information as to the barrel thickness necessary to withstand any particular gas pressure. And since the maximum gas pressure generated by various charges is known within narrow limits at all points along the bore, it is possible to determine the thickness of barrel throughout its length which is necessary for safety.

Conversely, if the barrel is ruptured, and the Maximum Strength of the steel from which it is made is obtained by actual test, it can be stated quite definitely that the gas pressure must have exceeded a certain value in order to produce the stress necessary to cause rupture.

In this connection it is important to know what are the absolute maximum gas pressures at different points along the barrel which can be generated by ordinary charges of powder. When a given weight of powder is consumed, or exploded, in a closed vessel the pressure developed is the maximum this weight of powder can give in the volume of the closed vessel. If this volume is the chamber, or bore, of a shotgun, one side—the wads and shot charge—moves and takes up heat from the powder gases, thus reducing the pressure. So the pressure must always be less in a gun barrel than in a closed vessel of the same volume, the amount by which the pressure is less being dependent on the amount of energy imparted to the shot charge and wads and the amount dissipated in heat.

Sir Andrew Noble measured the pressures developed by many propellants in closed vessels at various loading densities, and his researches have proved invaluable in ascertaining the absolute maximum pressures which can be developed in a shotgun barrel at various points along the bore by normal charges of ordinary shotgun powders.[1]

For purposes of convenience the gas pressures necessary to produce stresses if 15, 20 and 40 tons per square inch in the inner layer of a typical $2\frac{1}{2}$-inch 12-bore barrel are given in the table on next page, which also includes the normal gas pressures and the absolute maximum pressures which can be developed at various points along the bore by an ordinary charge of a shotgun powder.

The values of 15, 20 and 40 tons per square inch have been taken as examples in stresses simply for convenience, as 20 and 40 tons per square inch are the values of the Elastic Limit and Maximum Strength of the typical highest grade steel which is used in the manufacture of best quality gun barrels. In some grades of equally good steel the Elastic Limit is as specified, but the Maximum Strength is slightly less, being 35 tons per square inch. But the difference is of no practical importance because once the Elastic Limit has been passed the physical condition of the steel is so changed that

[1] Some typical results of Sir Andrew Noble's are given in the following table:

Loading Density.	Pressure in Tons per Sq. In. developed by			
	Ballistite.	Mark I Cordite.	M.D. Cordite.	Nitro-cellulose Powder.
0·05	3·0	3·3	3·0	3·0
0·10	6·5	7·0	6·5	6·4
0·15	10·9	11·7	10·5	10·0

All the propellants mentioned in this table actually give higher closed-vessel pressures than shotgun powders such as Schultze, Smokeless Diamond, E.C., etc., because they are wholly converted into gas, while the shotgun powders contain 10 per cent. or more of inorganic ingredients which cannot be converted into gas. Accordingly if we take the closed-vessel pressures for the nitro-cellulose powder as being correct for a shotgun powder such as Smokeless Diamond, the pressures are really being placed at an excessive level. Moreover, these pressures are also reduced by cooling and by work.

different tests of the same type of steel may give somewhat different results ; and it can be assumed for all practical purposes that the Maximum Strength of the highest-grade gun-barrel steel varies from 30 to 50 tons per square inch, and that 40 tons per square inch is a normal value.

TABLE XXX

NORMAL AND MAXIMUM PRESSURES AND PRESSURES NECESSARY TO PRODUCE DIFFERENT STRESSES IN AN ORDINARY 12-BORE SHOTGUN BARREL

Distance from Breech in Inches.	Pressure generated by 33 Grains Smokeless Diamond in a 2½-inch 12-bore Barrel.		Pressure necessary to Stress the Inner Layers of a typical 2½-inch 12-bore Barrel to		
	Normal.	Maximum Possible.	15 Tons per Sq. In.	20 Tons per Sq. In.	40 Tons per Sq. In.
1	2·80	30·30	5·00	6·70	13·40
2	2·80	10·10	5·00	6·70	13·40
2½	2·76	7·50	3·75	5·00	10·00
3	2·69	5·90	4·29	5·72	11·44
4	2·50	4·05	3·77	5·02	10·04
5	2·19	3·06	3·29	4·38	8·76
6	1·78	2·42	2·87	3·82	7·64
7	1·49	2·01	2·57	3·42	6·84
8	1·26	1·70	2·27	3·02	6·04
9	1·08	1·47	1·99	2·65	5·30
10	0·95	1·29	1·74	2·32	4·64
12	0·75	1·04	1·52	2·02	4·04
14	0·67	0·84	1·37	1·82	3·64
16	0·49	0·74	1·25	1·67	3·34
18	0·41	0·64	1·25	1·67	3·34
20	0·35	0·57	1·29	1·72	3·44
22	0·30	0·51	1·33	1·77	3·54
24	0·26	0·46	1·33	1·77	3·54
26	0·23	0·42	1·37	1·82	3·64

N.B.—All pressures are given in tons per square inch.

The important point is really the Elastic Limit. Once this is exceeded the shape of the barrel can be changed. If the Elastic Limit of the internal layers only is passed the outer layers may possess sufficient tensile force to compress these inner layers, when the increase in the size of the barrel will be so slight as to be almost imperceptible, the barrel merely taking up a slight permanent "set."

But if all the layers of the wall are stressed beyond the Elastic Limit they will not recover their original shape after being stretched and will remain permanently elongated.

When the walls of a barrel are elongated permanently as the result of a stress produced by internal gas pressure the diameter of the barrel is greater than it was originally, and the barrel is said to be "bulged."

If the Maximum Strength of the steel is exceeded the barrel will rupture or burst.

It must be realised, however, that the pressures given as being necessary to stress the barrel to 40 tons per square inch are actually less than those necessary to rupture a barrel which has this maximum strength. This is because the Gunmakers' Formula only gives the pressure for stressing the *inner layers* of the barrel to 40 tons. When the stretch of the barrel has become comparatively great, as it must just before bursting, all parts of the wall of the barrel exercise an equal hoop tension. And to calculate the gas pressure necessary to stress all the layers of the barrel to 40 tons per square inch a different formula is employed.[1] It is, however, sufficiently accurate to assume that the pressure necessary to burst a barrel is about 10 per cent. higher than that required to stress the inner layer to the maximum strength.

In the case of cheap guns the steel used for the barrels will frequently have considerably lower Elastic Limits and Maximum Strengths than the values I have given, and in such cases the barrels will be bulged or burst respectively by gas pressures which would have had no effect on barrels made of high grade steel.

I have frequently heard sportsmen eulogising the old Damascus twist barrels and declaring that this material

[1] Professor Alger gives the bursting formula as

$$P = t \times \frac{3(R - r)}{R + 2r}$$

was superior to steel in that it stretched without bursting. This belief is due to the frequency with which bulges used to occur in Damascus barrels. But so far from these bulges being a sign of the superiority of this material they were proof of its inferiority, as they indicated very low Elastic Limits. In the case of steel barrels similar gas pressures would have produced no permanent elongation because the steel would have resumed its original form on the pressure being removed owing to the steel being more elastic than Damascus.

If the physical condition of the steel is changed by submitting it to excessive heat, as explained in Volume I (pages 32 and 33), it loses its elasticity and strength, and the Elastic Limit and Maximum Strength are both lowered very considerably. In such circumstances a barrel can be bulged, or even burst, by considerably lower gas pressures than those given in Table XXX.

There are two points in connection with Table XXX which are worthy of attention.

The first, and by far the more important, is that the gas pressures necessary to stress the barrel to 15, 20 and 40 tons per square inch at 2½ inches from the breech are appreciably lower than the pressures necessary to produce the same results at 3 inches, and slightly lower than those which give corresponding results at 4 inches. This is because the wall of the barrel is thinner at 2½ inches from the breech than it is at 3 and 4 inches, because the chamber cone begins at 2½ inches. So it will be realised that the junction between the chamber and the chamber cone can be a weak spot in a barrel. In actual practice there is no extra risk owing to this fact, because the gas pressure must always be falling away at this distance from the breech, and a pressure which would stress the barrel excessively at 2½ inches would mean a still higher pressure in the chamber, which would also stress that part of the barrel excessively.

The second point is that the barrel seems to become stronger after a distance of 20 inches from the breech is exceeded. As a matter of fact it is stronger because the muzzle end of a barrel is invariably made thicker than the middle to allow for recessing and choke.

Although Table XXX gives particulars of a 2½-inch 12-bore barrel the general principles which it sets out apply equally to all gauges of barrels chambered for all lengths of cases. These principles may be summed up as follows :

(1) The gas pressure is always greatest in the chamber and falls away very rapidly immediately in front of the chamber until a point is reached which is approximately twice the length of the chamber from the breech. After this point is passed the rate of fall in the pressure becomes more gradual as the distance from the breech is increased (*vide* Plate X, Volume II).

(2) The gas pressure acts in this manner irrespective of its intensity.

(3) The gas pressure necessary to bulge or burst a properly designed barrel of good quality steel can only be produced by a normal powder charge in the immediate neighbourhood of the breech and chamber. Therefore the powder cannot be held responsible for any burst which occurs more than, say, one inch in front of the chamber.

These are three very important principles, and once they have been grasped we can leave this brief survey of the general principles involved and proceed to consider in detail the three different classes of bursts which were given at the beginning of this chapter.

PRESSURE BURSTS

The first of these classes comprises bursts which are caused by an excessive pressure generated in the cartridge-case. Such a pressure may be the result of any one or more of the following causes :

The Use of an Unsuitable Powder. It should hardly be necessary to emphasise the importance of using only shotgun powders in cartridges intended to be fired in shotguns ; yet experimenters whose enthusiasm is greater than their knowledge will occasionally try unsuitable powders. In the case of black powder, for example, a very fine-grain powder is unsuited for shotguns and the pressure generated might be disastrous. Similarly no rifle powder, such as cordite, should be used in a shotgun cartridge.

The use of an unsuitable powder cannot occur when cartridges are loaded on anything approaching a large scale, as an isolated charge of a powder different from that being used for the bulk of the cartridges could not find its way into the loading machine. Consequently the only conceivable risk from this cause is that run by the amateur experimenter. In cartridges purchased from any responsible gunmaker the risk is too remote to merit consideration.

The Use of an Excessive Powder Charge. The powder charges in cartridges loaded by automatic machines will seldom vary by more than half a grain more or less than the charge for which the machine was set, as the hoppers of the machine will only hold these amounts of powder ; and if the charge varies from the mean by any appreciable amount the machine will no longer function. For this reason machine loaded cartridges must always be safer and more reliable than those loaded by hand in the ordinary way, and it is quite impossible for any single cartridge from a batch loaded by a machine to contain a powder charge which is appreciably greater than the rest.

The only risk in the case of machine loaded cartridges is that due to the omission of checking the weight of powder given by the hopper. As was explained in Volume II, the size of the hopper is affected slightly by temperature, and it may throw bigger charges in warm weather than in cold. But such variations are admittedly slight, and could hardly be sufficient in themselves to cause any dangerous pressure.

The most important reason for checking the weight of the powder charge thrown by the machine is that there is always the risk when using some foreign powders that the powder has not been properly standardised for bulk.

In such circumstances the machine might load over 40 grains of a 33-grain powder in every cartridge. This possibility was explained at length in Volume II, and so I will not enter into further details here.

When cartridges are loaded by hand there is a far greater risk of irregularity in the weights of the powder charges, and I have actually known a case in which a 12-bore hopper was used in loading 16-bore cartridges by a country ironmonger. In this particular instance the loader was also unfortunate in using a cheap continental powder which had not been properly standardised for bulk, and so there were two sources of error. The first of these resulted in the 16-bore cartridges being loaded with the bulk of powder which would have been correct for a 12-bore case. Normally this bulk would have weighed 33 grains; but the powder had not been correctly standardised for bulk, and the charge actually weighed 42 grains. The net result was that the cartridges contained 42 grains of powder instead of 28 grains!

This is a most remarkable instance of an excessive powder charge, but I have also known 43 grains of another variety of continental powder being loaded into an ordinary 12-bore cartridge. Here again the powder, which was nominally a 33-grain bulk powder, had not been correctly standardised for bulk, and the loader had never checked the weight of powder thrown by his hopper.

These two examples should emphasise the extreme importance of checking the weights of powder given by the hopper of a machine, especially when foreign powders are used.

Amateur experimenters will at times load cartridges with excessive powder charges, and there is sometimes the risk of an ignorant loader using a bulk powder measure when loading a dense powder, such as ballistite. But such possibilities need not be considered by the shooter who buys his cartridges from a reliable source.

THE USE OF AN EXCESSIVE SHOT CHARGE. This is not such a potent source of risk as the one which has just been discussed, since it is very difficult to load an abnormally heavy shot charge into an ordinary cartridge-case and maintain the strength of turnover or crimp when the standard powder charge and wadding are used. Further, there is the same safeguard in the use of loading machines which holds good for powder charges. At the same time loaders should always check the weight of shot charge thrown by a machine from day to day in exactly the same way as they should test the machine for the weight of powder.

Occasionally amateurs try to improve the pattern by adding sawdust or bone-dust to the ordinary shot charge and so filling up the spaces between the pellets. This adds to the weight of the shot charge, and is, therefore, not to be recommended.

When abnormally heavy shot charges are used in conjunction with suitably light powder charges, as is done in Low-Velocity loads, or in Maximum cartridges with the special slow burning Neoflak powder, there is no risk of excessive pressure.

THE ACCIDENTAL INSERTION IN THE CHAMBER OF A CARTRIDGE OF SMALLER GAUGE. But there is one way in which the weight of the projectile (normally the shot charge and wads) can be increased very considerably which deserves the most careful attention.

It sometimes happens that a few 20-bore cartridges get mixed up in a bag of 12-bore. When this occurs the shooter may re-load his gun after firing with a 20-bore cartridge. This will naturally be too small for the 12-bore chamber, and it will slip forward until it sticks in the bore. When the shooter again fires the lock of that barrel he will only hear the click of the falling tumbler, and on opening the gun he will see an apparently empty chamber, on which he may quite likely think that he forgot to re-load in his hurry and will remedy the omission at once. In doing so he will load an ordinary 12-bore cartridge in his gun with a 20-bore cartridge in front of it.

The risk from such a procedure should be obvious, but the exact nature of the risk will depend on the position occupied by the 20-bore cartridge. This will be governed by the diameter of the rim of the cartridge-case and that of the front end of the chamber or cone. As a rule, a 20-bore cartridge will stick in a 12-bore gun with its base a little way *ahead* of the front end of a 12-bore cartridge when it is actually loaded in the chamber, and a situation will then arise which will be considered under the heading of "Obstructional Bursts." But sometimes the 20-bore cartridge will stick in such a position that *its base will just rest on the top of a 12-bore cartridge when the latter is loaded in the chamber*. In this position it really amounts to an additional projectile which the expanding gases produced by the combustion of the 12-bore powder charge will be required to expel, and in such circumstances the pressure generated may be very high.

I have taken a combination of a 12-bore gun and a 20-bore cartridge as an example, because this combination is far the most common. A 28-bore cartridge can be inserted similarly into a 16-bore gun and offers an almost exact parallel to a 20-bore cartridge in a 12-bore gun and the same results would follow. A 28-bore cartridge can also just be loaded into a 20-bore gun with a 20-bore cartridge behind it when the gun can be closed; and in very exceptional circumstances a 16-bore cartridge will stick similarly in a 12-bore gun.

Given a normal 12-bore gun and a correctly gauged 16-bore cartridge such a thing is an impossibility, as the 16-bore cartridge is too large to permit of its insertion sufficiently far into a 12-bore chamber to leave room for a 12-bore cartridge to be loaded behind. But in the *Field* of October 7th, 1922, a correspondent pointed out that he had recently purchased some 16-bore cartridges of British manufacture some of which could be inserted right home in a 12-bore gun. I thereupon wrote to this gentleman, who kindly sent me two of the smallest cartridges from the lot which he had bought. I tried these cartridges in three dozen guns of as different types as possible and found that only in the left barrel of one gun was it possible to load a 12-bore cartridge on top of the 16-bore one. And even in this case the gun could not be closed without the exercise of more than an ordinary amount of force. In the majority of cases it was impossible to insert a 12-bore cartridge for more than an inch and a half into the chamber when the 16-bore cartridge was already there.

The rims of these two somewhat undersized 16-bore cartridges measured 0·8034 and 0·8035 of an inch respectively.

Now the maximum cartridge sizes and the minimum chamber sizes, as accepted by the trade, are published. But there are no published accepted minimum cartridge sizes or maximum chamber sizes. The actually published and accepted sizes are 0·813 for the maximum diameter of a 16-bore rim, and 0·800 for the minimum diameter of the front end of a 12-bore chamber. Naturally cartridges are smaller than the maximum limit ; while, on the other hand, gun chambers are larger than the minimum limit. In the latter case, however, the difference is not great in carefully bored chambers ; and need not exceed, say, 0·002 of an inch. In old and worn chambers, however, this excess may very likely be greater.

But it was quite clear from this case that there was a danger from undersized 16-bore cartridges although the danger could only become real through the combination of an exceptionally wide 12-bore chamber and an exceptionally small 16-bore cartridge. So, as far as practical considerations were concerned, the danger was not very common. Nevertheless its very possibility was something to avoid, and consequently the British manufacturers slightly raised the minimum factory working limit for the rim diameters of 16-bore cartridges, which was the best step they could take towards the elimination of what risk there was. This minimum factory working limit has been rigidly enforced ever since, with the result that I do not think there is any danger to be feared from undersized 16-bore cartridges of British manufacture.

In the case of some foreign cartridges, however, the risk can be considerable, and in the *Field* of October

22nd, 1925, there appeared the report of an accident due to this cause. In this particular instance the cartridge-cases were of continental manufacture and out of twenty-three which I measured no less than twenty had rims of less than 0·800 of an inch in diameter, some being as small as 0·780. That is, the majority of these cartridges were sufficiently undersized to permit their being inserted right home in *any* 12-bore gun when a 12-bore cartridge could be loaded on top.

The danger attendant on the intermingling of 12-bore and 20-bore cartridges is now well known and generally appreciated. In fact so much so that many sportsmen eschew 20-bore on this account and select a 2-inch 12-bore or a 16-bore when they want a gun lighter than a 12. It cannot, therefore, be emphasised too strongly that a similar danger can exist from the accidental intermingling of 12-bore and 16-bore cartridges if the latter are not gauged most carefully during manufacture. That such a process can be omitted entirely is proved by the example I have just given, and consequently sportsmen who buy cheap continental 16-bore cases will be well advised to test them in a 12-bore gun so as to see how far they will drop into the chamber.

The possible combination of a 28-bore cartridge in a 20-bore gun was, to the best of my belief, first pointed out publicly by a correspondent to *Game and Gun* in May, 1938, and came to me, I confess, as a surprise. There is, however, not the slightest difficulty in inserting a 28-bore cartridge into an ordinary 20-bore gun, loading a 20-bore cartridge on top, and then closing the gun. This will be realised from the fact that the minimum permissible diameter of a 20-bore chamber at a distance of $2\frac{1}{2}$ inches from the breech is 0·685 of an inch, while the working sizes for the rim diameters of 28-bore cartridge-cases adopted by Imperial Chemical Industries, Ltd., are 0·665 for the minimum and 0·672 for the maximum, and it is probable that the manufacturers of most foreign brands of high-grade cases adopt similar limits. This means that the diameter of the largest 28-bore rim must always be smaller than the front end of the smallest 20-bore chamber.

But the difference in diameters is not sufficient to allow the 28-bore cartridge to slip down the bore as it can in a 16-bore gun, and it will be held by the chamber cone close in front of the 20-bore cartridge even when it is not actually resting on the front of that cartridge. When this latter condition is fulfilled the 28-bore cartridge will produce the effect of an abnormally heavy projectile, just as a 20-bore cartridge does when it rests on the top of a 12-bore cartridge in a 12-bore gun. But if there is even a little space between the base of the 28-bore cartridge and the front of the 20-bore cartridge, the conditions are changed and will be considered later under the heading of "Obstructional Bursts."

There is also the possibility of the front cartridge being fired by the discharge of the one behind, especially when a crimp turnover is used. Such a thing is extremely unlikely to occur when an over-shot wad is used as this wad is flat and comparatively soft. But with a crimp closure there is no over-shot wad, and it would, at any rate in theory, be possible for a shot pellet to strike the cap of a cartridge lodged in front and so discharge the cartridge.

A 12-bore barrel is larger than a 20-bore chamber and consequently the presssure developed by firing a cartridge of the latter size in a chamber of 12 gauge dimensions would tend to be very low, and the same general result would be given by firing a 28-bore cartridge in a chamber of 16 gauge dimensions. Accordingly I never investigated the possibilities seriously, since the risk attending the firing of any gun with a cartridge of smaller size forming an additional projectile seemed to me to be sufficiently great in itself to justify the very gravest warning and to leave the matter there.

For the weight of the front cartridge, added to that of the shot charge of the correct cartridge, combine to make so heavy a projectile that a pressure much higher than usual is demanded to produce movement. And this pressure increases abnormally the rate of burning of the powder, while the heavier projectile moves more slowly. These last two conditions combine to produce abnormal combustion, and an abnormal amount of powder is consumed in a relatively small volume. The effect approaches combustion in a closed vessel and a high chamber pressure is consequently developed.

But even so the pressure is not always sufficient to burst a really strong gun, and there are many instances on record of a 20-bore cartridge being fired out of a 12-bore gun in this manner without damage to the gun.

The risk attending such reckless experiments—for in some cases the gun was fired deliberately and knowingly, the shooter declaring that there was no danger—was always very grave, and it is unlikely that the action of any gun which was not of exceptional quality or fitted with an efficient top extension would stand the strain without showing distress. Nevertheless it is a proven fact that a burst from this cause is not necessarily inevitable.

But the discovery that a 28-bore cartridge could be loaded in front of a 20-bore cartridge in a 20-bore gun—for it was a discovery as far as I was concerned—created different conditions, since the 28-bore cartridge not only fitted a 20-bore barrel much more snugly than it did a 16-bore barrel or than a 20-bore cartridge did a 12-bore barrel, but it also produced a greater percentage increase in the weight of the projectile than it did with a 16-bore cartridge or than a 20-bore cartridge did with a 12-bore.

And at about this time the Belgian F.N. zinc cartridges with no over-shot wad and a crimp turnover were becoming fairly common, while the paper tubed cartridge with the crimp turnover appeared very shortly afterwards both in Great Britain and America.

Now it was obvious that the crimp sealing of the case and the elimination of the over-shot wad changed the condition of great improbability of the front cartridge being fired to one of what seemed to be great probability, since the shot pellets from the rear cartridge would have unobstructed access to the cap of the front cartridge directly the crimp was opened by the initial generation of the powder gases.

Accordingly, in 1938 and 1939 I carried out a number of experiments with the object of ascertaining the probable total increase in pressure which would normally be incurred by the combined discharge of both cartridges.

Since it seemed obvious that the greatest increase would be obtained by the combination of a 28-bore and 20-bore cartridge in a 20-bore gun, I began by firing a series of 20-bore cartridges alone in a pressure barrel so as to obtain the mean pressure. I then loaded up a number of 28-bore cases into dummy cartridges of exactly the same total weight as ordinary 28-bore cartridges and fired them in the same pressure barrel with their bases resting on a 20-bore cartridge. I purposely used dummies so as to eliminate any possibility of a double discharge.

Finally, I fired live 28-bore cartridges in the same barrel and in order to ensure a double discharge I stuck short "strikers" on to the centres of the over-shot wads of the 20-bore cartridges. These "strikers" functioned perfectly and in every case a double discharge was obtained.

The mean results of two series of ten shots with the dummy 28-bore cartridges gave increases in pressure of 46 and 56 per cent. But when the 28-bore cartridges were fired also, giving a double discharge, the mean increase in pressure was no less than 140 per cent.

This means that in the case of ordinary 20-bore cartridges developing an average normal pressure of, say, 2·75 tons, the pressure could become about 4·3 tons when a gun was fired with a 28-bore cartridge resting on the front of the 20-bore cartridge and when the 28-bore cartridge was not discharged as well.

If both cartridges were discharged the pressure would be raised to about 6·6 tons.

Similar combinations of 20-bore and 12-bore cartridges in a 12-bore gun gave increases of 30 and 50 per cent. in pressure when the 20-bore cartridge was not fired.

When both cartridges were fired the increase was 120 per cent.

Assuming a normal pressure of about 2·75 tons for the 12-bore cartridge on its own, this would mean that we should be prepared to expect a pressure of anything between 3·6 to something over 4 tons if a 20-bore cartridge were fired with its base resting on the front of the 12-bore cartridge in a 12-bore gun *provided the smaller cartridge were not fired as well.* If the original pressure of the 12-bore cartridge was a bit more lively the pressure developed by the double projectile would be correspondingly greater.

If both cartridges were fired the pressure would most probably be over 6 tons.

Similar experiments with 28-bore cartridges in a 16-bore gun gave an increase in pressure of 40 per cent. when the smaller cartridge was fired as a projectile and without being discharged as well. The outbreak of war intervened with the completion of these tests. But I was confident that the double discharge of 28-bore and 16-bore cartridges in a 16-bore gun would give an increase of about 130 per cent. I confess that I was surprised by the increase in pressure caused by the double discharge of a 20-bore and 12-bore cartridge in a 12-bore gun. The tight fit of a 28-bore cartridge in a 20-bore barrel would naturally produce a big increase, and that obtained by the double discharge of a 28-bore and 20-bore cartridge in a 20-bore gun did not seem unduly great. But the 20-bore cartridge lies so much more loosely in a 12-bore barrel that I did not anticipate so big a change. Further experiments in 1952 confirmed the possibility of these increases. It may be that in an ordinary barrel, which is not bored so tightly as a pressure barrel, the results might be somewhat lower. But even if they were the increase in pressure could never be anything but disastrous and it is always wiser to anticipate the maximum increase possible. If this is done the full danger is realised, and the more this danger *is* realised by sportsmen as a class the less the risk which may be incurred.

There is admittedly always the chance of a lucky low round. But there is an equal chance of an unlucky high one.

Finally, I would emphasise again that even these results were given only when the base of the front cartridge was actually resting on the top of the one behind. For, as has already been explained, if the front cartridge is a little distance ahead it acts as an obstruction, when an entirely different situation arises, which will be discussed in the next chapter.

THE USE OF CARTRIDGES TOO LONG FOR THE GUN. The pressure is raised very considerably by using cartridges which are appreciably longer than those for which a gun is chambered. It is, for example, distinctly dangerous to fire $2\frac{3}{4}$-inch 12-bore cartridges in a gun chambered for the ordinary $2\frac{1}{2}$-inch cases. One might think that this would be so obvious that no shooter would ever do such a thing; yet it is done quite frequently, and the gun or the cartridges usually receive the blame for any damage which arises.

THE USE OF ALL-BRASS CARTRIDGES IN AN ORDINARY GUN. Similarly it can be dangerous to use thin brass, or all-brass, cartridges which are specially designed and loaded for chamberless guns in a gun chambered for ordinary paper cases. The thin brass cases hold larger charges of powder and shot than do the paper cases, while the wads are larger in diameter.

Some "Thin Brass" cases are lined with a paper tube when their internal diameter is the same as that of an ordinary cartridge. Such cartridges are naturally perfectly safe to use in ordinary guns.

Cartridges of the type of the Belgian F.N. 2-inch zinc cartridges with a crimp turnover can also be used with safety in ordinary guns, for in these the felt wad is much thinner than usual and during its passage up the bore assumes a form something like that of a partially closed umbrella. In fact the majority of pressures developed by these short zinc cartridges were decidedly on the low side, a fact which probably helped the patterns.

A Cracked Action

In this particular case the damage was not due to any excessive pressure. The action was abnormally weak and lacked the support afforded by an efficient top extension. But the principal cause of the cracking was the physical condition of the steel which had been completely spoiled by over-heating

Similarly other types of all-metal cartridges specially designed for use in ordinary guns can be used with perfect safety, since the type of powder and wadding are selected so as to function correctly in what may be regarded almost as special conditions. But if there is any doubt the cartridges should be submitted for proper tests. As recently as June, 1947, I tested some Italian all-brass cartridges which developed pressures up to 3·72 tons, and were, therefore, definitely unsuitable for use in an ordinary 2½-inch 12-bore.

THE STORAGE OF CARTRIDGES IN EXCESSIVE HEAT. Some sportsmen like to store their cartridges in a hot cupboard, and frequently such cupboards are almost like ovens. This exposure to heat reduces the moisture contents of the powder and increases its violence.

The best method of storing cartridges was explained in Volume II.

THE USE OF IMPROPER WADDING. The substitutes for felt or air-cushion wads which are ordinarily used for wadding, such as cork or feltine, tend to lower the pressure; but occasionally some exceptional material may be used which can raise the pressure to a dangerous level. It was pointed out in Volume II that some years before 1914 experiments were made in which grains of rice were loaded between two card wads instead of the felt wad, and that this was a most dangerous procedure as the pressures developed were very high. Since 1920 I have come across cartridges in which sawdust had been used in a similar way. It cannot be impressed too strongly on both sportsmen and gunmakers that such departures from the normal may be highly dangerous, and experiments of this nature should only be made in a pressure barrel.

THE IMPROPER SEALING OF THE TURNOVER. As has already been explained *ad nauseam,* a tight turnover will raise the pressure. But it is doubtful whether a turnover made in the ordinary way will ever raise the pressure to the danger level, no matter how tightly it is made. Should, however, the end of the turnover be sealed to the over-shot wad by glue, or an excess of varnish, the pressure generated may become excessive. This is a point, therefore, which should not be forgotten.

Let us now turn to a consideration of the effect produced by an excessive pressure.

First of all it must constantly be kept in mind that pressure is caused only by the expansion of the gases generated by the combustion of the powder in the cartridge-case, and that this origin of pressure must always be the same irrespective of any cause contributory to the raising of the pressure above the normal limit. Failure to appreciate this elementary truth has given rise to much misunderstanding; so it is impossible to emphasise its importance too strongly.

It should, therefore, be remembered that the rise and fall of pressure in a shotgun barrel will always follow the general lines of the curve given in Plate X of Volume II. The actual pressures may be higher than those given in this diagram, but a pressure curve must always approximate to this form. That is it will rise very rapidly from the base of the cartridge-case and reach its maximum within the length of the chamber of the barrel. Once this maximum point has been reached it begins to fall away, at first very rapidly. But after a distance from the breech equal to twice the length of the chamber, or a little more, has been reached, the rate of fall in pressure becomes more gradual. And when a distance of approximately half-way up the barrel is reached the fall becomes so gradual that the pressure remains comparatively constant until the shot charge leaves the muzzle.

In other words, the pressure must always be maximum in the immediate neighbourhood of the breech, and cannot possibly ever be very high much in front of the chamber.

It is for this reason that gun barrels are always made thicker and stronger at the breech end, but in spite of this extra thickness there is really less reserve of strength at the breech than there is farther up, because the pressure will always be much higher near the breech than farther up the bore.

This should become quite clear after a study of Table XXX. In the third column of this Table appear the maximum pressures which can possibly result from the combustion of 33 grains of Smokeless Diamond in a 12-bore barrel. These maximum values are given for different distances from the breech, and they are all based on the closed vessel pressures given by this charge of powder.

That is, as has already been explained, the bore has been assumed to be completely sealed at the stated intervals in the Table, and so the whole of the charge will have been converted into gas in the volumes specified, thus developing the maximum pressures possible.

And here it may be stated that the closed vessel pressure of 30·3 tons which occurs at a distance of 1 inch from the breech could not be obtained in actual practice. For to do so would mean that the whole of the powder charge would have to be converted into gas before the wads and shot charge had begun to move. Such a rapid conversion of powder into gas would really be a detonation ; and this, as will be seen in Chapter XIX, cannot occur in an ordinary shotgun cartridge.

It may be urged that the maximum pressures which have been given in Table XXX are only those which can be generated by 33 grains of Smokeless Diamond in a 12-bore barrel, and that charges of 36 grains of this powder are used in special loads. This is true, but the increase in the maximum pressures possible resulting from the extra three grains of charge would be comparatively so slight as to make little, if any, practical difference in the general inferences which can be drawn from this Table. The maximum pressure possible in the chamber would be increased, but beyond five inches from the breech the maximum possible pressure would not reach the limit necessary to stress the inner layers of the barrel to 15 tons per square inch.

Similarly, the Table is sufficiently correct for other

33-grain bulk powders, such as E.C.; for the 36-grain powder, Modified Smokeless Diamond; for 42-grain bulk powders, such as Schultze; or even for dense powders, such as Ballistite or the Neoflaks.

In actual practice, therefore, the values given in Table XXX can be regarded as being sufficiently correct for all ordinary powder charges in a 2½-inch 12-bore barrel. And the differences which can exist in any other size of barrel between the normal and maximum possible pressures and the pressures necessary to stress the inner layers of that barrel as specified can be assumed from this Table with an accuracy sufficient for all practical purposes.

So we arrive at the conclusion—if indeed we have not reached it already—that *whatever the powder charge and whatever the gauge of the barrel, the danger from an excessive pressure must always lie in the immediate neighbourhood of the breech, as it is here that the maximum pressure occurs.*

This danger has to be met by the barrel *and the action*, and whichever is the weaker will give way provided the pressure is sufficiently high.

There can be no doubt that in the great majority of guns, especially guns in which the barrels are made from the very best-quality steel, the barrels are considerably stronger than the action. Consequently when the pressure exceeds the safety limit in such a gun the action will tend to crack across the bar. When this occurs the breech end of the barrels is immediately separated from the face of the action and the gas escapes, thus relieving the pressure.

An action is undoubtedly strengthened by an efficient top extension, but even so very few actions will withstand a pressure of 7 tons, and a high-grade barrel will withstand such a pressure without showing any effect beyond a bulge; while if the barrel were somewhat thicker in the breech than usual there would not even be any appreciable " set " as the inner layers of the chamber would not have been stressed sufficiently beyond the elastic limit to cause permanent elongation of the outer layers.

So it will be realised that the most likely result of an excessive pressure is the cracking of the action across the bar.

An excellent example of such an accident is shown in Plate VII (A). This was a best-grade 16-bore gun which was smashed by the pressure generated by overloaded cartridges. These cartridges actually contained 42 grains of a continental powder instead of the standard 28 grains, and were the cartridges to which I referred on page 343. The 1-inch pressures developed by these cartridges were measured in a pressure barrel, and varied from 5·8 to 7 tons.

In spite of this very high pressure the barrel had not apparently suffered, although it is possible that the chamber was very slightly enlarged owing to the inner layers of the walls of the chamber having been stressed just beyond the elastic limit.

It should be remembered in this connection that this was a 16-bore gun, and that owing to the smaller diameter of the bore the barrel is stronger, thickness for thickness, than that of a 12-bore gun. This will be seen at once by substitution of suitable values in the Gunmakers' Formula. A 12-bore barrel would probably have shown a slight enlargement in the chamber.

The bar of the action, however, was cracked more than half-way across and the head of the stock was smashed.

As can be seen this gun was not fitted with a top extension, yet even so it withstood several rounds before it was smashed. No higher praise could be given for the workmanship, design and quality of material used. But it is not easy to understand how the shooter could have continued to fire after noticing the very heavy recoil given by the first few rounds.

This case provides a most excellent and typical example of the result of a "smash" caused by a very excessive pressure, and the point to note is that the damage was produced in the action and at the breech.

I will now give two examples of guns burst by excessive pressures in which the barrels were weaker than the actions. In both of these cases, as would be expected, the barrels burst.

The first of these is shown in Plate VIII. This was an old and cheap 12-bore gun which had never been nitro proved, and the barrels were certainly made of an inferior-quality steel.

The excessive pressure in this case was caused by the firing of a $2\frac{3}{4}$-inch cartridge in the gun which was chambered only for the ordinary $2\frac{1}{2}$-inch case. The effect of this pressure was to burst the barrel throughout the length of the chamber, which was completely opened out, as can be seen in the photograph. The two barrels were also separated, the brazing, which was not of good quality, giving way.

The second example is shown in Plate XVI. This is particularly interesting as, to the best of my belief, it is the only recorded case of a 12-bore gun being burst by the accidental insertion of a *16-bore* cartridge in front of the 12-bore cartridge, and is the case to which reference was made on page 346.

The gun was a medium-grade weapon which was manufactured shortly before 1914 and was fitted, as can be seen, with a cross-bolt top extension. It was probably due to this fact that the action turned out to be stronger than the barrels, although the latter were rather on the light side.

In this case it will be seen that the right barrel was completely severed in two immediately in front of the chamber, a place where, as has already been pointed out, barrels usually tend to be less strong than elsewhere. The wall of the chamber was also split open along its entire length.

It is worthy of record that the action was not damaged in any way, and that the gun is still in use after being fitted with a new pair of barrels. This speaks highly for the good workmanship and design of the action, as well as for the quality of steel of which it was made.

Although at first sight the three examples of bursts which I have just given may appear to differ considerably one from the other, there is one very important point—in fact the most important point of all—which they share in common. This is the position of the damage: for in each case the damage was effected in the immediate neighbourhood of the breech.

In view of the fact that all three bursts were the direct result of excessive pressure, this is really what would be expected. But it is important that the student of this subject should learn to see the wood as a whole rather than individual trees in detail; and whenever a burst occurs the situation of the actual damage is most important evidence in determining the cause of the accident.

And in the case of high pressures there is another most important witness which should always be examined if possible. This is the fired cartridge-case of the round which actually caused the damage.

No unfired cartridge ever fits absolutely tight in the chamber, for were it to do so loading would be difficult. There is always a clearance between the brass head of the cartridge-case and the chamber, and the pressure generated on combustion of the powder expands the brass head and causes it to fit the chamber tightly. If the pressure is high the soft brass of the head takes an impress of the extractor, and the higher the pressure the more pronounced this impress. The result is that it is impossible for any abnormally high pressure to be generated without the fact being recorded by the tell-tale extractor mark on the fired case.

The photographs in Plate XXI (A) and (B) show this extractor mark plainly. The second of these photographs is of a $2\frac{3}{4}$-inch 12-bore cartridge which was fired in a gun chambered for $2\frac{1}{2}$-inch cases. The barrels were knocked off the face of the action by the resulting high pressure, and thus the head of the cartridge was unsupported when the gas escaped through the rim, splitting the rim.

In Plate XX (A) the photograph shows an ordinary 2½-inch cartridge in which the pressure had been raised to a very high level owing to the cartridges being stored in a very hot place. The extractor mark is again obvious, and the rim is enlarged although not actually split.

The strength of this extractor mark must naturally depend on the individual gun ; and so a comparison should always be made, if possible, between the fired case of the round under suspicion and normal cases which have been fired in the same gun. It will be found that the extractor mark is always much more pronounced when the pressure is high.

Another indication in a fired case of a high pressure has been mentioned in connection with the photographs in Plate XX (A) and (B) and this is the condition of the rim. An *enlarged* rim is a sure sign of a high pressure.

And yet another sign of pressure is to be found in the appearance of the cap of the fired case. If the pressure was high the cap will have been forced backwards and out of its proper seating in the head of the case ; it will be more flattened ; and the indentation of the striker will be more pronounced than usual.

This last sign is not so easily detected by an inexperienced observer, but once anyone has seen two or three caps which have been unseated by high pressures he will know what to look for. An experienced investigator can tell almost at a glance from the appearance of a fired case whether the pressure was on the high side, and can even make a very shrewd guess as to the actual pressure which was generated. Photographs showing the effects on caps of high and normal pressures are given in Plate XX (C).

In the case of a gun which is already "off the face" a comparatively moderate pressure will frequently cause *split* rims, but in these circumstances the extractor mark and appearance of the cap will indicate whether the pressure was sufficiently high to be regarded as abnormal.

And here it may be mentioned that if a gun is "off the face" and gas escapes through a split rim, the escaping gas may cause damage. I have known such a thing happen. Cartridges which developed pressures which were admittedly high, but certainly not dangerous, were used in a gun which was "off the face" in the first place. These cartridges would not have damaged a sound gun; but owing to the rim splitting the jet of gas thus produced by one round broke the cross-bolt top extension.

All shooters should realise that if they use a gun which is obviously "off the face" they can blame no one but themselves should an accident occur. For almost anything may happen if cartridges which are at all violent are used in a gun which gives split rims in the normal course of events. Such a gun has no reserve of safety, and to continue to use it is to seek trouble.

But let us return to the subject of Pressure Bursts. It has been seen that the danger is greatest in the immediate neighbourhood of the breech. And it can now be stated definitely that a burst or smash caused by an excessive pressure must always occur in the immediate neighbourhood of the breech; further, that such damage will either be a cracking of the action across the bar, or else the bursting of the barrel in, or immediately in front of, the chamber.

Damage such as this is strong evidence that the burst was caused by a high pressure, provided the sectional design of the action and the quality of the metal are all that they should be. Corroborative evidence may be found in the condition of the brass head of the fired case which actually caused the accident.

Conversely, if a burst occurs in front of the chamber cone and there is no damage to barrels or action in the immediate neighbourhood of the breech, and the gun has not been knocked "off the face," it can then be assumed with confidence that the burst could not possibly have been caused by a high pressure, and some other explanation must be sought.

CHAPTER XVII

BURSTS CAUSED BY OBSTRUCTIONS IN THE BORE

IN the last chapter the problems presented by Pressure Bursts were considered in detail, and in the final paragraph it was stated that any burst which occurs more than an inch in front of the chamber cannot be the direct outcome of excessive pressure generated in the cartridge-case. The fact, however, remains that if a barrel bursts anywhere only two explanations are possible: either the gas pressure at the site of the burst was too great, or else the wall of the barrel was too weak. And so both these two possibilities must be studied in turn.

If the gas pressure at some point between the front of the chamber cone and the muzzle is sufficiently high to burst a sound barrel, something out of the ordinary must have occurred which resulted in the pressure being raised abnormally at the site of the burst. There is only one way in which the pressure can be raised locally in a barrel once it has begun to fall after reaching its maximum level in the chamber: this is by the presence of an obstruction in the bore.

So we now come to the second of the three classes of bursts which were tabulated at the beginning of the last chapter.

OBSTRUCTIONAL BURSTS

This class of burst is far the most common, and it is safe to say that at the very least 70 per cent. of all the bursts which occur, if not more, are caused by obstructions in the bore. Indeed, so much more common are obstructional than non-obstructional bursts that gunmakers are frequently inclined to jump too quickly to the conclusion that when a burst occurs some way up a barrel it must have been due to an obstruction. There is, however, no valid excuse for such a mistake ; nor can it ever be made if the fundamental causes of an obstructional burst are properly understood.

It is, accordingly, extremely important that the actual reason should be understood why an obstruction in the bore increases the pressure locally.

The first theory put forward to explain the high local pressure caused by an obstruction suggested that the pressure was due to the compression of the imprisoned air between the obstruction and the rapidly advancing projectile. It is quite conceivable that if the obstruction were such that it sealed the bore completely and was almost immovable the imprisoned air would be compressed sufficiently to produce a high local pressure. But when searching for a correct explanation any theory which only fits in with certain particular, and very abnormal, conditions must be disregarded. And the imprisoned air theory can be disregarded owing to the fact that a barrel can be burst just as easily by a tubular obstruction, which must obviously allow the air to escape, as by one which seals the bore.

The next theory suggested that the pressure was the direct result of the compression of the moving shot charge, or of the obstruction, or of both, which was caused by the impact. Here again it is possible in certain circumstances that the longitudinal compression of the shot charge and the obstruction would cause an outward lateral expansion sufficient to produce a certain degree of local pressure. But that this is the real cause of all obstructional bursts can be disproved as readily as can the imprisoned air theory. For experiments have been carried out in which the shot charge was replaced by a brass cylinder of the same weight, and an identical cylinder was inserted in the bore of a pressure barrel as an obstruction. After firing, both these cylinders were recovered, when it was found that there were no indications of material lateral expansion, and certainly none to explain the very high local pressure which was actually measured with a piston and crusher.

Both these theories can, therefore, be dismissed.

"WAVE" PRESSURES. The true explanation was first indicated by the great French scientist, Vieille, who probably made more experiments with explosives than any other person who has ever lived. In 1890 Vieille published his classical researches on "Wave" Pressures under the title *Etude des Pressions Ondulatoires* which was included in the *Memorial des Poudres et Salpêtres*.

Now when a given weight of explosive is fired in a closed vessel the pressure developed must always be the same since it depends on the volume and temperature of the gases generated by the explosive. Accordingly the method of firing and the disposition of the explosive charge in the closed vessel cannot affect the maximum pressure unless some other factor is brought into play.

Vieille made experiments in closed vessels of long cylindrical shape which were very similar to gun barrels, being 0·87 inches in diameter and 34·9 inches long. In these vessels he fired different charges of various explosives, but the results he obtained with the French Poudre S, which is very similar to Schultze, will be sufficient to indicate now the general nature of all these results.

A charge of Poudre S which gave a loading density of 0·2 in the closed vessel was first of all placed uniformly along the whole length of the vessel and then fired. The pressure obtained was 5·7 tons at all points in the closed vessel.

An identical charge was then settled down at one end of the closed vessel and fired, and the pressure at the ends of the vessel was found to be 13 tons, although in between the ends it was normal for the loading density.

The difference in pressure developed between uniform loading and end loading increased, in the various experiments made, with the rate of combustion of the explosive, the density of loading, and the length of the closed vessel.

Vieille proved that the abnormal end pressures which were given by end loading were due to the movement of the hot and very elastic powder gases in the direction

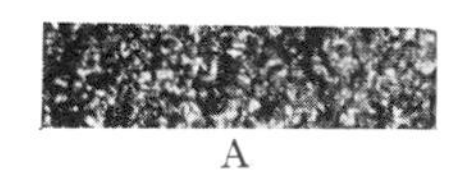

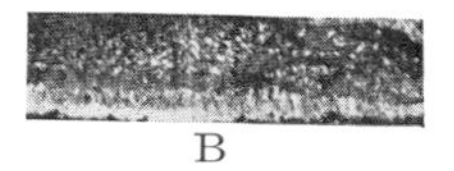

A B

(A) A slightly enlarged Photograph of the Fractured Surface of the Cracked Action shown in Plate XVII

The coarse, granular nature of the structure can be plainly seen. This is a sign of over-heating

(B) A Fractured Surface of a bit of steel of identical composition, but which had not been over-heated

In this case the surface shows a fine-grained, "silky" appearance

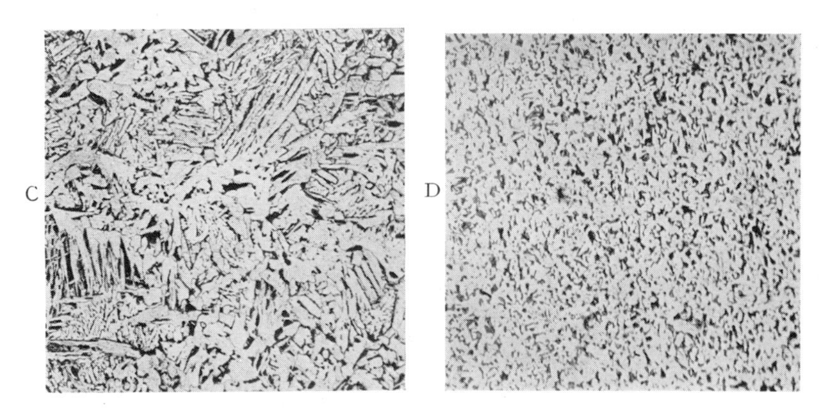

C D

(C) A Photo-micrograph of the steel used in the Cracked Action shown in Plate XVII taken at a magnification of 50 diameters

(D) A Photo-micrograph of a bit of steel from a high-grade action also taken at a magnification of 50 diameters

of the length of the vessel. When the explosive charge was evenly distributed along the whole length of the vessel and fired, gas was given off simultaneously throughout the length of the vessel and an even pressure developed. But when the explosive charge was placed entirely at one end of the closed vessel, the gases given off naturally rushed forwards along the length of the vessel until the forward layer of gases was suddenly checked by the closed end. When this occurred the gases which were behind the extreme forward layer overtook this layer and began to pile up against it, with the result that the extreme forward layer was compressed with great violence. It was this compression of the extreme forward layer of gases which caused the high pressure at the end of the vessel opposite to the place originally occupied by the explosive charge.

The situation can be compared to a crowd of people rushing up a blind alley without any regard for one another, when those at the extreme end of the alley will be squashed by the others pressing onwards, and they will bear the greatest pressure from the crowd pushing them against the wall.

Gases, however, are perfectly elastic, and therefore the pressure is very high at the extreme end of the vessel and drops very rapidly as this point is left.

The intense local pressure thus set up at the end of Vieille's closed vessel is known as a "Wave" pressure, and the maximum height of this wave pressure is very local.

The wave pressure at the far end of the long closed vessel was reflected backwards and an exactly similar situation was then set up at the opposite end of the vessel, which accounted for the pressure being so high at both ends.

After this the wave pressure was again reflected forwards and backwards, with gradually decreasing violence, until the movement finally died away. This action was shown by suspending a closed vessel as a pendulum and noting the swing.

In order that the great increase in pressure due to the wave should be appreciated I am quoting more of Vieille's results in the following Table.

TABLE XXXI

RESULTS OF VIEILLE'S INVESTIGATIONS OF WAVE PRESSURES

Explosive used.	Loading Density.	Pressure in Tons at ends of closed Vessel when loading is		Percentage Increase in Pressure due to wave.
		Evenly distributed.	At one end only.	
French B.F. . .	0·1	7	11	57
French B.F. . .	0·2	15·5	47·5	207
French B.S.P. . .	0·2	13·0	29·7	128
Poudre S. . . .	0·2	5·7	13·0	128
Black Powder .	0·5	14·5	40·3	178
Nitro-Cotton . .	0·1	11·0	35·5	222

WHY AN OBSTRUCTION BURSTS A BARREL. Vieille's researches provide a key to the problem of obstructional bursts, for when a projectile travelling up the bore meets a stationary obstruction its velocity is suddenly checked and it then proceeds to move onwards pushing the obstruction with it. But the velocity of the projectile and obstruction together after the impact must be less than the velocity of the projectile alone immediately before the impact, and consequently the check in the velocity of the projectile has the effect of turning its base momentarily into the sealed end of a closed vessel, when the expanding gases will overtake it and set up a wave pressure. And this wave pressure, which is extremely local in its action, can be sufficient to bulge or burst a barrel.

This explanation of the actual reason why an obstruction in the bore should cause a high local pressure may be better understood if we take a concrete example.

Let us assume that a shot charge meets an obstruction

of equal weight at a point in the bore when its velocity is 1,000 f.s.

Immediately before the impact the powder gases near the shot charge will be moving at the same velocity as the shot, that is 1,000 f.s.; but the velocity of the gases will be less and less as the distance from the shot charge increases, and will be zero in the extreme end of the cartridge-case. For the sake of convenience all these gases can be divided into two parts : those which have a velocity over 500 f.s. and those which have a velocity less than this figure. The division between these two parts will be approximately half-way between the base of the wads and the extreme end of the cartridge-case.

This situation is shown in Phase I in Fig. 33, which shows diagrammatically the state of affairs immediately before impact.

Phase II in Fig. 33 shows the actual moment of impact. When this occurs the velocity of the shot charge and wads is suddenly checked ; and then, by the laws of dynamics, the shot charge, wads and obstruction all begin to move forward together with a velocity of 500 f.s.; that is half the previous velocity of the shot charge and wads, since the obstruction is of equal weight to the shot charge and wads put together.

Simultaneously with this check in the velocity of the shot charge and wads all the expanding gases which are moving at a higher velocity than 500 f.s. will begin to overtake the shot charge, wads and obstruction and rush forwards against the base of the wads.

The next phase occurs a fraction of time after the impact and is shown as Phase III in Fig. 33. All the gases moving faster than 500 f.s. are rushing forwards and compress the extreme forward layer of gas against the base of the wads. The compression of this layer of gas sets up a wave pressure which acts radially, or outwards at right angles to the axis of the bore, in exactly the same way that a wave pressure was set up at the extreme end of Vieille's closed vessel, and over a very small length of the barrel.

Because the shot charge is moving all the time, even though with reduced velocity after the impact on the obstruction, it is obvious that this wave pressure will act ahead of the spot where the first meeting between the shot charge and obstruction took place.

Since this wave pressure acts radially outwards the wall of the barrel is submitted to a very severe pressure all round its circumference, and if the pressure is sufficient to stress the barrel beyond the elastic limit of the steel a permanent bulge *all round the bore* is the result. Such a bulge is known as a "Ring Bulge," as it has the appearance of a ring on a finger.

If the wave pressure is sufficiently severe to stress the barrel beyond its maximum strength a rupture, or burst, will result ; but even so there will always be elongation, which will take the form of a ring bulge, in that side of the barrel where rupture does not actually occur because the whole circumference of the barrel will have been stressed beyond its elastic limit over that part where the wave pressure acted.

Sometimes the barrel is completely severed in two by the wave pressure, but when this happens the two fractured ends of the barrel will always assume a funnel-like appearance, as a rupture all round the circumference is really the final development of a ring bulge. In a double-barrelled gun, however, each barrel provides support for the other, and consequently it is more usual for the actual burst to occur on the outward, or unsupported, part of the barrel. But the supported part of the barrel will show signs of the ring bulge, as will the adjoining part of the other barrel.

So it will now be seen that when a projectile meets an obstruction there is a sudden change in velocity, and that this sudden change in velocity sets up a radial wave pressure which bulges, and possibly ruptures, the barrel at a point ahead of the original site of impact.

MR. JONES'S CONFIRMATORY EXPERIMENTS. In 1903 the late Mr. F. W. Jones carried out a long series of experiments to check the truth of this theory and his

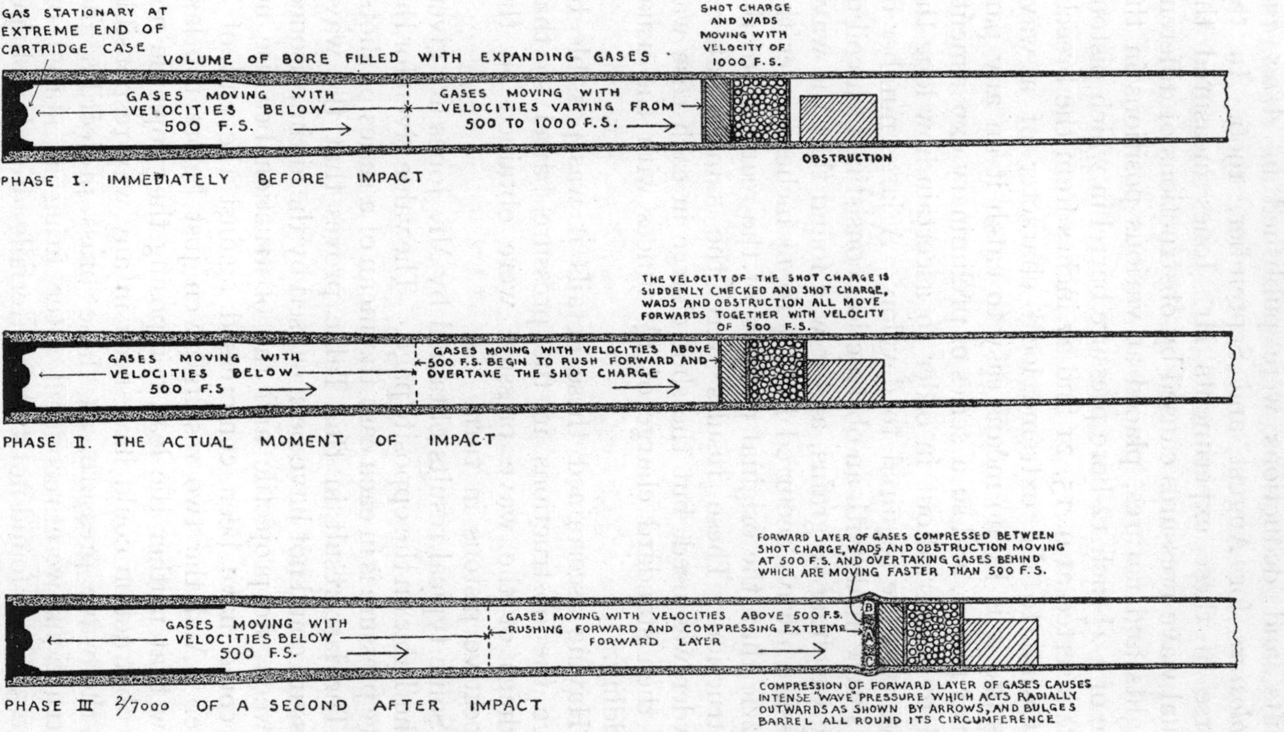

Fig. 33.—Diagram to illustrate how an obstruction in the bore bursts a barrel.

results and deductions were published in *Arms and Explosives* for August and September, 1906. In the course of these experiments Mr. Jones measured the actual wave pressures caused by obstructions of different weights and natures, placed at various positions in the bore of a 2½-inch 12-bore pressure barrel in which pistons were inserted at 9, 15, 21 and 27 inches from the breech.

Owing to the extreme local character of a wave pressure it is by no means easy to catch it on any particular piston, and so a series of preliminary experiments had to be carried out in order to ascertain how long the wave pressure required to develop. A large number of tests were made with an obstruction consisting of a coil of wire weighing 70 grains, and it was found that the wave pressure always occurred from ¾ to 1¼ inches nearer the muzzle than the original position of the rear face of the obstruction. These results were the same whatever powder was used, but the shot charge in each case was the then standard charge of 1⅛ ounces with the usual wadding.

Having ascertained these details it was possible to place the obstructions in the pressure barrel so that readings of the wave pressure were obtained on the respective pistons in turn.

Some typical results obtained by Mr. Jones are given in the Table on the opposite page. The value given for the wave pressure is in each case the mean of a series of shots.

The last result in this Table proves that the wave pressure could not have been caused by the air imprisoned between the projectile and the obstruction because no air could have been compressed against the end of a tube.[1] And the two results given just before the last show that neither the lead composing the projectile nor the obstruction could have been in any way responsible for the wave pressure, as these brass projectiles and obstructions were recovered after firing as stated on page 363 and found not to be materially altered in shape.

[1] This same fact was also proved by bursting ordinary barrels with obstructions made of coils of wire.

The first four results show how the intensity of the wave pressure is increased with the distance of the obstruction from the breech; while the fourth, fifth and sixth results at 27 inches show how an increase in the weight of the obstruction raises the wave pressure.

Now the farther the shot charge travels from the breech the greater is its velocity at any moment, and

TABLE XXXII

WAVE PRESSURES DEVELOPED BY DIFFERENT OBSTRUCTIONS AT VARIOUS POINTS IN A 12-BORE BARREL

Projectile.	Obstruction.		Distance of Wave Pressure from Breech.	Wave Pressure in Tons.
	Nature.	Weight.		
$1\frac{1}{8}$ oz. shot and usual wadding	Shot and wads	539 grs.	9 inches	5·9
"	"	"	15 "	6·4
"	"	"	21 "	7·8
"	"	"	27 "	8·3
"	"	270 grs.	27 "	7·1
"	"	135 "	27 "	3·4
"	Solid brass cylinder	539 "	27 "	9·0
Solid brass cylinder, weighing $1\frac{1}{8}$ oz. usual wadding	"	"	27 "	8·6
"	Brass tube	"	27 "	7·9

consequently any check to its movement caused by an obstruction of fixed weight will produce a greater *change in velocity* the farther this check occurs from the breech.[1]

Also at any given point in the barrel the *change in velocity* will be greater as the weight of the obstruction, which causes the check, is increased.[1]

It will, therefore, be realised that the first six results in Table XXXII completely endorse Vieille's researches,

[1] If V is the velocity of the projectile at the moment of impact, W the weight of the projectile and M that of the obstruction, then, by the laws of dynamics, the velocity immediately after impact will be

from which it was evident that the wave pressure is due to the movement of the powder gases relative to the projectile. *For the greater the change in the velocity of the projectile the more excess velocity will the powder gases have, and consequently the more intense will be the wave pressure.*[1]

The reader may quite naturally wonder what happens to the air imprisoned between the advancing shot charge and an obstruction which seals the bore; so such a situation deserves to be considered.

$V \times \frac{W}{W + M}$, and the change in velocity will be $V\left(1 - \frac{W}{W + M}\right)$. If W and M are constant and V is increased, so will the change in velocity be increased.

Similarly if V is constant and M is increased, the change in velocity will also be increased.

[1] Mr. Jones developed a rough empirical rule for estimating the force of the wave pressure which he based on the fact that the wave pressure must be a function of the change in the velocity of the projectile due to its meeting an obstruction. This change will be $V\left(1 - \frac{W}{W + M}\right)$, and if this reduction in velocity is multiplied by 0·0123 the product represents the approximate rise in pressure due to the wave.

For instance, at 21 inches the velocity of the shot charge would be about 1,200 f.s. When M = W, the reduction in velocity at this distance is 600 f.s. This figure multiplied by 0·0123 gives 7·38 as the value for the rise in pressure due to the wave, to which must be added the normal gas pressure at 21 inches, namely 0·33 tons, making a total pressure of 7·71 tons, which approximates very closely to the value of 7·8 tons actually obtained by experiment and given in Table XXXII.

The comparative accuracy of this rough empiric is shown further by the following comparison of calculated and average observed wave pressures.

Calculated	Average observed
3·4 tons	3·4 tons
5·7 ,,	7·1 ,,
6·8 ,,	6·5 ,,
7·6 ,,	7·0 ,,
8·0 ,,	7·9 ,,
8·3 ,,	8·6 ,,

The great majority of obstructions do not make an air-tight fit in the bore; but should one do so, the imprisoned air is compressed until the pressure behind the obstruction is sufficient to overcome both the inertia of the obstruction and the resistance to movement offered by the free air in front. When this degree of compression has been attained the obstruction and shot charge will be moving forward together with a common velocity which must be less than the maximum velocity attained by the shot charge before the obstruction began to move. So there must be a change in the velocity of the shot charge, although this change will be more gradual than when the air is free to pass by the obstruction. But it certainly causes an intense wave pressure as was proved by Mr. Jones's experiments. However, the exact effect on the wave pressure due to the change in velocity being more gradual is unknown.

From the very nature of a wave pressure in a barrel it follows that the length of barrel on which the intense pressure acts is very small. Attempts at catching the wave pressure on pistons in experiments indicate that this length is about one-tenth of an inch. The intense pressure acting radially outwards over this small length of barrel produces a ring of indentation at the point where this wave pressure existed. This is the ring bulge and it must always be present in a barrel burst by a wave pressure.

From this it will be clear that it is absolutely impossible for a barrel to be burst by an obstruction in the bore without the barrel showing that this has occurred by the tell-tale ring bulge.

SUBSEQUENT WAVE PRESSURES CAUSED BY AN OBSTRUCTION. Let us now turn to a consideration of what happens after the wave pressure has been developed, that is after the situation shown in Phase III in Fig. 33.

Two possible conditions may exist: either the wave pressure was sufficiently violent to burst the barrel, or it was not.

If the barrel is burst the gas escapes and the pressure is immediately relieved, while the shot charge and obstruction continue to move up the bore under the influence of the velocity they possessed at the moment of the action of the wave pressure. Thus the shot charge and obstruction will leave the muzzle of the burst barrel.

If the wave pressure was not sufficient to burst the barrel the situation can become more complicated. The shot charge and obstruction will continue to travel along the bore under the influence of the expanding powder gases, but the wave pressure will be reflected backwards and will occur again at the extreme end of the cartridge-case. It will then rush forward once more and may overtake the shot charge before it has left the muzzle, in which case it will act again immediately behind the wads. It will now, however, be very much less intense because the shot charge will have moved farther on and so the gases will have less excess velocity than they had when the first wave pressure was formed.

From this it may appear that no less than three ring bulges may be produced by one obstruction. In practice, however, this is hardly possible because it will be seen from Table XXX that the pressure necessary to stress the chamber only to the elastic limit is greater than one which will burst the barrel at any point more than 8 inches from the breech. So it is almost impossible for a wave pressure to lack the violence required to burst a barrel half-way up and yet be sufficiently intense to bulge the barrel at the breech.

However, it is possible for the *third* wave pressure to be sufficiently violent to bulge the barrel some way ahead of the site of the first wave pressure, in which case one obstruction would be responsible for two ring bulges. I had never seen such a case until December, 1946, when I examined a gun which had two ring bulges in the right barrel, one about 3 inches from the breech and the other, which was less pronounced, nearly 3 inches farther up. In addition to these two ring bulges, the action was smashed at the angle. The cause of this damage was a fairly heavy obstruction in the bore just clear of the chamber—almost certainly a bit of cleaning material as the accident occurred at the first shot of the day—which was struck by the shot charge when the resulting wave pressure stressed the thick part of the barrel beyond the elastic limit and produced the first ring bulge. The shot charge and obstruction then continued to travel up the bore while the wave pressure was reflected back to the breech. Here it lacked the violence needed to stress the thick breech end of the barrel beyond the elastic limit, but the pressure at the angle of the action was sufficiently intense to split the body of the action. Some of the gas escaped, forcing the cartridge forwards into the chamber of the left barrel, but the relief was not sufficient to prevent the rest of the gas being reflected back up the bore of the right barrel, when it caught up the advancing shot charge and obstruction and thus produced a third wave pressure which stressed the barrel beyond the elastic limit and so produced the second ring bulge. Incidentally, this was the only burst or smashed gun which I have seen in which the left cartridge had not been fired as well as the right when the damage occurred in the right barrel. The explanation undoubtedly is that the gas was reflected back down the right barrel with such rapidity that the cartridge in the left chamber was pushed forwards before the left lock could be jarred off or before the involuntary pull on the left trigger had had time to develop.[1]

OBSTRUCTIONS VERY NEAR THE MUZZLE. The next

[1] Wave pressures recurring down the bore are a regular phenomenon in heavy artillery, especially in some big naval guns. In these guns the charge is about 6 feet long, and consists of a very slow burning variety of cordite so as to ensure well-sustained pressures throughout the length of the bore. This charge ignites so comparatively slowly that gas is generated by the rear portion before proper combustion has started in the extreme front. The effect of this is that the front portion of the charge acts as an obstruction to the expanding gases generated in rear, and causes a wave pressure which is reflected backwards and forwards during the passage of the shell along the bore.

point which deserves attention is the effect of obstructions very near the muzzle. It has been shown that the wave pressure needs a little time to develop and that, in consequence, it always occurs at a point in the barrel from about $\frac{3}{4}$ to $1\frac{1}{4}$ inches in front of the position occupied by the rear end of the obstruction before the impact.

From this it will be realised that if an obstruction is situated so near the muzzle that its rear end is $\frac{3}{4}$ of an inch, or less, from the muzzle the wave pressure will not have had time to develop before the shot charge has left the muzzle. In this case the wave pressure will actually occur just outside the muzzle, when it will of course be dissipated in the air without damaging the gun.

This fact is of extreme importance in determining the limit of the position of choke in a barrel. For the constriction of the choke checks the velocity of the shot charge, as has been explained in Volume II, which means that choke really acts in exactly the same way as an obstruction.

When the shot charge enters the cone of the choke it has attained its maximum velocity, and so it will have time to travel the greatest possible distance before it is overtaken by the wave pressure. This distance is about $1\frac{1}{4}$ inches farther on than the position of the obstruction, which is in this case the cone of the choke. So it will be seen that if the parallel in front of the choke is longer than about $1\frac{1}{4}$ inches there is a risk of the shot charge being caught up by the wave pressure before it has left the muzzle, when a ring bulge will probably be produced very close to the muzzle.

But if there is an abnormally deep recess just behind the choke, or if the cone of the choke begins too abruptly, the shot charge may be checked sufficiently by the *rear* part of the cone to cause a wave pressure to develop; and in such a case the wave pressure may catch up the shot charge before it has quite entered the parallel, when a ring bulge will be formed at the front end of the cone or the beginning of the parallel.

The same result may occur if the felt wad is very

hard and incompressible, for it will then have difficulty in entering the cone of the choke, when the rear end of the cone will act as an obstruction. In a properly designed choke the check in velocity is gradual as the shot charge and wads travel up the cone, and only becomes definite when the front end of the cone is reached, which is too close to the muzzle for the wave pressure to have time to develop.

When a ring bulge is formed near the muzzle from any of these causes the choke is said to be "lifted." Various explanations are frequently offered, but the real one is that it is the effect of the wave pressure caused by the check in the velocity due to the choke; and it is only when the choke is ill designed, or the wadding is too hard, or the velocity of the shot charge is abnormally low, that the wave pressure can catch the shot charge up before its exit from the muzzle.

Incidentally this fact provides conclusive evidence in disproof of the theory that the ring bulge is caused by the expansion of the lead of the shot charge. For were this the case a ring bulge would be produced in the cone of the choke in every gun, and by every shot.

TYPES OF OBSTRUCTIONS

We can now pass to the problem of how obstructions find their way into the bore of a gun. There are two general ways in which this happens:

(1) They can be inserted by some act of the shooter independently of the cartridge.

(2) They can be left behind in the bore as the result of a faulty cartridge.

All obstructions must come under one of these headings, so let us take them in turn.

The following are typical of those which can be inserted by the shooter.

Cleaning Material. Bits of cleaning material, usually tow or rag, are sometimes left in the bore at the end of one day's shooting and not noticed at the beginning of the next. To the careful man such an accident may appear almost impossible ; but in actual practice it is a very fruitful cause of bursts, especially abroad when the cleaning of the gun is delegated to some native servant or orderly. One would think that the final act of cleaning a gun would always be to look through the barrels in order to see that the work was complete. But in spite of what seems to be obvious, cleaning material *is* frequently left in the bores of guns. Accordingly all shooters should make it an immutable rule to look down the barrels before starting off on a day's shooting.

Since a bit of cleaning material can be left at any point in the bore a burst from this type of obstruction can occur anywhere in the barrel. But if the material is left in the chamber so that it touches the front end of the loaded cartridge it will not act as an obstruction but will cause an increase in chamber pressure, since the shot charge must have acquired a certain amount of velocity before a wave pressure can be developed. An obstruction situated but an inch ahead of the chamber will allow the shot charge sufficient time to acquire requisite velocity, and the wave pressure produced can be enough to burst the best barrel if the obstruction is heavy. For it must be remembered that it is the magnitude of the *change in velocity* that is the deciding factor in the intensity of the wave pressure ; and if the obstruction is sufficiently heavy there can be a bigger change in velocity when the shot charge is only moving at 500 f.s. than would be caused by a very light obstruction when the shot charge was moving at 1,200 f.s.

Any accident that may arise from cleaning material left in the bore can be regarded only as the outcome of gross and unpardonable carelessness.

MUD OR SNOW. This is probably the most common type of obstruction there is.

Mud, earth or snow can be picked up in the muzzle of a gun by scraping it accidentally on the ground when negotiating some fence. A bit of stick or twig will sometimes get pushed into the muzzle when going through a hedge or thick undergrowth. And peat from the edge of a grouse butt can be picked up by brushing the side of the butt with the muzzle, or when leaving a gun standing with its muzzle resting against the side of the butt.

Some sportsmen are of the opinion that there is only danger when the mud, or similar type of obstruction, completely seals the bore ; and that when the bore is only partially sealed no harm will be done. This idea is, of course, quite wrong ; and the danger is identical whether the bore is completely sealed by mud or only partially obstructed. But since the wave pressure always acts ahead of the original position of the obstruction, any mud or snow which does not extend more than $\frac{3}{4}$ of an inch down the muzzle will not cause any damage because the obstruction will have been carried out of the muzzle by the shot charge before the wave pressure can develop. So in this respect an obstruction in the extreme muzzle has a similar effect as regards the wave pressure as has choke.

But if the mud reaches farther down the barrel, as it generally does, the muzzle will be bulged or burst.

Obstructions of this type usually stick in the bore from 1 to 6 inches from the muzzle, and so the burst or bulge as a rule occurs in approximately the last 5 inches of the barrel. But it is quite possible for the obstruction to slip farther down, in which case the burst or bulge will be farther down too.

Such bursts cannot be regarded as so much the result of carelessness as of accident, and many shooters seem quite unaware of the danger. The best precaution is to take great care to avoid bringing the muzzle of the gun in contact with the ground or anything else. And if such a contact is even suspected one should always unload and look down the barrels to make sure that all is clear.

Personally I always carry a pull-through in my pocket when out shooting so as to be able to remove any obstruction that might find its way in by accident. I have only once had to use it, but the very fact that it has been used proves the value of its presence.

THE ACCIDENTAL INSERTION IN THE CHAMBER OF A CARTRIDGE OF SMALLER GAUGE. I have already dealt with this possibility at considerable length in the last chapter, and so will not repeat myself here beyond stating that the danger of an obstructional burst only arises when there is a space between the rear end of the front cartridge and the front end of the second cartridge. If this space is only an inch the shot charge will have sufficient time to acquire ample velocity to produce an obstructional burst through a wave pressure being developed by the change in that velocity. For although the velocity of the shot charge may not be very high so near the breech it must not be forgotten that the obstruction is very heavy, and thus the *change* in the velocity of the shot charge will be considerable.

Usually a 20-bore cartridge will stick quite ½ an inch in front of the loaded 12-bore cartridge in a 12-bore gun, and a 28-bore cartridge will stick a similar distance ahead of a 16-bore cartridge in a 16-bore gun, while a 28-bore cartridge tends to stick less than ¼ of an inch in front of a loaded 20-bore cartridge in a 20-bore gun. But, as I have stated in the last chapter, I do not think a 16-bore cartridge is very likely to cause an *obstructional* burst in a 12-bore gun as it would generally stick with its base resting on the end of the loaded 12-bore cartridge, when a *pressure* burst would probably be the result.

The further forward the smaller cartridge sticks the more violent will be the wave pressure.

A burst of this type can only be caused by the accidental intermingling of 20-bore and 12-bore cartridges, or of 28-bore and 16-bore cartridges. So the best precaution is to avoid any possible risk from this cause by keeping these respective sizes of cartridges quite separate.

But even if a shooter is sufficiently unfortunate as to load a 20-bore cartridge in a 12-bore gun he will receive warning that something out of the ordinary has occurred by getting an apparent miss-fire. *So it should be an invariable rule always to look down the barrels on the sus-*

picion of a miss-fire, especially if the chamber appears empty when the gun is opened.

From the very nature of the obstruction the burst must always occur a little distance in front of the chamber cone.

It is just possible that the impact of the over-shot wad of the 12-bore cartridge against the cap of the 20-bore cartridge might fire the latter, and in the case of crimp cartridges, where there is no over-shot wad, the chances of the 20-bore cartridges being fired are increased. The pressure developed by the 20-bore cartridge in the 12-bore barrel would be less than normal but its effect would be to act as an extra check to the velocity of the 12-bore charge, when the change in that velocity would be greater. This would mean a more violent wave pressure. Thus it will be realised that the only effect of such a double discharge would be to intensify the wave pressure produced, and that the resulting burst would be caused by the wave pressure whether the 20-bore cartridge were fired or not. In fact the firing of the 20-bore cartridge would make no difference to the result.

We now come to the second general class of obstructions, namely those which can be left behind in the bore as the result of a faulty cartridge.

It occasionally happens that a weak cap may fail to ignite the powder charge properly, especially if the powder is of a gelatinised type and the weather is very cold, as was explained in Volume II. In such circumstances combustion is not complete, or may not even occur at all, when there will be insufficient gas pressure to propel the shot charge and wads out of the muzzle, although there may be enough to push them some distance up the bore. On the gun being opened the empty cartridge-case is ejected and if another round is then loaded and fired an obstructional burst is practically inevitable. And because the weight of the obstruction will be identical with that of the projectile, as both consist of a shot charge and wads, the change in velocity will be great, which means a very intense wave pressure.

Nowadays, when both caps and powders are so

efficient, an accident from this cause is happily rare. But if the caps and powder are not properly matched it is quite possible for faulty ignition to occur; and so the importance of obtaining cartridges in which the caps really do suit the powder will be appreciated.

With hand loaded cartridges a single powder charge is sometimes omitted altogether by an oversight, and then the only propelling force would be due to the explosion of the cap, which would probably leave the shot charge and wads lodged a little distance up the bore. But with machine loaded cartridges such accidental omissions of individual charges are almost impossible, and so it is clear that the best safeguard for this type of accident is to purchase cartridges of known reliability.

Faulty ignition may also be due to a very abnormally weak striker blow. Some years ago I came across a case of this nature, and investigation showed that the right lock was so rusty that it was hardly possible for the tumbler to fall. This was in a best grade gun, too, and it only emphasises the extreme importance of examining the locks periodically.

When a shot charge is left in the bore it is possible for the shot itself to fall out when the barrels are dropped for re-loading, leaving the felt wadding behind. In this case the weight of the obstruction would be comparatively light, and so the wave pressure would not be nearly so severe as that caused by the whole shot charge. In fact I have known an instance of a felt wad being stuck in the bore a little distance ahead of the chamber cone which did not cause even a ring bulge when a round was fired. The shooter knew the wad was there and did not intend to fire another shot through that barrel; but on his way home he forgot and took a sudden chance. No harm was done simply because the change in velocity produced by the light obstruction close to the breech was insufficient to develop a wave pressure violent enough to stress the rather thick wall of the barrel to its elastic limit. So no permanent elongation was produced in the form of a ring bulge.

In all cases of faulty ignition the shooter receives definite warning, and if he heeds this he will avoid an accident. If the entire shot charge and wads are left in the bore there will be no report, as this is caused by the powder gases escaping from the muzzle at high tension ; and if the shot charge does not leave the muzzle the powder gases behind it cannot do so either.

Then when the empty case is ejected, or extracted, a very abnormal amount of smoke will be seen emerging from the open breech. If there was no powder charge in the cartridge there would be no smoke ; but then there would not have been any report either, and this in itself should arouse suspicion that all was not well.

So the shooter should make another rule, namely always to look down the bore if there is anything in the least abnormal with the sound of the report, or if an abnormal amount of smoke issues from the breech after unloading, or the recoil is abnormally low.

Then should a " cut off " (see Volume II) occur, the paper tube of the case may sometimes be blown some way up the bore when it will make a most dangerous obstruction. Usually, however, the paper tube will remain in the chamber in which case it will not be found possible to reload that barrel. But in any event the shooter, or loader, would probably notice the fact that a whole cartridge-case had not been ejected, only the brass head ; and he should then look down the bore at once to see where the paper tube is stuck. With a non-ejector gun a cut-off could not occur without being noticed.

But there is one type of obstruction which can be left behind in the bore after the discharge of a cartridge which gives no warning, and against which no precaution can be taken. It is, therefore, in some ways the most dangerous obstruction of all ; but happily it is so rare that the possibility is scarcely worth consideration.

This obstruction is the over-powder card wad. If this wad is inserted into the cartridge-case slanting by the loader or loading machine it may happen that it is turned edgeways, and during combustion is not expelled from the bore with the other wads and the shot charge. And even if this does occur the thin card wad is so light that it will not always cause a sufficient change in the velocity of the shot charge to develop a wave pressure violent enough to burst, or even bulge the barrel. It must, however, be realised that it is quite *possible* for a thin card to burst a barrel, especially if the barrel is worn and thin. Bursts have undoubtedly been produced in this way, and consequently if anyone is so extremely unfortunate as to experience such an accident, he should not throw scorn on his gunmaker when such an explanation is offered.

There have also been cases of a cap anvil being blown some way up the bore and becoming a very light obstruction. But as a rule the shot charge seems to ride over the anvil which then causes a "pimple" in the barrel. A "pimple" is the exact opposite of a dent, and gunmakers were not infrequently asked to reduce the pimples caused in barrels by anvils. But with tubular anvils such an accident is far less likely to occur.

SOME EXAMPLES OF OBSTRUCTIONAL BURSTS

I will now give particulars of a few examples of typical obstructional bursts, all of which are illustrated in the various Plates. For by a study of these examples the student will be enabled to form a good general idea of the main characteristics of this class of accident.

The first thing to remember is that a ring bulge is an essential accompaniment of any obstructional burst. If a ring bulge is present the burst *must* have been caused by an obstruction of some sort: absence of a ring bulge is conclusive evidence that there could not have been any obstruction present, and so another explanation for the accident must be sought.

I have already explained that a ring bulge is a short bulge all round the circumference of the barrel which gives a similar appearance to a ring on a finger, or a snake which has swallowed an egg. Sometimes the wall of a

PLATE XIX

(A), (B) and (C) Examples of Lamination in fractured surfaces of gun barrels.
(D) " False " lamination in a fractured surface.

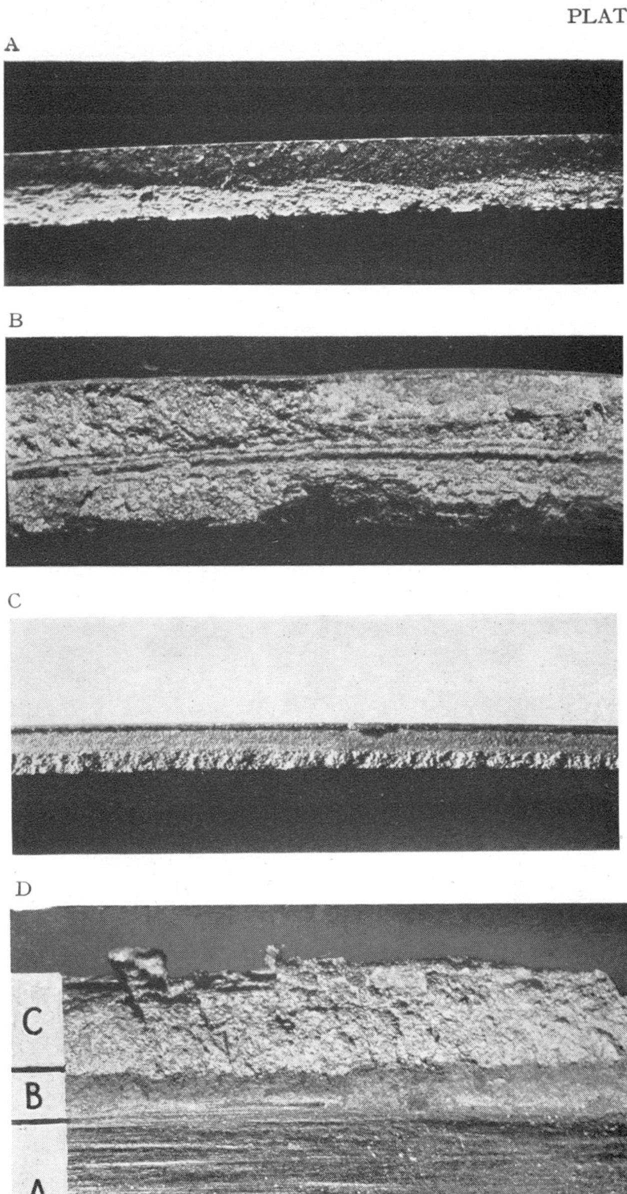
A
B
C
D
C
B
A

barrel is of uneven thickness in different parts of its circumference. In such circumstances the thicker part of the wall naturally has more strength to resist the radial pressure and so does not suffer the same degree of permanent elongation as the thinner part, which means that the bulge will be more pronounced in that part of the circumference where the barrel is thin and less so where the barrel is thick. This is no very rare occurrence and does not mean, as I have known suggested, that the internal pressure was uneven but merely that the barrel lacked symmetry in strength. In fact if the wave pressure is very slight and the wall of the barrel abnormally thin in one part it is possible for that thin part only to suffer permanent elongation, and be bulged, while the rest of the circumference of the barrel shows no bulge. But even in such an extreme case the thin portion of the wall would show the narrow circumferential swelling which is typical of a ring bulge, and of a ring bulge alone, and no experienced investigator would be misled by such a phenomenon. The best way to detect a faint ring bulge is to look along the foreshortened barrel in exactly the same way as was suggested for detecting dents on page 276. A pronounced ring bulge is obvious once one knows what to look for ; but in case the reader cannot visualise one exactly, a photograph of a ring bulge in a single tube is shown in Plate IV (A).

Plate IV (B) shows a ring bulge at the muzzle of a double-barrelled gun which was produced by some mud being picked up in the bore. An important point to notice in this photograph is the manner in which the rib is bent at the site of the bulge. This invariably happens as the rib is softer than the barrel, and personally I always look along the rib foreshortened first of all when I am examining a burst barrel for signs of a ring bulge.

Two excellent and quite typical examples of obstructional bursts are shown in Plate V.

The one in Plate V (A) occurred, as may be seen, about 8 inches from the muzzle, and was almost certainly caused by some mud picked up in the barrel which slipped farther down when the gun was raised for firing. Evidence of a ring bulge is quite clear. The top rib, which was farthest from the camera, is bent at the site of the burst; and the bottom rib (nearest the camera) is bent downwards and actually fractured at the same place. The severed portions of the barrel protrude outwards all round its circumference and have assumed a funnel-shaped appearance; while the fractured strip of barrel at the point of rupture is plainly bent down and then up. The left barrel has also been affected by the wave pressure, and has been bent at the site of the burst, as may be seen from its divergence from the straight edge of the ruler.

The burst shown in Plate V (B) occurred about 18 inches from the breech and was caused by the shot charge and wads being left in the bore owing to faulty ignition. Here again evidence of the ring bulge is quite clear. The top rib (nearest the camera) is bent at the site of the burst, and the fractured ends of the barrel are splayed outwards all round the circumference and have assumed a funnel-shaped appearance similar to that seen in Plate V (A). Incidentally the general similarity of these two bursts is very marked.

An obstructional burst at a point about 5 inches from the breech is shown in Plate VI. This was the result of the accidental insertion of a 28-bore cartridge in front of a 16-bore cartridge in a 16-bore gun. Once more the ring bulge is very clear. The upper photograph (A) shows how the top rib is bent at the site of the burst, and the lower photograph (B) shows the severed portion of the barrel which has assumed a concave shape at the site of the burst.

Plate VII (B) is an example of a double obstructional burst, that is a burst in each barrel. The cause in this case was undoubtedly cleaning material left in each barrel by an Indian orderly. The gun burst at the first shot of the day from the right barrel. This jarred the left barrel off too, which also burst. It would seem to be a fact that when a burst occurs in the right barrel the left barrel is usually discharged also. I do not suggest that this is an inevitable consequence of the right barrel bursting, but with only two exceptions whenever a burst in the right barrel has come under my notice enquiry has elicited the fact that the left barrel was also discharged.[1] This may be due to the extra jar given to the gun by the burst: or it may be that the shooter unconsciously presses the left trigger immediately the burst occurs in the right barrel. It would be easy to understand that any shooter would be so disconcerted by a burst occurring that he might easily make some involuntary movement or contraction of his trigger hand which might account for the left trigger being pressed.

The two ring bulges in this double burst are not quite so much in evidence as in the previous examples, since the right barrel was completely severed in two, and the left nearly so. But the fractured ends of both barrels show a distinct circumferential splay outwards with a tendency to assume the funnel-like appearance to which attention was called in the cases of the bursts shown in Plate V. And the narrow strip remaining of the left barrel is bent outwards at the site of the burst. Further, the rib also shows unmistakable signs of two ring bulges at the point 1 for the right barrel, and at 2 for the left. In fact, the rib is again a most excellent witness.

These examples which I have given could be multiplied almost indefinitely, as there is a most pronounced and unmistakable similarity between all obstructional bursts. But I think I have indicated a sufficient number of ring bulges to show how unmistakable such a bulge can be, and how comparatively easy it is to detect.

[1] In December, 1947, I reported on a smashed gun in which the action was broken right through at the angle and the stock shattered by a very excessive pressure. The barrels of this gun, which was of medium quality, were quite undamaged. The actual break was caused by a cartridge in the right barrel, and in spite of the terrific jar which the action must have sustained, the cartridge in the left barrel was not discharged but was forced forwards into the chamber by the escaping gases just as in the accident described on page 375. This provided the second exception within my own experience.

CHAPTER XVIII

MORE ABOUT BURSTS

AT the beginning of Chapter XVI it was explained that all bursts could be divided into three classes. The first two of these classes have now been dealt with, and so there only remains the third class, that is bursts which are due to some abnormal weakness of the metal of the barrels or action. Such weakness can be the result of one or more of the following causes:

(1) Wear and tear.
(2) Faulty workmanship or design.
(3) The use of inferior metal.
(4) Flaws in the metal.

And since each of these causes is a question of extreme importance I propose to take them in turn before we return to the subject of actual bursts.

WEAR AND TEAR. Provided it is not accompanied by neglect, I do not believe that ordinary fair wear and tear can ever reduce the strength of a barrel sufficiently to cause a burst. The deciding factor is corrosion, and this is the outcome of neglect. A barrel can become so pitted by rust that the thickness of the walls is reduced to a dangerous extent, and if this pitting is concentrated along a line, or over some comparatively small area, the resulting weakness to the barrel may easily prove fatal.

Then pitting in a barrel can be taken out, but this entails the enlargement of the bore until all the corroded parts of the wall have been removed. Were this operation carried out near the breech the gun should be reproved as the enlargement of the bore might easily be sufficient to transfer the barrel to the next size larger in gauge. But if the enlargement is only carried out in the forward part of the barrel this question does not arise.

Then in the course of time the constant friction

between the bore and the shot charge and wads which is produced at every shot, as well as that of cleaning, can help to reduce the thickness of the barrel. But the effect of this fair wear and tear is so comparatively slight that I cannot imagine it producing any tangible result, even in the course of a lifetime. However, when it is combined with such enlargements as the removal of pitting and the polishing of the inside of the bore during periodical overhauls, the net result is that the walls of the barrel can eventually become so thin that they will finally give way. But even so, such a condition could only be brought about in a very old gun.

The most dangerous place of all for corrosion to become established is under the rib, as rusting can then go on unchecked for a long time. I have seen a gun in which the right barrel was so badly corroded under the rib that the wall was eaten nearly completely through by rust. This gun had otherwise been well looked after, and the owner had no suspicion that any rust had formed. Yet the process of rusting must have been going on for a considerable time, and the barrel eventually burst at the weak spot.

Incidentally this case presents yet another argument in favour of sending guns up to the maker, or some competent gunsmith, for periodical overhauls.

FAULTY WORKMANSHIP OR DESIGN. Faulty workmanship can arise from carelessness or ignorance. Carelessness in manufacture will never occur in a high-grade gun by a good maker, and the chances of ignorance are comparatively slender. But in the manufacture of some very cheap guns, in which every possible penny is saved in the cost of production, both carelessness and ignorance are much more common. This applies especially to actions, which are frequently made much too light in sectional design across the bar (see Volume I, Chapters II and IV), while the angle between the face and the bar is sometimes left very sharp instead of being rounded, and the " table " is sometimes cut away carelessly so as to reduce its thickness to an unnecessary extent.

In the early days of breech-loaders there were frequent conversions of muzzle-loading guns to breech-loading, and a very common cause of accidents was too great encroachment on the thickness of the walls of the chamber in boring the holes for the extractor legs. There was not the metal to spare in many muzzle-loaders to allow these holes to be made without impairing the strength of the barrels, while if a hole was in the least bit out of the true the weakness produced was accentuated.

At the present time it is probable that all converted muzzle-loaders which are still in use, and which are likely to burst, have already done so. But this origin of bursts can still exist in some very cheap modern guns as I have reported on a burst caused in this way in a very cheap American gun.

Accidents produced by any such cause can only be attributed to carelessness. Ignorance, however, can be just as dangerous, if not more so, and the ignorance that prevails on the subject of brazing is quite astonishing.

The risks attending the operation of brazing were mentioned in Volume I, the chief of which is the possibility of overheating the barrels. When this is done the physical nature of the steel is entirely changed, the fine grain structure being destroyed (see Volume I, pages 29 and 30). The metal is then quite soft and the elastic limit and maximum strength are very low.

The whole process of brazing is full of pitfalls, and it is extremely doubtful whether the workmen employed on the brazing of many cheap guns appreciate these possible pitfalls in the very least. They work by a sort of rule of thumb and I never cease to marvel that accidents arising from faulty brazing are not comparatively common, whereas in actual fact they are extremely rare.

In about 1943 a new type of brazing "solder" was introduced called "Easyflow," which makes an even stronger union than the ordinary spelter and which can be worked at a much lower temperature. I know some gunmakers who use it with the greatest success. The careful use of "Easyflow" should eliminate entirely all risk of overheating since it runs at a temperature of 650° C., which is well below the critical temperature of steel.

But barrels are not the only part of a gun which can be weakened by overheating. The action itself can be rendered quite unsafe in the same way, although in its case no question of brazing can arise. It was explained in Volume I that the action body is stamped out of forged steel. In order to do this the steel bar must be heated, and the higher its temperature the more easily the stamping can be made. So it will be appreciated that the cost of the work can be reduced a trifle if the steel is overheated and rendered very soft, and that sometimes this temptation becomes too great.

THE USE OF INFERIOR METAL. Good steel has a higher elastic limit and maximum strength than poor-quality steel: but it costs more, and so inferior steel is often used in the action bodies and barrels of cheap guns. This means that they are not so strong, and consequently lack that reserve strength possessed by the highest grade steel which can be so useful in any abnormal occurrence. The actual price of the action bodies and tubes in the rough may not be so very much less than that charged for those made of better material; but the makers of many of these very cheap guns frequently try to save every penny wherever they can.

FLAWS IN THE METAL. The way in which flaws can occur in the forgings from which barrels are ultimately made has been described with sufficient detail in Volume I (page 23). In the higher grades of steel the whole of the top of the ingot, which contains the greater proportion of the impurities or "slag" is cut off and thrown away; but in the cheaper forgings this is too wasteful, and so there is considerable risk of some of the impure part of the ingot being included in the billets from which the tubes are drawn.

When steel is drawn it has a pronounced grain which is really comparable to the grain of the trunk of a tree.

Any local impurities, such as particles of "slag," are then drawn out in this grain, thus forming a longitudinal "seam" in the tube, the length of this "seam" naturally depending on the original size of the particle of "slag." A flaw of this nature is usually termed an "inclusion of slag."

Sometimes, however, a small bubble of air or gas may be formed in the cooling ingot, and if this occurs in the billet it will be drawn out longitudinally with the grain, when there will not be complete cohesion between the particles of steel where it exists. This kind of flaw is frequently called an "inclusion of gas."

Flaws caused by inclusions, either of slag or gas, can vary from being very deep and pronounced to being so slight as to be invisible. Obviously the better the quality of the forging the less chance of a flaw, so the risk of flaws must be much greater in barrels made from very cheap tubes. Nevertheless it must be realised that there is always just a possibility of a flaw being present in the very best quality tube, for no matter how great the care exercised in manufacture it is impossible to make absolutely certain that any casting is entirely free from an inclusion of some sort. By submitting the cooling ingot to pressure (see Volume I, page 24) the chances of an inclusion are rendered so slight that they can be regarded as negligible for all practical purposes ; but the remote possibility of its existence must always be recognised.

This very brief description of the formation of flaws should be sufficient to impress upon shooters the extreme importance of having the barrels of their guns made from tubes which are above suspicion. Unfortunately a considerable section of the gun trade seem to fail to appreciate this importance, and cheap continental tubes are used for barrels to a great extent. When a sportsman buys a gun by some British gunmaker he is probably quite unaware that the tubes from which the barrels are made are possibly the cheap production of some continental factory, and this is naturally a point on which the vendor of the gun remains silent.

The really best makers never use anything but high-grade British tubes for their barrels, and this is one of the many differences between their guns and those made by makers whose standing is not so high.

I do not wish to suggest that no foreign tubes are as good as British. In fact I feel sure that some of the best makes of continental tubes would probably be hard to beat. But such tubes would be just as costly as British; and the gunmaker who uses foreign tubes is actuated wholly by motives of cost. And I certainly think that sportsmen should realise this fact, and make a point of enquiring into the origin of the tubes whenever they buy new guns.

Flaws caused by inclusions are not nearly so likely to occur in actions, because actions are not drawn to the same extent as barrels; so the flaws would be much more local, and would almost certainly be detected during the work of cutting out the action body.

Flaws, however, can be caused in other ways. For instance, there is always the danger of producing cracks in steel articles during brazing or soldering. If the part to be brazed is of irregular shape it will not expand with perfect regularity, and so be subjected to some localised surface stress when being heated in contact with the brazing fluid or soldering alloy. The contours of the breech ends of ordinary barrels are sufficiently regular to obviate the setting up of any localised stress; but in the case of over and under guns the breech ends of the barrels are sometimes very irregular in form and shape, and there is a possibility that this irregularity of form may introduce stresses due to a consequent irregularity of heating, which is not ordinarily met with in the usual type of gun with horizontal barrels. So this is a matter which gunmakers who build over and under guns should consider very carefully.

Again, flaws can be started in a sound barrel or action, especially if the physical nature of the steel is not quite perfect, by some abnormal stress generated by an excessive pressure. It is thus possible for a gun to be weakened to a dangerous extent by some particularly violent cartridges without any visible sign becoming evident at the time.

It is also possible for numbers which are impressed on a barrel starting a flaw, especially if they are in a straight line. And there is also one recorded instance of the impressing of a Proof Mark starting a flaw.

But these possibilities are remote and they can hardly be said to enter the field of practical politics. The danger of flaws being produced by violent cartridges is, however, real; as sportsmen usually seem to be so callous that they prefer to use up a box of cartridges which are obviously abnormally violent rather than discard them all after experiencing one or, at the most, two exceptional rounds. And it is the repetition of the abnormal stress which is more likely to start a flaw than a single isolated round.

SOME EXAMPLES OF BURSTS CAUSED BY ABNORMAL WEAKNESS OF THE METAL

Before going any further in our study of the problems which arise in connection with abnormal weaknesses in the metal of barrels and actions, it may be of advantage if I give some examples of actual bursts which have been caused solely by such weaknesses, as these examples should help us in our consideration of how these weaknesses can result in accidents.

The first of these examples is shown in Plate IX (A). This burst was really the result of what can only be regarded as faulty workmanship in a cheap gun. During the process of "striking up" the rib, that is fitting it to the barrels, a longitudinal cut was made in the barrel along the line of junction between the edge of the rib and the right barrel. This cut weakened the barrel, and a fracture ultimately occurred along this line.

The next two examples are given in Plate IX (B) and (C), and are so similar as to be almost identical. In both cases the gun was very old and the walls of the barrels had become so worn that they were scarcely thicker than tissue-paper. The result was that they could not withstand indefinitely the stress imposed by firing, and they ultimately gave way.

It should be particularly noticed that in none of the three bursts in Plate IX is there any sign of a ring bulge. The ribs are all perfectly straight. Nor is there any opening out of the ends of the severed portions of the barrel in the form of a funnel such as can be seen in the photographs given in Plates V and VII (B).

By a rather remarkable coincidence all these three bursts occurred in different parts of the country but within a few days of each other; and all three pairs of damaged barrels were on my table at the same time.

I once examined a burst almost identical to those shown in Plate IX (B) and (C), being due to the wall of the barrel having been reduced in thickness by excessive boring out with a view to reducing traces of a bad dent, which raised yet another question. It was caused by the first shot of the day, and that part of the bore in front of the burst was clean, while the part behind the burst was fouled in the normal manner. This gave rise to an impression that the shot charge must have left the barrel by the hole caused by the burst instead of by the muzzle.

Such a thing could not possibly happen, because the burst could not have occurred until the wall of the barrel was stressed by the gas pressure; and the gas pressure could not have acted until after the shot charge had passed the seat of rupture, since the shot charge must always be in front of the expanding gases.

The explanation for that part of the bore which was in front of the burst being clean is as follows:

The fouling is the residue deposited by the powder gases, and when the barrel burst all the gases took the easiest method of escape and left by the hole made by the burst instead of overcoming air resistance in propelling the shot charge forwards and escaping by the muzzle. Consequently no residue was deposited in front of the burst.

The shot charge, however, would continue to travel along the bore with the velocity already acquired, and the felt wad would clean any traces of fouling left by the shot, thus giving that part of the bore ahead of the burst an appearance of being quite clean.

The next two examples are both due to flaws and are shown in Plates X and XI. In the one shown in Plate X (A) the flaw was due to an inclusion of "slag" in the original ingot, and when the ingot was drawn a longitudinal "seam" was produced in the metal. The "seam" begins at the point marked 1, and runs in a straight line to the point 5. The actual burst occurred along this seam. An examination of the fractured edges of the barrel between the points marked 1 and 2 will show that the metal of the barrel seems to consist of two layers of varying thickness, the outer layer being dark. This discoloration is due to the presence of the slag, which produced a fissure penetrating in places to half the thickness of the wall.

After the accident cross-sections were made of the barrel at 3, 4 and 5, and the fissure could be clearly seen under the microscope at these points. At the point 3 it was still very deep; but the farther it ran from the breech the shallower it became. The photo-micrographs of this fissure taken at these points are shown in Plates XII and XIII. That in XII (A) is only magnified to 100 diameters, as if a higher power had been used it would not have been possible to include the whole depth of the fissure in the field of view of the microscope. It will be noticed that the outer half of the fissure is very fine, and that it widens in the lower half. A photograph of this lower half only, magnified to 250 diameters, is shown in Plate XII (B).

At the point 4 the fissure had become less deep, and the whole of it could be included in the field of view of the microscope when magnified to 250 diameters. A photograph taken with this power is shown in Plate XIII (A).

At the point 5 the fissure had become considerably

more shallow, but rather wider, and a photograph of it here taken at a magnification of 250 diameters is given in Plate XIII (B).

These photo-micrographs are conclusive proof of the existence of this flaw, and the metallurgic examination revealed the cause as inclusion of slag. Although the flaw is so clearly visible between the points 3 and 5 it is almost certain that this is because it was opened a certain amount beyond the actual burst when the accident occurred. It is extremely doubtful whether it could possibly have been detected by visual examination before the accident.

But in this particular gun there was another contributory cause to the burst, namely the poor physical nature of the steel of the barrels near the breech end. This was the result of overheating during brazing; and at the breech end the fine grain structure of the steel had been completely destroyed, leaving the steel in its softest and most dangerous coarse grained condition.

This was indicated in the first place by the coarse granular structure of the fractured edges of the metal. When steel of a proper physical condition is ruptured, the fractured surfaces should appear fine and fibrous. If it is coarse and granular there is a strong reason to suspect overheating. A metallurgic examination confirmed the suspicion aroused by the condition of the fracture, but showed that at a distance of about 10 inches from the breech the steel was only partially affected by the incorrect heat treatment, and the structure was in an intermediate stage between the most coarse grained condition prevalent at the breech and the correct fine grained condition which existed at the muzzle where the heat had not reached.

Photo-micrographs showing the structure of the steel of this barrel at the breech, 10 inches from the breech, and near the muzzle were given in Plates III (B) and IV (A) and (B) of Volume I.

Another very similar example of a burst caused by a flaw is shown in Plate X (B). In this case the flaw was possibly due to a small air bubble in the original casting which produced a short seam when the ingot was drawn. But I believe that the true explanation was that the number on the barrel was impressed with too great force and thus set up a local stress in the metal along the line of the number. An examination of the photograph will show that the fracture occurred exactly along the line of the bottom of the figures comprising the number, which had certainly been impressed deeply. This flaw extended from the points 1 to 2 in an absolutely straight longitudinal line, and the burst occurred along this line.

During the investigation it was suggested that the burst might have been due to excessive pressure developed in the chamber. But such an explanation was impossible. The burst actually began at the point 1, which was 4 inches away from the breech, and extended to the point 2, a distance of 8½ inches from the breech. On measuring the thickness of the barrel at these points and substituting these values in the Gunmakers' Formula it was seen that pressures of 12 and 7 tons would be required respectively to burst this barrel, if it had been sound, at distances of 4 and 8½ inches from the breech. Such pressures would mean corresponding 1-inch pressures of 13·5 and 15·5 tons. These pressures were absolutely impossible. Not only did the fired case of the cartridge which caused the burst show no indications of any lively pressure, but the rest of the cartridges taken from the same box all gave normal results. And most important of all, the barrels were absolutely tight on the face of the action although there was no top extension. The action could not possibly have withstood a pressure even approaching 13·5 tons without cracking, and it was as good as ever.

The existence of the flaw was indicated by the absolutely straight fracture in the line of the "grain" of the barrel, and the extraordinary smooth surfaces of the ruptured edges.

Further, there was no sign of any elongation or bending in the steel along the lower edge of this straight fracture.

The first of these points suggested the presence of some longitudinal flaw.

The second is conclusive proof that the steel at the site of the burst could not have been stressed beyond its elastic limit, let alone to its maximum strength, if it had been sound. The fact that a rupture had occurred without elongation was conclusive proof that the steel could not have been sound along the line of the burst.

The similarity of the two bursts shown in Plate X is very marked, and is emphasised still more by the top views of both which are given in Plate XI. In both cases the site of the actual burst is situated along an almost straight longitudinal line, nor is there any suspicion of a ring bulge, both the ribs being absolutely straight. The two photographs in Plate XI should be compared with that given in Plate VI (A), when the difference between the two bursts which we have just been considering and an obstructional burst will be obvious.

Two more examples of bursts caused by flaws in the barrel deserve attention in order to make our study of the problem more complete.

The first of these is shown in Plate XIV (A) and was a ·410 gun of Belgian manufacture in which the lumps were brazed on to the barrels. This fact happened to preserve the flaw almost completely and conclusive evidence of its existence was, therefore, obtained. It will be seen that a crack opened up longitudinally in the " grain " of the steel in the right-hand barrel and extended from A to B, where it vanished and was presumably continued underneath the two lumps. The fractured surfaces at C showed a distinct " layering " of the metal where the slag, which was the cause of the flaw, had been situated before the seam opened and the slag itself was blown away by the escaping gases. This " layering " of the metal almost looks like geological stratification and is technically known as " lamination." And when lamination is present in a ruptured surface it provides conclusive evidence of the existence of a flaw.

But the fact of the lumps being brazed on prevented much of the actual flaw from being blown away immediately under the lumps, and so a cross-section of the barrel was made at D. The flaw was one of the worst I have seen, reaching more than half-way through the wall of the barrel and being wider in the middle of the wall than at the outer surface. A photo-micrograph of the central portion of the wall of the barrel at the point D is shown in Plate XV (A) and, I think, speaks for itself.

This flaw was pronounced but not so deep at E and had almost petered out at F.

The next example is shown in Plate XIV (B) and, as can be seen, a barrel which opened out along a " seam " at the forward end. The photograph shows how straight this seam was and how it followed the grain of the steel. The fractured edges of both sides of the seam showed pronounced lamination and there was no doubt whatever that the burst was caused by a flaw, although in this case the actual inclusions of slag which constituted the flaw had been carried away by the escaping gases.

It will be noted that in neither of these last two examples is there any suggestion of a ring bulge elongation of the steel other than a gentle opening along a straight seam.

But there is one feature common to all the seven bursts which I have given as examples of the result of abnormal weakness of the metal which should receive the most careful attention. *This is the entire absence of any signs of great violence.*

In all the bursts shown in Plates IX, X and XI all that has happened in each case is that a flap has been lifted up from the wall of the barrel, comparatively gently, the edge of the flap coinciding with the line of greatest weakness, while in the bursts shown in Plate XIV there was merely a comparatively gentle opening of the barrel in the form of a straight and narrow split.

There is none of the twisting, bending back, distortion and general shattering effect which is such a marked accompaniment of the obstructional bursts.

Nor is there the obvious effect of extreme violence which severed the right barrel of the gun shown in Plate XVI, or caused the wreck shown in Plate VIII.

Even in the example shown in Plates X (A) and XI (A) only a flap of metal was raised from the wall of the chamber and barrel, and in this barrel the metal was in its softest state owing to overheating.

It will be noticed that I have referred to the "grain" in the steel. Plate XV (B), (C) and (D) gives three photomicrographs of longitudinal sections of barrels which have been "etched" with dilute nitric acid so as to reveal the structure of the steel and taken at a magnification of 100 diameters. The dark parts consist of iron carbide, the compound of carbon and iron, and the light portion is free iron, or ferrite, for in the steel used for barrels the percentage of carbon is too low to permit all the iron being turned into the compound of iron carbide. The longitudinal grain in the metal is very distinct and shows straight streaks of ferrite running between the structure of iron carbide.

The steel shown in plate XV (B) contains just about 0·4 per cent. of carbon. Those in XV (C) and XV (D) slightly less. It may be stated that the first of these steels was British and the other two were continental.

I will give one more example, but this time of an action cracking as the result of faulty manufacture. This action is shown in Plate XVII, and at first sight it might appear to be a typical result of excessive pressure. But there was no evidence to corroborate this diagnosis. In fact, all the evidence went the other way. In the first place the gun was chambered for 12-bore $2\frac{3}{4}$-inch cases, and ordinary $2\frac{1}{2}$-inch cases were being used at the time, which would tend to reduce the pressure.

The next point was that the cartridges used at the time were standard factory loaded cartridges, and that the rest of the cartridges in the box were fired off without anything peculiar being noticed in the way of violence. And, as has already been pointed out, it is extremely unlikely for one single round in a batch of cartridges loaded in bulk in a factory to produce a very abnormal pressure when all the others give satisfactory results.

And finally, most important of all, was the fact that the fired case of the round which actually caused the accident showed no indications of high pressure.

It was emphasised in Volume I that these light box-lock guns were naturally very weak across the bar, and that what may be described as this "congenital" weakness was normally counteracted by:

(1) The addition of a top extension.

(2) Rounding the angle between the face of the action and the bar.

(3) Maintaining the thickness of the "table" of the bar, as well as a sectional design which is likely to give the maximum strength possible.

(4) The use of high-quality steel.

Now, first of all, this particular gun had no top extension at all, and the angle between the action face and bar was not rounded, but was cut very sharp. Further, the "table" was very thin, and was not even of the same thickness over each lock, being ·09 of an inch thick over the left lock and only ·08 of an inch thick over the right lock. There could have been no valid reason for this reduction in thickness over the right lock, and such a reduction indicated that proper care had not been exercised in manufacture.

But the omission of the top extension, and especially the sharp angle between the action face and the bar, were in themselves enough to account for excessive weakening of the action at the most critical point.

And in addition to these faults in design there was the question of the metal. The coarse granular structure of the fractured surfaces suggested overheating. The two photographs in Plate XVIII (A) and (B) give a comparison between the fractured surface of this action and that of a fracture of a bit of steel of identical composition, but which had not been submitted to excessive heat. Both photographs are slightly magnified in order to make the difference more evident. It will be seen that the photograph on the left shows a very coarse granular structure, while that on the right has a fine grain structure.

The suspicion of overheating which was thus aroused was completely confirmed by a metallurgic examination. Plate XVIII (c) is a photo-micrograph of a portion of the steel cut from the bar of the action at the site of the fracture, and this shows an "acicular," or needle like, structure, which always tends to weakness, and which was due to the steel having been overheated. The photo-micrograph in Plate XVIII (D) is that of a bit of steel from a high-grade action. The carbon content is only slightly higher but the carbide is evenly distributed.

But the metallurgic examination also showed that the steel itself was of a very mild nature, the carbon content being only 0·1 per cent., which is about the same as that of wrought iron. A very slightly higher carbon content (say 0·2 per cent.) would have given considerably higher tensile strength, while the extra cost would have been trifling. But in some of these low-priced guns everything is sacrificed to cheapness, and there can be little doubt that the overheating occurred when the action body was stamped out, because the hotter the metal the easier it is to make the stamping.

So it will be realised that this cracking of the bar was due to the following causes:

(1) Inferior metal.

(2) Faulty workmanship. The action had been overheated and the recessing for the accommodation of the locks had been carried out carelessly.

(3) Faulty design. There was no top-extension, and the angle between the face of the action and the bar was much too sharp.

Such a combination of faults is, we must hope, uncommon: but it shows the inherent possibilities of a cheap gun.

THE PROTECTION AFFORDED BY PROOF

In the two previous chapters I tried to explain how it was that pressure and obstructional bursts were actually brought about. But so far no attempt has been made to explain *why* some abnormal weakness in the metal may ultimately cause a burst barrel or a smashed action. I have purposely delayed dealing with this question until it was possible also to deal with the question which was asked at the end of Chapter XV; namely, Is Proof an absolute safeguard against an unreliable gun being placed on the market?

The six examples given respectively in Plates IX (A), X (A), X (B), XIV (A), XIV (B) and XVII are all obvious examples of unreliable guns. Yet all six had passed Proof which undoubtedly submitted them to a much more violent strain than that imposed by any subsequent cartridge, not excepting the cartridge which actually caused the rupture in each case. So the reader may easily wonder how it was that these guns could withstand the severe test of Proof and yet give way subsequently under the influence of a normal pressure.

There is a widespread belief among gunmakers that if a gun has once passed Proof it cannot possibly burst unless submitted to a pressure higher than that developed by Proof. Unfortunately this belief is quite erroneous, and is, in fact, contrary to all metallurgic knowledge and experience. Steel, in common with other metals, is subject to fatigue, and if any structure of steel is constantly submitted to a certain stress it may eventually give way, even though it would be quite capable of withstanding that same stress, or a higher one, for a limited number of times. *It is not the intensity of any particular stress which causes rupture so much as the constant repetition of the stress*. A sound barrel or action can withstand this constant repetition of stress indefinitely because there is a sufficient reserve of strength. But if any part of a barrel or action is, or becomes, abnormally weak it will not possess the reserve of strength necessary to withstand the ordinary stress imposed by firing for an indefinite number of times. It may be able to do so twenty times, a hundred times, or even a thousand times ; but it will eventually give way exactly like the cracked pitcher which went to the well once too often.

When the wall of a barrel is weakened in some particular place by pitting or a flaw, the sound part of the wall has to do all the work of withstanding the strain which should normally be untertaken by the whole wall. And the effect of even some relatively deep pitting or flaw is not to be gauged by the reduction in the thickness of the wall alone, but by the stress concentration which can occur at the base of the pitting or flaw.

The constant repetition of this stress concentration can eventually overcome the resistance of the wall, and a burst will occur when the steel has become too tired to withstand the strain any more.

It will be noticed that I have used the word "tired" instead of "fatigued," which is more commonly associated with metals. But I have done so purposely, because the kind of "fatigue" which can produce a burst in an unsound gun is not quite the same phenomenon as that universally termed "fatigue" in the strictest metallurgic sense.

Metallurgically speaking, "fatigue" is the effect produced by constant stressing of some metal structure *up to its elastic limit.* A fracture which is produced in this way is known as a "fatigue fracture," and when the ruptured surfaces are examined they will be seen to have assumed a very distinct and definite concoidal form. Most true "fatigue fractures" give this appearance, and it is definite proof that the structure in question was stressed up to its elastic limit a very great number of times.

The most common type of true fatigue fracture is that which is produced in the back axle of a motor-car by a flaw. The existence of the flaw throws extra stress on the sound metal, and if the flaw is sufficiently serious the sound metal may be stressed up to its elastic limit at every revolution. Then in course of time the axle breaks with a true fatigue fracture.

In science, it is essential that certain definite terms should be applied to certain definite conditions; hence it has come about that the term "fatigue" is only applicable in the strictest sense to a peculiar condition produced in metal by a particular type, or strength, of stress.

So when a gun with a flaw in the barrel bursts, it is scientifically incorrect to state that the burst was due to "fatigue," as this term is used in metallurgic parlance to denote another special type of fracture. Nevertheless the barrel bursts because it has experienced a kind of fatigue, and when explaining the reason from the practical view-point of a non-scientific sportsman the burst can reasonably be attributed to a kind of fatigue, provided the strictest metallurgic meaning of the word is remembered.

But let us return to the question of Proof.

It will not be difficult to understand that a barrel containing a flaw may be sufficiently strong just to withstand the Proof pressure, both in Provisional and Definitive Proof. But if it has only withstood these pressures with but a small margin to spare it will almost inevitably give way in course of time under the constant repetition of stress imposed by firing a number of shots. The fact that the barrel has once, or even twice, withstood successfully a pressure of 5 tons is no guarantee whatever that it will be able to withstand for an indefinite number of times any pressure lower than 5 tons; or that it can only be burst when a 5 tons pressure is exceeded.

All engineering structures are so designed that the materials used in these structures have a certain Factor of Safety. This means that the working load on any given piece of material used in the structure is much less than the breaking stress.

If the breaking stress of the piece in question is, say, five times the maximum working load, the Factor of Safety is said to be five. In boilers, for example, the Factor of Safety is from four and a half upwards, while the test pressure employed varies from one and a half to twice the maximum pressure. In a shotgun, on the other hand, the Factor of Safety is probably not more than two and a half or, at the very most, three. But since the test pressure applied in Proof is nearly twice the normal working load it will be seen that a gun is more severely tested than a boiler, because the test pressure applied approaches more nearly the bursting pressure.

However, the Factor of Safety in a gun or any other structure depends on the strength of the material used; and since this is not ascertained in each individual gun as carefully as it is for every piece of steel used in a boiler, the Factor of Safety of a gun cannot be said to be known as accurately as that of a boiler. And yet there are authenticated cases on record of boilers having burst because of latent flaws.

It is, therefore, quite ridiculous to maintain, as some gunmakers do try to maintain, that the fact that a gun has passed Proof is conclusive evidence that it must have been sound in every respect.

Proof can, in fact, weaken a gun by accentuating a flaw which may already exist.

The reader may, therefore, quite naturally wonder why the pressure given by Definitive Proof is not increased. The reason why this would be impossible is that the *actions* would never withstand a higher Proof pressure. For in Definitive Proof it is really the action which is being tested, not the barrel. As can be seen from Table XXX a sound barrel of good steel can withstand a considerably higher pressure than that given by Proof without distress. But the action would not. And so it is the strength of the action which limits the strength of Proof, which means that a barrel considerably weaker than the normal can pass Definitive Proof without much difficulty. This Proof charge may strain it, however, and weaken it; just as it is possible to test a gut salmon cast with a pull of 10 lb. and so strain it that it would not withstand another pull of more than 2 lb.

If Definitive Proof were made more severe guns would

all have to be heavier on account of the stronger actions which would be necessary, and sportsmen would not like to go back to heavier guns.

A better plan would be to make the Provisional Proof more severe. But no matter how severe this were made within reason there would always remain the risk of an unsound barrel being just strong enough to pass. And such a barrel would certainly give way in course of time.

The best plan of all would be to incorporate in Provisional Proof one or more of the methods of "Crack Detection" which have been developed so successfully since about 1935. X-rays are used regularly in all big steel works for the detection of flaws in steel, but it is at present doubtful whether the results are always quite so definite when examining a tube as they are in the case of flat plates. Further, the cost of the plant is very heavy, while the examination of every specimen means the taking of a photograph which needs a specialist to interpret. Such work would add enormously to the cost of Proof, which is at present fixed by the Gun Barrel Proof Act of 1868. The Sorting Bridge method of detecting flaws is also liable sometimes to misinterpretation. But "Crack Detection," both Magnetic and Fluorescent, has proved very satisfactory and is comparatively cheap and simple. In the Magnetic method the steel specimen to be tested is first magnetised and then immersed in a special "ink," which is really paraffin in which a very large amount of minute particles of magnetic oxide of iron are in suspension. Any flaw in the specimen makes a break in the magnetic field and the tiny particles arrange themselves along this break, thus disclosing the flaw.

In the Fluorescent method the specimen is first painted with a special fluid and then examined under ultra-violet light when any cracks become immediately visible. But in this method the cracks must be in the actual surface of the steel, while in the Magnetic method sub-surface faults or inclusions can be disclosed.

PLATE XX

Magnetic Crack Detection is a comparatively new method of detecting longitudinal flaws in shotgun barrels. The principle is based on the fact that when a longitudinal flaw in a piece of drawn steel occurs, the flaw causes a break in the circumferential continuity of that piece of steel. The method is to magnetise the barrel or tube and place it in a special "ink" contained in a copper trough. The "ink" comprises what may almost be termed an "emulsion" of very fine particles of steel suspended in paraffin. A copper rod is run down the tube, protruding slightly at each end. These two ends are attached to the middle of an electric circuit.

When the current is switched on the tube is heavily magnetised and, if there is any break in the continuity of the steel, the fine particles collect along the line of that break, and form a very definite and pronounced streak along the outer circumference of the tube. This method is, as near as possible, foolproof and, as will be seen from the photograph overleaf, the results can be really startling in their clarity.

Plate A. Photograph showing split in the grain of the steel of the right-hand barrel. This was visible to the naked eye.

Plate B. Photograph showing two longitudinal splits in the grain of the steel of the left-hand barrel. These were quite invisible to the naked eye, but are here seen revealed by Magnetic Crack Detection.

In the previous edition of this volume I merely mentioned the possible value of Magnetic Crack Detection, but further experience has convinced me that this value can only be obtained fully by testing with a *finished* barrel. A barrel in the tube stage is not sufficiently smooth for the special "ink" to adhere to the line of the crack. Magnetic Crack Detection, therefore, cannot be used to full advantage on a barrel in the "tube" stage.

Author's Note: I am indebted to Messrs. Metropolitan Vickers, Ltd. for their great kindness in spending so much time and trouble in showing me the technique of this method in operation.

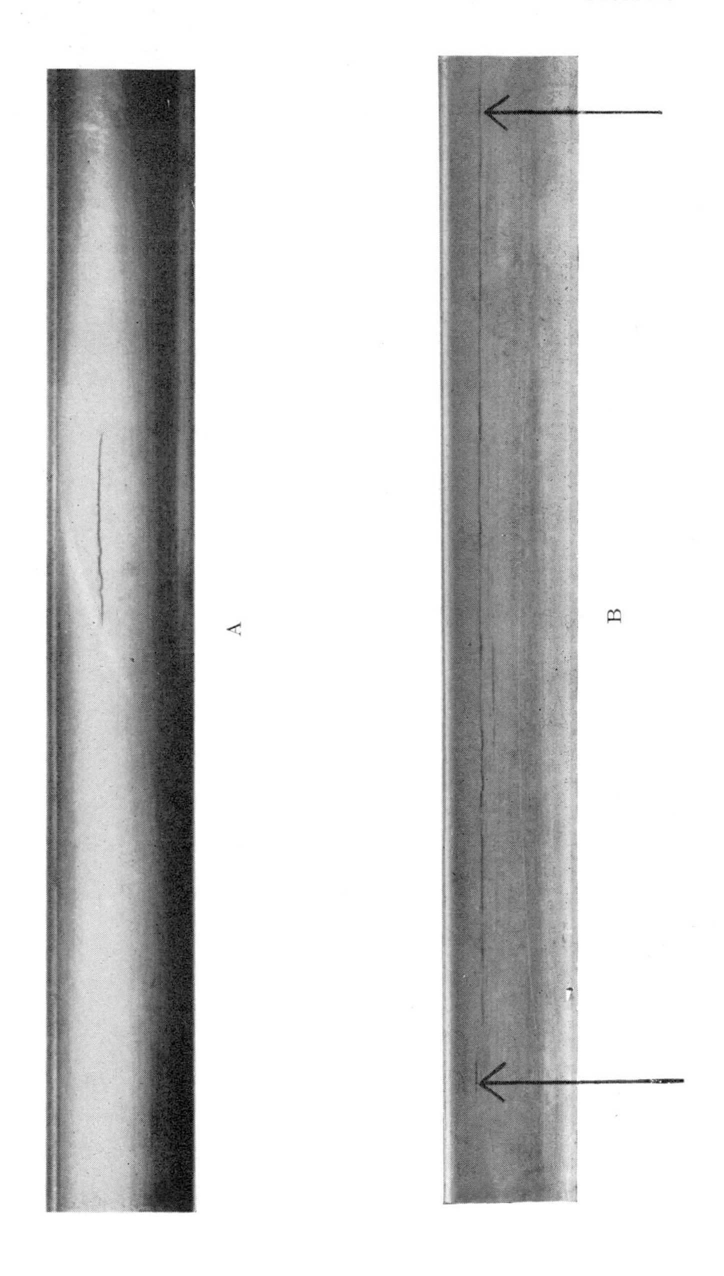
A
B

But in any case no such additional examination could be carried out without increasing the cost of Proof, which is already insufficient to cover the costs entailed in carrying it out. This is not surprising as it will be generally realised how the costs of all labour, material, rents, and indeed everything, have gone up in the past century. But the fact that the actual prices for all the Proofs are fixed by an Act of 1868 means that there can be no increase until a new Act is passed. The time for such an Act is long overdue and it can be but hoped that if and when it does come it will permit the Proof Authorities to incorporate other tests in Proof besides the firing of Proof charges should they deem such tests to be useful, and also to increase the prices of Proof to a reasonable degree. It may well be that the rapid advance of scientific research may open out new and better methods for the detection of flaws, and it will be a tragedy if the hands of the Proof Authorities are tied by an Act of 1868.

So although Proof cannot in any way be regarded as an infallible safeguard, it is undoubtedly the best that can be provided as far as all practical purposes of sport are concerned, and under existing conditions, especially as although Proof may possibly weaken an unsound barrel it can also at times *strengthen* one which is sound but rather on the light side. This is a very interesting point: but in order that the reader may understand it the more readily I will first make an apparent digression.

Before the introduction of wire wound guns the almost universal system used in the construction of naval ordnance or other heavy artillery was the shrinking on of a number of tubes, each over the others. The principle underlying this procedure was as follows:

The innermost tube of all was made comparatively thin, and the next tube was so made that its internal diameter was slightly less than the external diameter of the smaller one. It was thus impossible to fit the larger tube over the smaller when cold; but if the larger tube was heated it expanded sufficiently to permit its being slipped on over the smaller tube. The larger tube was thicker than the smaller, and consequently stronger; so as it contracted on cooling it *compressed* the inner tube.

This process was repeated several times until the gun was built up of a number of tubes, each shrunk on over the others.

The effect of this procedure can be explained best by considering only the two innermost tubes of all.

Owing to the pressure exerted by the outer tube the steel walls of the inner tube are kept in a state of constant compression. So when any internal pressure is applied which tends to expand this inner tube this pressure will first have to stretch the tube to its original form, and will then have to stretch it up to its elastic limit and maximum strength before rupture will occur. From this it will be seen that a certain amount of pressure will, in the first instance, be taken up in stretching the tube to its original size and overcoming the compression which is exercised by the outer tube. This means that the total pressure necessary to stretch the tube to any specified degree above its original form will have to be greater than would have been the case had there been no initial force of compression to overcome. In other words, the tube will be stronger.

And when a number of tubes are shrunk on over each other the total strength of the whole piece is greatly increased, because each individual tube must be expanded before any stress can come into play in the tube immediately outside; and in the case of every single tube a certain amount of residual compression must be overcome before it can be expanded.

This digression may appear unnecessary, but it provides an excellent example of the manner in which stresses act in a gun barrel. Such a barrel admittedly consists of a single, or mono-bloc, tube; but the walls of this tube must always be regarded as being made up of a very large number of very thin layers. And each of these layers must be stretched in succession before any stress can act on the layer immediately beyond.

A process known as " Auto-frettage " utilises this fact and has been used successfully for strengthening the mono-bloc tubes used in several makes of Breech Loading and Quick Firing guns in this country ; while the system has also been employed with various kinds of guns and howitzers in America, Japan, and several continental countries.

In this process of Auto-frettage an internal hydraulic pressure is introduced in a mono-bloc tube sufficient to stress the inner layers of the tube beyond their elastic limit. When this pressure is removed, these inner layers do not resume their original dimensions of their own accord but tend to remain larger. This tendency stretches the inner layers of the tube, thus bringing into tension the outer layers of steel, and so enabling them to support the inner layers against further pressure. And since the hydraulic pressure is so arranged that only the very innermost layers are stretched, the state of tension which is forced on the outer layers compresses the inner ones, leaving them in a state of residual compression.

The final effect is then the same as if the barrel were built up of a number of shrunk-on tubes.

If the chamber of a barrel is rather on the light side, or if the steel has a rather low elastic limit, it sometimes happens that Provisional Proof, or even Definitive Proof, can stretch the inner layers of the chamber beyond their elastic limit, and thus introduce the process of Auto-frettage in the breech end of the barrel. When this occurs the barrel will be stronger than it would have been had the Proof pressure been slightly lower and not stressed the inner layers beyond their elastic limit.

So it will be seen that in spite of some admitted shortcomings there can be decided advantages in the present system of Proof ; and if any change were made it would seem better to increase the severity of the test imposed by Provisional Proof on tubes. Even at the present time numbers of faulty tubes fail to pass this test : and the greater the severity, still smaller would be the percentage of faulty tubes which would get through, and this would mean that the possibility of a gun being sold with an unsound barrel would be slighter even than it is at present. For when the enormous number of guns made every year is remembered, the percentage of accidents due to flaws is infinitesimal. And should an unsound gun be sold the chances are that it will give way before very many rounds have been fired. For the kind of fatigue which causes unsound guns to burst sets in, as a rule, comparatively quickly: and the greater the number of shots that are fired through any gun the less the risk of any latent flaw being present. In fact any gun which has withstood 1,000 rounds can probably be regarded as being cleared of suspicion.

So when all things are considered it will be realised that Proof does provide a very real safeguard; and further, one which has been largely responsible for the high reputation enjoyed by British guns all over the world. Perfection, however, is almost impossible of attainment; and the protection afforded by Proof is not absolute and would not be absolute even if additional measures of testing were incorporated.

THE DIAGNOSIS OF A BURST

Whenever a burst does occur the exact cause is naturally a matter of considerable importance. Consequently I propose to offer some suggestions as to the steps which should be taken in order to make a thorough investigation of the accident.

In order to give the investigator every possible chance of arriving at the truth the gun should be sent up for examination as soon as possible, *and without being cleaned*. Accompanying the gun should be the fired case of the cartridge which actually caused the burst; if possible the fired case of the round immediately preceding the burst; a few fired cases, and as many unfired cartridges as possible, up to, say, twenty, of the batch which was being used at the time.

With this evidence available it should be possible to diagnose the cause of the accident with certainty.

Let us first of all assume that the burst has occurred in one of the barrels.

In the last chapter it was stated that by far the most common cause of burst is some obstruction in the bore, and so the first thing to do is to look for evidence of an obstructional burst, that is for a ring bulge. Such a bulge, as has been explained, can best be seen by foreshortening the barrel; and if a ring bulge is detected the cause of the burst becomes established beyond any shadow of doubt.

But even if the investigator is thus quite confident that the burst was due to an obstruction, it by no means follows that the owner of the gun will be equally satisfied without further proof. Every effort should, therefore, be made to try to ascertain what the obstruction could have been; and in this connection the owner of the gun should be asked to give replies to the following questions:

(1) Was the accident caused by the first shot of the day through the barrel which actually burst?

If so, there would be strong reasons for presuming that the obstruction consisted of some cleaning material left behind in the bore.

(2) If the accident was not the result of the first shot of the day, what was the result of the shot from the barrel which burst immediately previous to the one which caused the damage? Was the bird actually killed?

The object of this question is to ascertain what chances there could have been of a charge of shot being left behind in the bore.

(3) Did anything in the least abnormal occur in the case of the shot fired through the burst barrel immediately before the round which caused the burst? That is, was there a miss-fire? Was the report quite normal? Was there any abnormal amount of smoke issuing from the breech on unloading?

These questions are merely intended to investigate still further the possibility of a charge of shot being left in the bore by the previous round.

(4) If there was an apparent miss-fire immediately before firing the round which caused the burst, was the chamber apparently empty when the gun was opened for re-loading ?

The reply to this question should provide a clue as to whether there was any possibility of a cartridge of a smaller size having been loaded by accident and become stuck at the head of the chamber.

(5) Was the shooter out with a party, and, if so, was any member of the party using a smaller bore of gun ? If so, what size ?

(6) Does the shooter, or any member of his household, own a gun and cartridges of smaller gauge than the one which burst ? If so, of what size or sizes ?

Both these last two questions may help to clear up the possibility of the burst being caused by the accidental intermingling of cartridges.

(7) Under what conditions was the shooting taking place ? That is, was the shooter walking up or driving ?

There is generally more chance of picking up some obstruction in the muzzle when walking up than when driving. But if the shooter states that he was grouse driving, he should be asked the nature of the butt he was in. If it was made of peat, as it probably would be, it would be quite reasonable to suppose that he had picked up some peat in the muzzle of his gun ; especially if the burst occurred near the muzzle.

(8) What was the nature of the ground on which the shooter was standing, or over which he was walking, at the time of the accident ? That is, was it soft plough, sandy, grass, heather, etc. ?

This question is really a " follow up " to the previous one, and the reply should indicate the chances of some obstruction having been picked up in the muzzle of the gun.

The answers to these eight questions and the actual

position of the burst in the barrel should between them provide sufficient data to determine the nature of the obstruction with comparative certainty. But the fired case of the round which caused the burst and also that of the round immediately preceding the burst should also be examined for confirmatory evidence.

For instance, I know that one fired case of a round which actually caused a burst was noticed to have *unburnt* grains of powder sticking to the *outside* of the case at the extreme front end; that is where the turnover would be straightened out. Now it was clearly impossible that these grains could have come from the cartridge itself, as the turnover would have to be straightened out before any powder gas or grains could leave the case. So it was evident that these unburnt powder grains must have been in the chamber *before* this cartridge was loaded, and that when the turnover was unrolled they were pressed against the outside of the case. This indicated that combustion had not been complete in the previous round, which suggested that the shot charge had been left in the bore.

This fact was further emphasised by an examination of the fired case of the round immediately preceding the accident, as there was still some unburnt powder inside the case.

A similar examination should be made of any other fired cases of cartridges from the lot which contained the one which caused the burst, as it is possible that indications of incomplete combustion may also be found in them. And if the combustion was not complete in the majority of rounds, it is quite reasonable to suppose that in one round it was so incomplete that the shot charge was left in the bore.

And in order to complete the investigation a most careful examination should be made of as many live cartridges as possible from the same batch. Some should be opened, and the weights of the powder and shot charges checked in order to test for regularity of loading. This step should never be omitted, as I once examined a batch of cartridges in which the powder charge had been omitted altogether in several rounds.

Then all the remaining cartridges should be tested for ballistics; that is pressure and velocity, and if possible recoil. If the ballistics, especially the pressures, are weak and irregular, there can be a presumption that the ignition is at fault. But if the ballistics are all normal and regular, the odds are that the cartridges are not at fault.

But in the case of an obstructional burst the really essential evidence is the ring bulge. If there is a ring bulge, there must have been an obstruction; and the absence of a ring bulge is conclusive proof that there could not have been an obstruction.[1]

If, therefore, the burst was not caused by an obstruction it must have been the result of some excessive pressure or of some abnormal weakness in the barrel.

A pressure burst, as was explained in Chapter XVI, can only occur in the immediate neighbourhood of the chamber; and so if the burst occurred ahead of the chamber cone an excessive pressure can be ruled out of court. But if the burst occurred at the breech, and was the direct result of a high pressure, confirmatory evidence will be found in the appearance of the brass head of the cartridge which caused the accident. For it is utterly impossible for a very high pressure to be developed without it leaving its mark on the fired case.

Further evidence may be obtained by an examination of the fired cases from the same batch of cartridges, and

[1] The most difficult of all obstructional bursts to diagnose with certainty is a burst which is clearly the result of an obstruction, but which occurred suddenly in the middle of a series of shots, when there was no possibility of any mud or similar substance being picked up in the muzzle, and when the previous shot killed a bird. In such a case the explanation must be arrived at by a process of elimination; and when every possible alternative has been discarded the only explanation remaining is that the burst was caused by an over-powder card wad left in the bore. Fortunately, however, such accidents are very, very rare.

PLATE XXI

(A) A $2\frac{1}{2}$-inch 12-bore cartridge-case showing signs of an excessive pressure. The mark of the extractor is plainly seen between the points 1 and 2; and the rim is enlarged.

(B) A $2\frac{3}{4}$-inch 12-bore cartridge-case showing signs of an excessive pressure. The mark of the extractor is very pronounced between the points 1 and 2; and the rim is split from 3 to 4.

(C) The cap on the left shows signs of an excessive pressure. It is lifted out of its seating and flattened against the breech face and the indentation of the striker is very pronounced. A comparison should be made with the cap on the right which shows a normal striker indent and pressure.

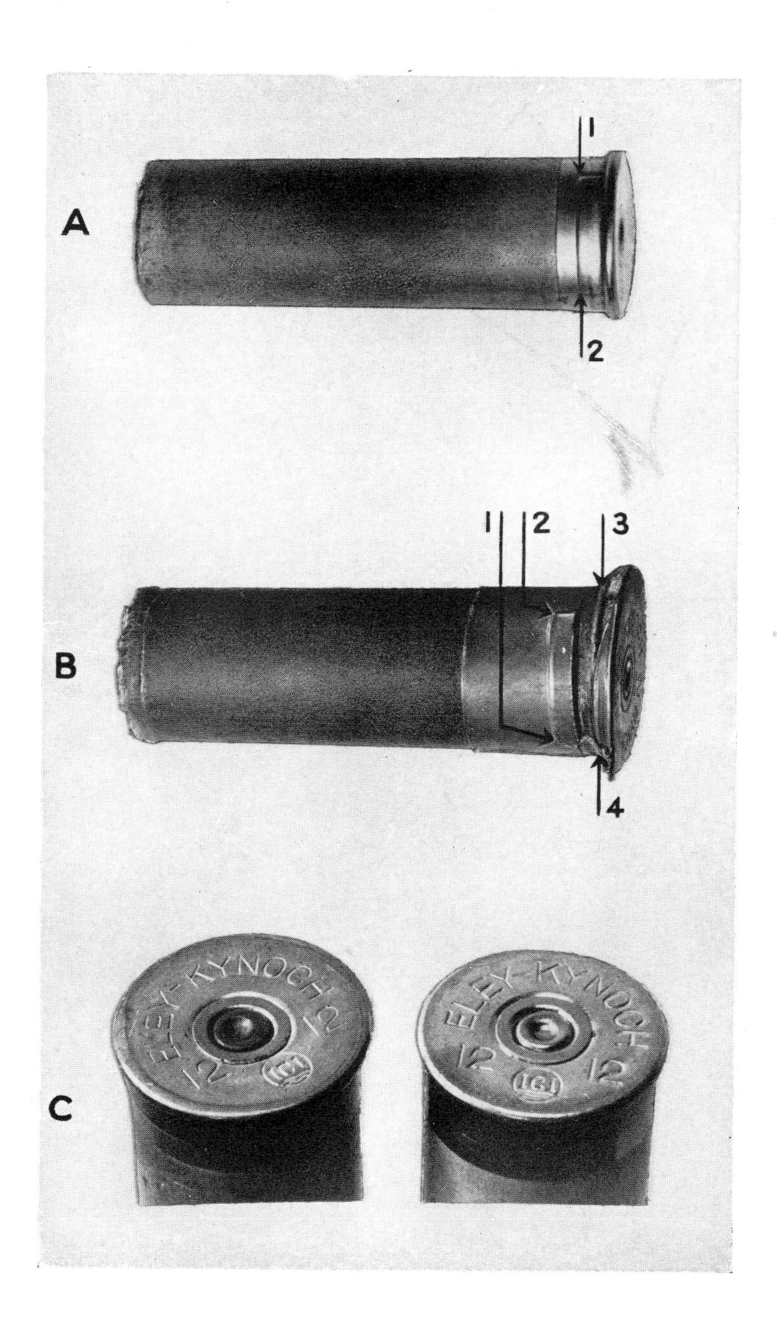
A
1
2
B
1
2
3
4
C
ELEY-KYNOCH 12
12
ICI
ELEY-KYNOCH
12
12
ICI

by testing as many unfired cartridges as possible from this batch for loading and ballistics.

As has been stated more than once, it is extremely improbable, if not impossible, for one isolated round to develop a pressure sufficiently high to burst a sound gun when all the other cartridges in the batch behave quite normally. So if the burst was caused by a high pressure there should be plenty of corroborative evidence in the other cartridges from the batch.

And since human nature is such as it is, there is always the possibility that the vendor of the cartridges will declare that the burst must have been caused by an obstruction, in spite of there being no ring bulge. It is, therefore, always advisable to obtain from the owner of the gun answers to all the questions suggested for the elucidation of an obstructional burst. These replies will help to establish the impossibility of an obstruction having been present.

If there are no confirmatory indications of any excessive pressure having been developed, the only remaining explanation is that the burst must have been due to some abnormal weakness in the barrel. And in any case this must be the cause if the rupture is situated in front of the chamber cone, and there is no ring bulge.

The first thing to do is to test the cartridges, examine the fired cases, and obtain answers to the questions which have already been given. These are important steps as they will provide useful additional negative evidence that the burst could not have been caused by an obstruction or pressure, and they may help to convince a doubting shooter, or gunmaker, of the real cause.

Then a most careful examination should be made of the fractured edges, both with the naked eye and a powerful pocket lens. If the weakness has been caused by rust or pitting, the fractured edges will show unmistakable signs of discoloration. But if there are no indications of rust or pitting, and the thickness of the wall of the barrel is normal, the investigator's suspicions will naturally be directed towards the possibility of a flaw.

If the fracture occurs along a straight longitudinal line and the fractured edges along this line are of a different appearance from those of the flap of metal which must have been lifted, suspicions of a flaw will become almost a certainty. And in such circumstances it is essential that the barrel should be submitted to an expert for metallurgic investigation. When this metallurgic evidence corroborates the suspicions of a flaw, the matter can be said to be definitely settled. It must, however, be remembered that metallurgic evidence of a positive nature is only confirmatory evidence. When such evidence cannot be found the other evidence of the presence of a flaw is not necessarily invalidated; and it is quite incorrect to assume that because no evidence of a defect in the metal is revealed by the microscope, no defect could have existed. It is possible for the actual burst so to disturb the surfaces of the fractured parts as to render microscopic examination abortive, and the absence of proof obtained by a microscope of the presence of a flaw is no proof of the absence of a flaw in the metal.

But should there be any distinct lamination in the surface of a fracture the evidence of a flaw can be regarded as definite even if no inclusions are found, for inclusions are usually carried away with the escaping gases when a barrel opens out along a seam. And in order to help the reader to recognise lamination when he sees it three typical examples have been given in Plate XIX. The top three photographs are the surfaces of longitudinal fractures, or splits, in barrels along the grain of the metal and the "layering," or lamination, is obvious.

The bottom photograph is of interest as it is an example of what may be termed "false" or "apparent" lamination, which was caused in the following manner.

The right barrel of a gun burst owing to a flaw in the chamber, and the metal opened out along a seam near the top of the barrel. The outside flap of metal was blown outwards and bent downwards against the sharp edge of the flat of the barrel, with the result that the barrel wall was snapped off along this edge in exactly the same manner as a thin piece of wood could be snapped off when placed over the edge of a table and the outer portion was bent downwards.

In the photograph the layer A is the outside edge of the flat of the barrel, which corresponds to the table edge just used as a simile, while the fractured surface of the barrel wall consists of the layers B and C. It might be thought that these two distinct layers were lamination, but actually the dividing line between the layer B and the layer C is the neutral axis of the wall. When the barrel wall was bent over outwards the outer and bottom portion, which was pressed against the edge of the flat, was forced into a state of compression. At the same time the inside of the wall, which was farthest from the flat, was forced into a state of tension as it was gradually stretched when the barrel wall was bent outwards. When fracture finally occurred the areas under tension and compression showed different characteristics as can be seen plainly in the photograph, which shows the neutral axis very clearly.

If there is the slightest doubt as to whether the burst was caused by an excessive pressure it will be better to measure the thickness of the wall of the barrel at both ends of the rupture, when use can be made of the Gunmakers' Formula to determine the gas pressures necessary to stress the barrel to its maximum strength at these points. The maximum strength can either be assumed, or else actually be obtained by cutting a test piece of metal from the barrel. If this necessary pressure is at all high it would mean that the 1-inch pressure must have been higher; and this can be proved or disproved by the appearance of the fired case as well as by the condition of the action.

The metallurgic investigation should also include an examination of the physical structure and condition of the steel so as to find out whether the barrel had been overheated during brazing. For it should not be forgotten that overheating can so destroy the strength of the steel as to render it liable to fracture when subjected to very low stresses.

This last point is of special importance when investigating a smashed or cracked *action*. The vendor of the gun will almost certainly attribute the accident to an excessive pressure; and it is quite probable that he will be right, for a cracked action is usually a typical indication of a very high pressure.

But the example given in Plate XVII proves that a very high pressure is not necessarily the true explanation for an accident of this type, and the metal of the action body in the immediate neighbourhood of the fracture should be metallurgically examined for the state of its physical condition. If there are signs of overheating, or incorrect heat treatment, the cartridges can be absolved from blame, and the onus must be borne by the gun.

I trust that I have now said enough to indicate the lines on which an investigation into the cause of a burst should proceed. Confidence in the correctness of a diagnosis can only come by experience backed up by a knowledge and understanding of the subject. I have tried to outline sufficient of the subject in these three chapters to provide the necessary knowledge and understanding; experience, however, can only be gained by each individual for himself.

But before I close this subject I will mention that there is one type of " burst " which is occasionally encountered which is not a burst at all. For it sometimes happens that a shooter actually hits the barrels of his second gun with the shot from his first gun, which is in his loader's hands, when he turns round and fires at a bird behind. The barrels will naturally be severely damaged, but such an accident is quite unmistakable.

A burst is the result of some internal pressure in the barrel which is acting outwards, and so the ruptured portion of the barrel will always show an *outward* splay.

But when the barrels are hit at very close range by a charge of shot, the rupturing force is acting *inwards* as far as the near side of the barrels is concerned, and so the barrels will tend to close up at the site of the rupture. Further, there will be marks of lead on the outside of the barrel.

In such a case, as in fact in every case of a burst, the investigator must be guided entirely by facts in his search for the truth, and should avoid being influenced by statements made by any interested party if such statements do not appear to confirm the definitely established facts.

LIABILITY IN THE CASE OF A BURST

When a burst occurs the question of liability will naturally occur to the owner of a gun, both for the repair or replacement of the gun itself, and also for possible physical injury. In any accident of this nature there are three parties concerned: the owner of the gun; the vendor of the gun; and the vendor of the cartridges. It may be as well, therefore, to consider all three points of view as impartially as possible.

The owner of the gun is naturally distressed at the damage to his weapon, quite apart from the fact that he possibly has been damaged himself. And he will equally naturally wish to have the loss made good.

The vendor of the gun will be just as anxious to meet the owner in any reasonable way, because his reputation may suffer if the fact that one of his guns has burst becomes widely known.

The same applies to the vendor of the cartridges, who will certainly do everything in his power to prove that the fault could not have been in them.

Consequently the owner of the gun really starts in a better position as far as any compensation is concerned, because it will be distinctly to the other parties' advantage to settle with him generously and so regain his confidence in their goods. This is a point which some sportsmen seem sometimes to forget, and I have known them at times to take up what can only be regarded as a most unreasonable attitude.

If any accident happens to a gun which has not been Nitro Proved but in which cartridges loaded with nitro powder were being used at the time of the accident, the owner of the gun can have no sort of claim whatever on either the vendor of the gun or cartridges. And the more generally this fact is realised the better both for sportsmen and gunmakers, as much misunderstanding will be saved.

But if the gun has been Nitro Proved the problem may not be so simple.

If the burst was caused by an obstruction no blame of any sort can be attached to the vendor of the gun, nor can he be held liable in any way.

And the vendor of the cartridges could only become liable if it were proved that the obstruction was caused by a faulty cartridge, in which combustion had been incomplete and so resulted in the shot charge being left in the bore. It might be possible to prove this in a court of law, but I can imagine that there could be considerable difficulty in convincing a jury composed of men and women who knew nothing of the subject. And if the nature of the burst indicated that it had been caused by an over-powder card wad left in the bore, I should say that legal proof would be an impossibility.

Nor must it be forgotten that incomplete combustion may be the result of faulty ignition due to an abnormally weak striker blow. And so no sportsman should contemplate serious legal action unless his purse is very deep, and he enjoys losing money.

For in the vast majority of cases the obstruction is inserted by some act of the shooter himself, and in such circumstances he alone can be held responsible.

If the burst was proved to be due to excessive pressure which was the result of abnormal or incorrect loading, the vendor of the gun is cleared of responsibility, and the vendor of the cartridges must shoulder the blame.

But a burst caused by some abnormal weakness of the metal is in a different category. If this weakness is the result of corrosion of any sort or of wear and tear

PLATE XXII

It is a common sight to see a sportsman struggling to put a gun together, especially if it be a weapon to which he is not accustomed. Force is not infrequently used, and burred, or otherwise damaged, lumps are usually the result. The illustrations show the wrong and right methods of holding a gun to put it together. The wrong position is shown in illustration A, and here the barrels are held a long way from the breech ; the angle between the barrels and stock is nearly a right angle ; the lever of the action is not pressed, and the stock is held by the hand alone. The correct position is shown in illustration B. It will be noticed how the barrels are held with the back of the hand upwards close to the breech so that complete control is exercised over the lumps of the barrels and they can be coaxed into the slots of the action. The angle between the barrels and stock is much more obtuse, thus allowing the hook of the forward lump on the barrels to find its own position, while the thumb of the right hand is pressing back the action lever and so giving the lumps every chance to slip into the slots in the action. At the same time the stock is pressed against the right fore-arm, which steadies it.

If the barrels are held too close to the breech there is a risk of pinching the flesh of the hand in a most painful manner when the gun is closed.

Once the hook of the forward lump is felt to engage, it is a good plan to try to pull the barrels apart from the stock. If the hook has not actually caught no harm is done, while if it has caught this movement helps to close the gun.

(A) The Wrong Way

(B) The Right Way

no one can fairly be held liable. But if the burst was due to a flaw, the situation can become very complicated. For the vendor of the gun will naturally do everything in his power to show that the flaw must have developed after it was sold as the result of some very high pressure. But if a metallurgic examination shows that the flaw is the result of some "inclusion" the vendor of the gun is legally liable under Section 14 (1) of the Sale of Goods Act, 1893. And here it may be mentioned that the makers of high grade British tubes now use Crack Detection for examining their tubes before they are issued.

Should a metallurgic examination show that the physical condition of the steel has been impaired through overheating, the gunmaker should shoulder all the blame and bear every penny of the cost of the damage. Overheating is nothing but bad workmanship for which there cannot be any possible excuse. But whether this view would be upheld in a court of law is another matter.

Finally, it should be realised that the majority of bursts are really the outcome of carelessness or ignorance on the part of the shooter, and that in these cases he should shoulder whatever blame there may be.

PRECAUTIONS TO AVOID BURSTS

In view of the statement which I have just made I will now give a list of precautions which all shooters should adopt. If they do they really need have no fear whatever of any bursts other than those very rare accidents due either to an over-powder card wad being left in the bore, or else to some latent flaw in the metal of the barrels. And these two causes are really so extremely unusual that they need hardly be considered.

The precautions which I suggest are as follows:

(1) Always buy cartridges from a reliable firm. This will minimise the risk of faulty loading, etc.

(2) Always adopt every possible precaution to prevent different sizes of cartridges being intermixed.

(3) Always look through the barrels before starting out on a day's shooting.

(4) Always carry a pull-through when out shooting.

(5) Always unload and look through the barrels on the faintest suspicion of the muzzle touching the ground or undergrowth.

(6) Always look through the barrels after the trigger is pressed with no result. If a miss-fire, see if there is anything in the barrel; if the chamber is empty, see if a smaller sized cartridge is sticking in the bore.

(7) Always look through the barrels on the slightest suspicion of anything peculiar happening in the sound of the report, or the fall of the hammer.[1]

(8) Always look through the barrels if an abnormal amount of smoke is seen to issue from the breech after unloading.

(9) Always look through the barrels if the recoil seems abnormally weak. When shooting at game the normal recoil is not ordinarily noticed. But anything markedly abnormal usually is detected at once.

(10) Never continue to use any cartridges from any particular lot if one or two give an altogether excessive recoil.

(11) Always have guns overhauled periodically by a competent gunmaker (preferably the original maker).

Bursts are extremely unpleasant occurrences, and if these eleven precautions were always adopted I am

[1] I have known a case of a latent flaw developing during shooting, when the report sounded peculiar. This was undoubtedly due to the fact that the barrel had begun to "go," and so gave out a different note, just as a cracked bell gives out a different note to a sound one. In this case the shooter did look down the bore, but of course saw nothing. If he had examined the *outside* of the barrel he would probably have seen some indication of a "seam" in the steel which had suddenly become more evident. So if the bore is seen to be clear after a peculiar report it would be as well to examine the barrels themselves for any abnormal appearance. But, as has already been stated, such flaws are so comparatively rare that the examination of the barrels need hardly be regarded as a normal precaution, especially if the gun has fired over 1,000 rounds.

convinced that bursts would be distinctly more rare even than they are. I will, however, wind up the subject with a note of consolation.

One would think that a burst would almost always cause serious bodily harm. But happily this idea is not borne out by experience. Out of the several hundred different bursts which I have personally investigated since 1920 only four caused any hurt to the shooter. In some of the other cases the shooters had extremely lucky escapes: but they were escapes; and it can be comforting to know that so many bursts can occur without hurting either the shooter or anyone else.

CHAPTER XIX

ODDS AND ENDS

THERE now only remain for consideration a few comparatively minor subjects which could not properly be included in any of the preceding chapters. I am, accordingly, dealing with these various points in the present chapter.

DETONATION

The first, and most important, of these miscellaneous subjects is the question of Detonation. There is a comparatively common belief among both sportsmen and gunmakers that shotgun cartridges can " detonate " ; and I have frequently been told that a gun has been burst by the detonation of the cartridge, while I have on several occasions been offered this explanation in all good faith for perfectly obvious obstructional bursts. It may, therefore, be as well to consider first what a " Detonation " really is ; and then why such a thing cannot occur in an ordinary shotgun cartridge.

When any explosive is said to " explode " it is meant that the explosive charge is resolved into hot gases with great rapidity. In general terms all explosives can be divided into two classes : " High " Explosives ; and Propellants.

The former class includes such explosives as dynamite and gelignite, which are used for blasting ; the latter, explosives such as cordite (which is used for the propulsion of projectiles in ordnance, rifles, pistols and revolvers), and Smokeless Diamond (which is used in a similar way in shotguns).

Detonation is the ordinary way of working in the case of " High " explosives, while combustion is the normal method of working in the case of Propellants. In both detonation and combustion the explosive charge is completely resolved into hot gases, but the difference between the two actions can best be realised with the help of the following example.

In a 12-inch Naval gun the cords of cordite which make up the charge are about one-third of an inch in diameter, and when combustion takes place they are totally burnt up in about one-hundredth part of a second. But in the case of a shell loaded with T.N.T. similar layers of this substance are converted into gases in about one-millionth part of a second. So in the latter case the conversion into gases is just about 10,000 times as rapid as the former. This is the difference between detonation and combustion as applied to explosives: combustion is slow—very slow—as compared with detonation.

Once this point is understood it becomes possible to assign an accurate definition to the term "detonation," and probably the best definition of any is as follows.

Detonation, when applied to explosives, means that the explosive charge is resolved into hot gases with such rapidity that the walls which contain that explosive have not time to make any appreciable movement before the conversion into gases is complete.

In the case of a 12-bore 2½-inch cartridge this would mean that the whole of the 33 grains or 42 grains of the powder would be completely converted into gases before the shot charge has had time to make any appreciable movement in the cartridge-case, let alone push back the turnover. If this happened the pressure developed would be about 30 tons to the square inch, and such a pressure would shatter the gun into fragments.

However, not only has such an occurrence never happened with shotgun cartridge-cases and powders as manufactured to-day, but it never could happen.

In order to cause the detonation of high explosives, such as dynamite or gelignite, a detonator must be used. This is a metal capsule which contains some substance such as fulminate of mercury; and for use with ordinary blasting explosives a detonator contains a minimum quantity of 15 grains of fulminate of mercury. There are, in fact, very few blasting explosives which can be made to detonate by a detonator which contains less than 7 grains of fulminate of mercury; and it must be remembered that such explosives are peculiarly sensitive to detonation.

But when shotgun powders are tested as blasting explosives they are very insensitive to detonation; and even the most sensitive require a detonator containing at least 15 grains of fulminate of mercury to produce detonation. So when the possibility of a detonation occurring in a shotgun cartridge is being considered, we must search for some detonating force; and such a force will have to be the equivalent, at the very least, of a charge of fulminate of mercury equal in weight to nearly half the total charge of powder in the case of a 33-grain powder, or more than one-third of the total powder charge of a 42-grain powder. But where could such a colossal detonating force be hidden? In the cap? Let us see.

High explosives, as has been seen, need a special detonator to be placed in contact with them in order to ensure their detonation. The sudden wave of intense pressure set up by the detonation of the detonator causes the high explosives in contact with it to detonate also.

Now a shotgun cap cannot set up such a high wave, and is consequently only an "igniter." But since it is well known that caps commonly used in shotgun cartridges do contain a certain amount of fulminate of mercury, let us consider why it is that they can only act as igniters, and not as detonators.

It should be realised that detonators always contain substances which will detonate on ignition. Such substances "go off" very rapidly; and, therefore, as explosives they are only suitable for use as detonators or igniters.

The composition in an ordinary percussion cap

contains fulminate of mercury ; not only, however, is the amount very small, but there are also moderating ingredients in the composition which destroy its detonating capacity. Further, the total weight of the composition is only about half a grain. And apart from the fact that this small quantity is placed definitely in the safety zone because of its moderating ingredients, half a grain is only one-thirtieth part of the 15 grains which constitute the minimum necessary weight to cause detonation of a shotgun powder.

The function of a percussion cap is to produce a flame which ignites the powder, just as a match ignites a cigarette. And it is utterly impossible for a cap to detonate the powder in a shotgun cartridge, both because of the small weight of the priming composition and the chemical ingredients which go to make up that composition.

It now only remains to be seen whether it is possible for the combustion of the powder charge to change into detonation during the process of combustion.

There have been a number of definite instances when burning masses of T.N.T. and some other explosives, which were being accidentally consumed by ordinary combustion, suddenly detonated. So the reader may wonder whether it is not possible for the powder charge in a shotgun cartridge to begin the process of conversion into gas by the ordinary procedure of combustion, and then suddenly to assume a detonating rôle and detonate after a short interval of time, just as burning masses of T.N.T. have been known to detonate after ordinary combustion had been in progress.

It is true that in such circumstances no detonator was required to produce the detonation. But there are two factors which have always been present when detonation has followed combustion in the cases of burning masses of T.N.T. and other explosives : large amounts of explosives were involved ; and considerable time elapsed between the moment of first ignition and the subsequent detonation.

In the case of a shotgun cartridge both these factors of quantity and time are lacking; for the weight of powder is very small and the charge is totally consumed within ·003 of a second. Further, when large amounts of shotgun powders have been deliberately destroyed by burning, the jump from ordinary combustion to detonation has never been observed.

It can, therefore, be definitely stated that detonation subsequent to combustion is impossible in the case of any ordinary shotgun cartridge. And even if this sudden jump to detonation could take place, it could not occur until the shot charge had moved some distance up the bore—3 to 4 inches at least. Were detonation then to occur, the pressure generated would merely be the closed vessel pressure for this distance, and would not be dangerous because of the large space in which the powder gases would be contained.

So it will be realised that if a burst is ever stated to be due to the detonation of an ordinary shotgun cartridge an explanation is being offered which is not only unreasonable, but unthinkable. For, as has been shown, a detonation is something so different from ordinary combustion that there cannot be any confusion between the two. And all who are interested in shooting can be assured that ordinary shotgun cartridges are absolutely safe in this respect, and cannot, in any circumstances, detonate in a gun.

REINFORCED ACTIONS

It has been seen that the weakest part of the action is the junction of the bar with the body, and that this point can be strengthened by rounding the angle between the bar and the face of the action. Actions, however, can be strengthened still further by being so cut that an extra thickness of metal is left round this angle. Such an action is said to be "reinforced," and there can be no doubt that quite an appreciable increase in strength is thus obtained with only a slight increase in weight.

Reinforced actions, therefore, can be used with advantage in the case of box lock guns which have no top extension. But for ordinary side lock guns this type of action is hardly necessary.

Another method of strengthening the action of a gun, or rather of the attachment of the barrels to the action, is by means of "Side Clips." These are small projections on each side of the face of the action which prevent any tendency of the barrels to move sideways. Since the thrust of the discharge of the right barrel acts to the right of the centre of the action body, and that of the left barrel to the left of this centre, there must be a tendency for the barrels to move sideways in relation to the body of the action, and sometimes a slight horizontal looseness can be developed. Side clips help to prevent this looseness, and therefore add to the solidity of the attachment of the barrels to the action. They can, accordingly, be an advantage in guns which are habitually used with high pressure cartridges. But in ordinary guns side clips are quite unnecessary.

"VENA CONTRACTA" GUNS

A type of gun known as the "Vena Contracta" was brought out towards the end of the nineteenth century by Messrs. Lang. The principle underlying this type of gun was that the chamber was of usual 12-bore dimensions, while the bore of the gun was gradually contracted until it became a 20-gauge. After various experiments it was found that the best results seemed to be given when the barrel was reduced in size to its final dimensions about 6 inches in front of the chamber. The effect thus obtained was similar to combining a 12-bore chamber with a 20-bore barrel by means of a chamber cone about 6 inches long.

The purpose of this system of boring was to reduce

the weight of the forward part of the barrels, and so improve the balance, and at the same time obtain a slight reduction in the total weight of the gun.

But although the patterns obtained in various trials were quite satisfactory, and the pressures were not found to be excessive, the Vena Contracta gun never became firmly established ; and it seems probable that the departure from the usual was too great to be justified by the results achieved.

It does, however, seem possible that the Vena Contracta principle might be used again by gunmakers in their search for methods of reducing the weights of their guns. I doubt whether the full contraction from a 12-bore chamber to a 20-bore barrel will ever become permanently established. But a reduction to 14-bore or 16-bore would not be nearly so startling and might enable the gunmaker to fit 12-bore barrels of 27 or 28 inches in length, which would be lighter forward than a full 12-gauge. Such a step would admittedly be contradictory to the usual plan of enlarging the bore slightly, in order to improve patterns ; and I do not put it forward as a suggestion. The possibility of such a system of boring, however, should be recognised, although it could never become established without exhaustive trials.

SHORTENING BARRELS

A question which sportsmen are constantly asking is whether it is possible to shorten an existing pair of barrels without impairing the shooting of the gun to which they belong.

It should be quite obvious that since the choke is situated close up to the muzzle it would be quite impossible to remove any part of the muzzle without interfering with the choke in some way or other ; which can only mean that the shooting of the gun must be impaired.

The only type of boring which would not be affected by shortening the barrels is an absolutely true cylinder: and this boring is very rare.

It can accordingly be stated quite definitely that the shooting capacity of a gun will be spoiled by the removal of any part of the barrels at the muzzle end.

It is, however, possible for a skilled gunmaker to separate the barrels for some distance from the muzzle after they have been shortened, and then to swedge the ends of the shortened barrels down so as to make fresh constrictions. By this means a fresh choke can be introduced in any barrel; but the work is highly skilled, and therefore expensive, while the results are not always certain.

No sportsman should, therefore, definitely place an order for such work without first consulting fully with his gunmaker as to the chances of success. And if the gunmaker is doubtful about the results likely to be given by any particular pair of barrels, it will almost certainly be better to buy a new pair than to shorten old ones.

MISS-FIRES

When a miss-fire occurs the cartridge usually receives the blame, but in the vast majority of cases the fault lies in the gun.

As was explained in Volume II, there is a certain standard of sensitiveness for British caps which is gauged by the height from which a 2-ounce weight must fall on to a cap in order to explode it. The standard height is 14 inches, but most caps will explode when the weight is dropped from 12 inches, and some even when the height is only 10 inches. It is, therefore, a simple matter to test caps for sensitiveness; and if they pass the test the cause of the miss-fire must be searched for in the gun.

As a general rule, when a gun gives miss-fires there

is more than one cause, but the following are the principal faults which can singly, or in combination, give rise to miss-fires.

(1) A weak mainspring which gives a weak striker blow.

(2) An incorrectly shaped striker which does not indent the cap properly.

(3) The striker hole is not placed correctly, with the result that the striker does not hit the cap in the centre.

(4) The striker hole, or lock, or both, is clogged with dirt or rust. This will impede the fall of the tumbler and so reduce the strength of the striker blow.

(5) The mainspring is not properly seated, with the result that its full expansion is attained before the fall of the tumbler is completed, when a rebound action takes place which checks the tumbler at the end of its fall and reduces the force of the blow.

If miss-fires are experienced, the indentations made by the striker in the caps of as many cartridges as possible, both fired and those which have miss-fired, should be examined. It very occasionally happens that the cap is seated slightly below the level of the base of the cartridge ; but this can easily be seen if the straightedge of a ruler is placed across the base of the cartridge. If the cap is correctly seated, and the indentations appear weak, the fault must lie in the gun, and it should then be sent to the maker, or other competent gunsmith, for examination.

WEIGHTS OF TRIGGER PULLS

There is no recognised standard weight for the trigger pulls of a shotgun, but the left barrel almost always has a slightly heavier pull than the right because better leverage can be obtained on the rear trigger, and if too light it might be jarred off when the right barrel is fired. In single-trigger guns the leverage is the same for both locks, but even so experience has shown that a slightly heavier pull for the left barrel is by no means a disadvantage, as this eliminates the risk of the right barrel jarring off the left.

In any case it is a bad mistake to have trigger pulls too light, as the gun is then far more liable to be jarred off by any sudden shock or bump, even when it is at "Safe."

On the other hand, if the trigger pulls are too heavy, it is exceedingly difficult to release the tumbler without a jerk, and this can so disturb the alignment of the gun that a miss will be certain.

As a general rule, the trigger of the right barrel has a pull of from $3\frac{1}{2}$ to 4 lb., and that of the left from 4 to $4\frac{1}{2}$ lb. These weights have been found by long experience to be the most satisfactory, and all shooters will be well advised not to have their pulls set outside these limits.

DOUBLE DISCHARGE

Sometimes the recoil of the right barrel will jar off the left lock, and when this happens there is a "double discharge." This expression, however, is slightly misleading because both barrels of a gun cannot be fired absolutely simultaneously, since the second is fired as the result of firing the first. Nevertheless the two barrels go off with such a short interval of time between them that they appear to be fired simultaneously.

There is no doubt that such a double discharge imposes an additional strain on the action; and if it were to occur frequently, and the gun were not of best quality, the barrels would probably be lifted off the face of the action, even if more serious damage did not result.

There is no single cause for the apparent simultaneous firing of both barrels, but the most common causes are:

(1) The weight of the trigger pull of the left barrel is too light, with the result that the lock of the left barrel is

jarred off by the recoil developed by the firing of the right.

(2) The trigger of the left barrel protrudes slightly to the right (in the case of a man firing from the right shoulder), with the result that it is caught by the trigger finger after the first barrel is fired.

(3) The stock of the gun is too long for the shooter, with the result that the trigger finger is involuntarily slipped back on to the trigger of the left barrel.

PISTOL GRIPS

A Pistol Grip to the stock is invaluable in a rifle, as it helps to steady the hand when pressing the trigger, In an ordinary shotgun, however, it is, I think, a mistake. because it gets in the way of the trigger hand when it is slipped back after firing the right barrel to take up a grip for the firing of the left. So a pistol grip tends to slowness in the firing of the second barrel.

In a single-trigger gun, however, this does not apply ; and if the owner of such a gun prefers a pistol grip there is no reason why he should not have one.

And in the case of heavy wildfowl guns a pistol grip can be an advantage as it helps the shooter to obtain a firmer hold with his trigger hand, and so take more of the recoil. With these guns extreme quickness is seldom necessary for the second barrel.

SINGLE-HANDED GUNS

Those shooters who have had the misfortune to lose an arm must suffer a great and inevitable handicap. But in spite of this handicap much can be overcome by determination and perseverance, and although it is extremely doubtful whether a one-armed man could ever become a really good all-round shot, he might very easily become quite a useful shot and derive real enjoyment from this sport.

But since a severe handicap is inevitable it is useless to refuse to recognise its existence, and no one-armed shooter should think of using a gun which has not been adapted as well as possible to his peculiar requirements.

The first of these requirements is lightness ; but not only in the total weight of the gun, but also in the weight of the forward part. So it is essential that the centre of inertia of the whole gun should be situated as far back as possible. For this reason a 20-bore fitted with 25-inch barrels would seem to be a particularly good weapon.

Then, since the trigger hand has to take the whole weight of the gun and control the swing as well as press the trigger, a special grip becomes absolutely necessary. A good big pistol grip will be, for this reason, an advantage. But the best grip of all is that devised by Messrs. Woodward, which is really an abnormally enlarged and specially shaped pistol grip in which recesses are cut for the thumb and individual fingers. This grip can be attached to any gun and should be regarded as an absolute necessity for a one-armed shot.

And since the shifting of the grip which is necessary for firing the left barrel of a double-trigger gun might easily make the shooter lose his control of his weapon, a single trigger becomes equally necessary.

Two other points which deserve special consideration are ease of opening and closing, so as to render the work of loading as simple and safe as possible. For this reason an efficient self-opening gun will prove a great boon.

And finally, a rubber recoil pad will probably prove a welcome relief, as recoil will always appear heavier since there is only one arm available to help to receive it. Further, if the recoil pad is well varnished it will not tend to stick to the coat and the butt will slip more easily into position against the shoulder.

GUN HEADACHE

About twenty years ago some correspondence appeared in the *Field* on the subject of Gun Headache, and various contributors expressed the opinion that the real cause was a disordered liver, or over-indulgence in food, drink and tobacco. This explanation may be true in a certain number of cases, but I am quite sure that it is not true for all ; as I know men who are models of sobriety, and non-smokers to boot, and whose livers are reported to be perfectly normal, who yet suffer from gun headache. In many of these cases, however, the sportsman has suffered some severe injury earlier in life, and it seems that any serious injury to the head may possibly cause a predisposition to gun headache.

The late Dr. C. J. Heath, who was not only President of the Wildfowlers' Association but who also gained a high position in the medical profession, assured me that gun headache is really nothing more than a form of mild concussion produced by the repeated recoil. As a layman I will not attempt to offer any opinion on this statement, beyond saying that it certainly explains the fact that cartridges which develop a severe recoil are always more likely to cause gun headache than lightly loaded cartridges.

In any case, the remedy undoubtedly lies in reducing the recoil by the use of lightly loaded cartridges ; and sometimes only 30 grains of a 33-grain powder are used in conjunction with but $\frac{15}{16}$ of an ounce of shot in an ordinary 12-bore $2\frac{1}{2}$-inch cartridge. These very light charges, however, are not always effective against game unless they are very carefully loaded ; and consequently it is usually better to try first a combination of 33 grains of some 33-grain powder and 1 ounce of shot. If this is still too heavy a load the powder charge can be reduced to 32 grains.

Different kinds of powder, however, can also be tried with advantage, and it seems to be a fact that many sportsmen have been cured of gun headache by a change of powder. There can be no definite rule, as powders apparently affect individuals differently; and I have known at least one case of a sportsman who could only use Ballistite with comfort. Sufferers from gun headache should experiment for themselves, first by reducing the shot charge to 1 ounce, or slightly less, and then trying different loads of 33-grain powders. In no case should any 42-grain powder be used, as these develop a heavy recoil, and for the same reason very light guns should be avoided.

"ROCKET" CARTRIDGES

Tracer bullets have been used in rifles for so long that many shooters have probably been surprised that no serious attempt seems to have been made until quite recently to evolve an efficient tracer cartridge for shotgun work. As a matter of fact there has been quite a number of different trials in the past, but none proved very satisfactory; for the manufacture of an effective tracer shotgun cartridge is a very different affair from that of a tracer rifle bullet. In this last case the bullet itself provides accommodation for the tracer compound, and the pressure generated in any modern nitro rifle is more than enough to ensure ignition of this compound.

For it is the question of pressure which is the greatest difficulty which must be surmounted in the manufacture of a tracer shotgun cartridge. In Volume II the importance of certain properties of a cap flame were duly emphasised. The flame, which is in reality burning gas, impinges from out of the cap chamber on to the powder under considerable pressure; and it is this pressure with which it is forced on to the powder, as well as the actual temperature of the burning gases, which results in the proper ignition of the powder charge.

The problem of igniting the tracer compound is not dissimilar, as the two same factors are again essential: temperature and pressure. The temperature produced by the combustion of the powder charge in an ordinary shotgun cartridge is sufficient ; but the pressure is on the low side.

And there is yet another difficulty in the case of a shotgun cartridge which does not arise in a rifle bullet, which, as has already been stated, provides ready accommodation for the tracer compound. The pellets in a charge of shot are too small to act as such vehicles, and experiments made in coating them with substances which give off smoke have not been encouraging, because the amount of substance which will remain on the pellets will be too slight to produce much visible effect. Yet the shot charge must be normal, or one would not obtain correct data.

These difficulties, however, were overcome after exhaustive trials, and the "Eley Rocket Cartridge" was the result.

One of these original Rocket cartridges is shown in section in Plate XXIII, from which it will be seen that an extra pellet was added to act as a vehicle for the tracer compound. The addition of this extra pellet, or capsule, was really the only important difference between a Rocket cartridge and an ordinary game cartridge.

The capsule in question was just over ¼ inch long and about ¼ inch in diameter, comprising a small cylinder of copper, which is closed at the front end and left open in rear, with a "head" of lead attached to the closed front. This lead is added to provide the necessary weight and in the original cartridge was inserted inside the copper cylinder, which was the full length of the capsule and was, indeed, the capsule itself.

But later the capsule consisted of two parts : the short copper cylinder and the separate lead head which was riveted on to the front of the copper cylinder. The tracer compound was contained in the cylinder portion of the capsule, which was seated in the centre of a 1¼-inch felt wad which replaced the usual card over-felt wad. To make room for this wad the ordinary felt wad was not so thick as usual.

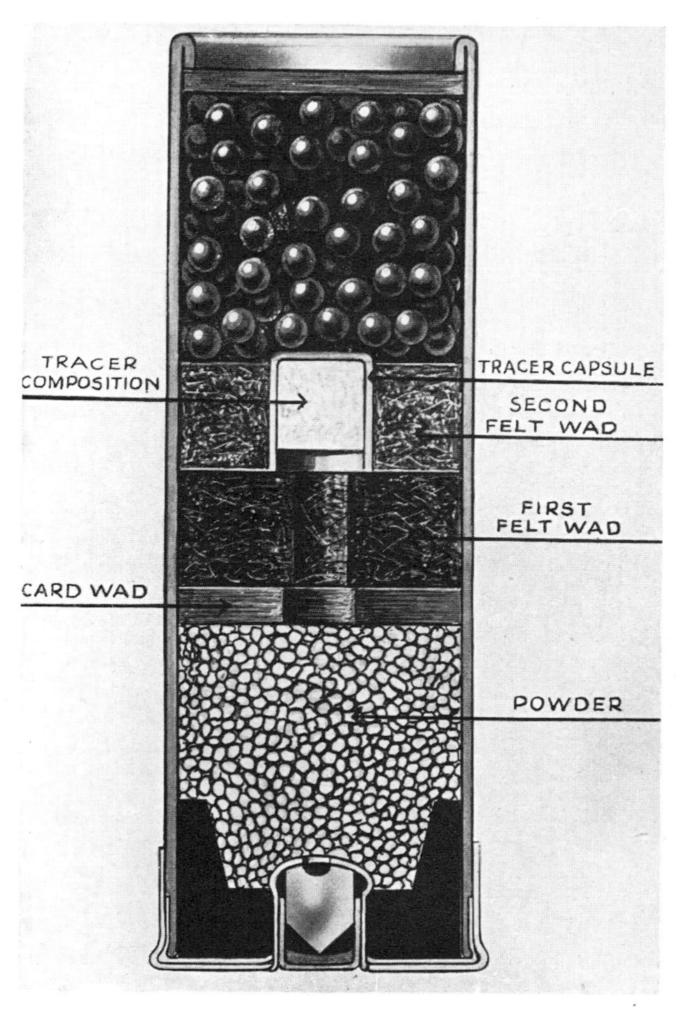

A Sectional Diagram of the Original Eley "Rocket" Cartridge

In order to allow the flame from the burning powder charge access to the tracer composition, both the card over-powder wad and the usual felt wad were perforated with a hole in their centres.

And so it will be realised that the only divergence from the normal was the use of a perforated over-powder card wad ; a somewhat thinner and perforated felt wad ; and a second felt wad, which held the tracer capsule, instead of the card over-felt wad.

The shot charge was the standard $1\frac{1}{16}$ ounce, and the powder charge was also standard. The effect was that the ballistics developed by this cartridge were in every way normal, and the shot charge behaved in exactly the same manner as the shot charge from an ordinary cartridge as regards pattern and velocity.

When the cartridge was fired the burning powder ignited the tracer compound, which kept burning as the capsule followed its trajectory for about 65 yards from the muzzle of the gun. The trajectory was thus defined by a bright line of flame when viewed from a flank, or by a bright spot of light when seen by the shooter himself or someone close to him.

In order to test whether the tracer capsule flew in the middle of the shot charge I tried a number of these cartridges on a pattern plate, and found that in every single case the mark of the tracer pellet was, for all practical purposes, in the middle of the pattern, never being more than 9 inches away from the exact centre.

I must confess that I am quite unable to offer any explanation as to why this tracer capsule did fly so centrally, and am forced to the conclusion that such good results must be dependent on the most careful loading. If the capsule were not inserted quite straight it might not have flown so accurately.

Theoretically these Rocket cartridges would appear to offer a degree of help which is so enormous that their use may seem almost to be unsporting. In actual practice, however, the help which they gave was not so easy to interpret as many would think. Anyone who has had much experience of tracer bullets will corroborate this point of view.

The reason undoubtedly is that any tracer projectile which carries some burning composition leaves a trail of light which defines the actual trajectory. This trail of light—or spot of light as it appears when viewed from the gun—hangs momentarily in the air and one is instinctively inclined to correct on the trajectory thus defined. In doing so, however, one forgets that the target is moving all the time, and so the relative distance between the target and the defined trajectory is not the same as that between the target and the passing projectile.

In the case of a miss behind a tracer cartridge—either gun or rifle—invariably exaggerates the error ; while in the case of a miss in front the error appears smaller than it actually is.

On one occasion when I was using a Rocket cartridge in the field I killed a crossing pheasant, and the trace was clearly visible passing just under the root of its tail. The gun next to me gleefully smacked the seat of his " plus fours " as an indication of where my shot had gone ; but the Rocket cartridge had libelled me grossly, because the bird was killed stone dead and was hit in the head.

This exaggeration of errors is helped by what is termed " persistence of vision," which is the inability of the brain to discard any image formed on the retina immediately that image is removed. For the image can exist only so long as the object which forms it is actually in the field of vision ; but there is a time lag in the brain's dismissal of the image.

If it were not for this time lag there would be no apparent continuity of movement when watching a cinema film and each photograph would appear as a separate picture ; and the series would be seen as a succession of fixed positions, each differing slightly from its predecessor, when the movement would appear as a series of jerks.

Similarly this time lag on the part of the brain, which renders it impossible to discard any image on the retina immediately, causes one to continue to see the foreshortened trace after it has actually burnt out. And so the apparent hanging of the trace in the air is rendered longer by persistence of vision and the bird has more time in which to change its position relative to that of the trace as fixed on the retina.

The original tracer capsule weighed about the same as a pellet of S.S.G. shot and such a pellet can inflict an unpleasant wound at over 100 yards. But, as has already been pointed out, the later form of capsule consists of two parts: the lead head and the copper cylinder, the former being riveted to the latter. As the tracer composition burnt during flight the riveted part of the lead was fused by the heat until finally the lead head and the copper cylinder separated, just as the last of the tracer composition was consumed.

The result was that two light projectiles replaced one comparatively heavy one and consequently any tendency to serious risks was almost negligible.

But although Rocket cartridges cannot, and do not, damage a gun, the use of steel shot can, and does. It is difficult to understand how any ordinary shooter can think of using steel shot, as the hardness of the shot would, one have thought, be so obvious that the risk of damage to a barrel should be equally obvious. But a few years ago several pairs of barrels were sent to I.C.I., all of which had been used for firing steel shot—probably small ball bearings. The cartridges used were loaded with small steel balls, mostly about $\frac{1}{4}$ inch in diameter, and the damage comprised deep scores in the bore, from the chamber to the muzzle, or to the site of the burst, if there was a burst, for these were fairly common.

It can be stated quite definitely that the use of steel ball bearings, or steel pellets of any sort, will invariably score the barrel, even if the ball bearings are copper coated. If sufficiently large they will actually distort the barrel or cause a burst. Damascus barrels usually burst about one foot or more from the breech. In the case of steel barrels a burst will usually occur at the muzzle—probably due to the check to the shot charge on entering the choke.

Some years ago, within the space of a few weeks, no less than five pairs of damaged barrels—all showing the same type of damage—were sent to I.C.I.

This suggested that some person, or persons, without being aware of the danger involved, was, or were, loading cartridge cases with steel ball bearings, or pellets of steel.

It cannot, therefore, be emphasised too strongly that the use of steel pellets of any size in shotgun cartridges constitutes a source of real danger, both to the gun and the actual user of the gun.

In the past there have been isolated cases of this nature, but the more recent experiences suggest that some person, or persons, was, or were, using steel balls for home loading of shotgun cases without, apparently, any idea of the potential danger for himself which he was laying up.

EXTREME RANGE

A question which is constantly cropping up is that of the possibility of danger to beaters or spectators at ranges of 200 yards and over. This is merely another way of asking what is the extreme range of an ordinary shotgun, so the question needs an answer.

It is very generally believed that the maximum range of either a rifle or a shotgun is obtained with an angle of elevation of 45 degrees. This would be true were the shot fired in a vacuum, but the resistance of the air makes a considerable difference, and the maximum range is actually obtained when the barrel of the rifle or shotgun makes an angle of a little over 30 degrees with the horizontal; and for all practical purposes it is sufficiently accurate to state that the maximum range is given by an angle of elevation of 30 degrees.

It is probable that the best information available in

connection with this subject is that obtained experimentally some years ago.[1] Series of shots were fired from an ordinary 2½-inch 12-bore gun with standard cartridges on a dead-calm day along a perfectly straight canal. The gun was fired from a rest, and the different elevations were obtained with a clinometer, while several observers with stop-watches took the times of flight.

[1] The calculation of extreme ranges is not an easy problem, because the velocities of the shot charges drop below the lowest values given in any ballistic tables. The best method to adopt is the "Quadratic Rule" method, but even this necessitates assumptions which cannot be definitely proved. The late Mr. F. W. Jones, however, evolved an empirical formula for the range of shot pellets when the gun is fired at an angle of 30 degrees elevation. Since this formula is based partly on the experimental results obtained with No. 6 shot it may need modification should further experimental results be obtained with different shot sizes. Consequently I will avoid any details of the method employed for obtaining the formula, which is:

$$S = C \times 40748 \times \log\left(\frac{4 \cdot 78}{\sqrt{C}} - 2 \cdot 3\right) + 26$$

where S is the Range in feet, and C the Ballistic Coefficient of an individual shot pellet.

The late Major J. H. Hardcastle gave me a rough empirical formula some years ago for the extreme range of shot which has the merit of simplicity. This formula is:

$$R = \frac{1500}{\sqrt[3]{N}}$$

where R is the extreme range in yards and N the number of pellets to the ounce.

This formula is really an assumption that the range for an elevation of 30 degrees is directly proportional to the Ballistic Coefficient and there is certainly neither theoretical nor experimental evidence for different shot sizes to support this assumption. Nevertheless, Major Hardcastle's formula probably gives results which are sufficiently near the truth for all practical purposes for shot sizes which are close to No. 6, but the more the shot size varies from No. 6 the greater will be the error.

With Mr. Jones's formula the extreme ranges for BB, No. 2 and No. 6, are respectively 328, 282 and 226 yards; while with Major Hardcastle's formula these ranges are 365, 310 and 232 yards.

The actual results obtained were as follows:

Elevation in degrees.	5	10	15	20	25	30	35	40	50	60	70	80	90
Range in feet	365	500	580	640	680	700	695	680	605	495	350	185	0
Time of flight in seconds	1·61	3·03	4·29	5·41	6·39	7·23	7·95	8·57	9·54	10·15	10·58	10·98	11·28

So if it is assumed that the extreme range for any ordinary shot size is just under 250 yards the error will not be material.

VERTICAL RANGE AND TERMINAL VELOCITY

Akin to the question of extreme range is that of the vertical range, or the height which the pellets of a shot charge will attain when the gun is fired vertically upwards. This question is of little practical value, but is quite frequently being asked by shooters with an enquiring turn of mind. In the case of No. 6 shot the vertical range is about 120 yards. Larger and smaller shot will attain greater and lower heights respectively, but the difference will not be much.

Another question dealing with the same subject is also common, namely, why is it that the shot charge does not return to the ground after being fired vertically upwards with the same velocity with which it started?

In a vacuum, where there is no air resistance, a projectile fired vertically would return to the point of departure with exactly the same vertical velocity as that of projection. This theoretical condition, however, cannot exist in actual practice on account of the resistance of the air.

This resistance prevents the projectile from going so high as it would in a vaccuum, and so, for this reason alone, it would not attain the same speed when it returned to the point of departure as it would have acquired in a vacuum, because it would not have so far to fall.

Further, during its return to earth the velocity which the projectile acquires through gravity is reduced by the air resistance, and so there is a second reason why the velocity of the projectile when returning is less than that with which it started.

All shooters know how a charge of shot will often drop almost like rain. The reason for its low velocity when falling is, however, not entirely to be found in the reduced height which it attains owing to the resistance of the air but also in what is known as "Terminal Velocity."

When a pellet of shot, a bullet or shell, a bomb, or anything else for that matter, is falling the only force which is pulling it downwards is that of gravity, and this force is directly proportional to the weight of the falling body. But the faster any body moves through the air the greater becomes the air resistance, and when any projectile is falling from a height there comes a point when the force of the air resistance becomes equal to the force of gravity.

Once this point has been reached the projectile continues to descend with uniform velocity. If the air resistance tends to slow it down a bit gravity at once takes charge and pulls it down faster; but directly a certain speed is attained the air resistance becomes sufficiently powerful to put on the brake. Thus it happens that the two forces, one positive and one negative, balance each other when a certain speed has been reached and so prevent the projectile from falling any faster. This critical speed is known as the "Terminal Velocity."

It will be realised that this terminal velocity is dependent on two things: the force of gravity acting downwards and the air resistance acting upwards. The former is dependent on the weight of the projectile; the latter on its capacity for overcoming air resistance. A big-diametered, blunt-nosed projectile will not slip through the air so easily as a long, lean and sharply pointed one, while a spherical ball will be affected more by air resistance than any elongated bullet or shell. And so, other things being equal, a spherical ball will have a lower terminal velocity than an elongated bullet of the same weight because the latter can travel faster through the air before the critical degree of air resistance is created.

The existence of terminal velocity will be appreciated when one considers falling rain. This velocity naturally varies with the size of the drops, but can never be anything but very low which explains why rain does actually fall so gently, although when the drops are big they come down more heavily.

It is exactly the same with a charge of shot and the terminal velocity of No. 6 shot is only round about 30 f.s., which explains why it drops so gently.

CHAPTER XX

THOUGHTS ON SHOOTING

OUR study of the whole subject of the Gun and the Cartridge is now complete, and it is with some diffidence that I add this final chapter. I have felt, however, that it might not be out of place to offer a few ideas rather than suggestions on some of the problems which are inseparable from the actual use of a shotgun in the field. Hitherto, throughout all three volumes, I have been dealing to the best of my ability with definite facts ; and it is with reluctance that I leave them in order to air purely personal views, which may possibly not be shared by readers who are more competent to instruct in actual shooting than I am. But my own experience in the past has convinced me that there are many beginners who are but too anxious to obtain some help from books. So it is for them, and them alone, that I am attempting this chapter, even though I am sure that shooting, just like casting a fly, can never be learnt from the written word. At the present time the actual handling of a gun in shooting is taught most efficiently at numerous shooting schools. Yet it is probable that when certain definite facts are understood the beginner may be able to profit all the more from shooting school lessons.

Shooting with a shotgun means shooting at a rapidly moving target ; and the difficulty of shooting at any moving target consists of firing at a point exactly the right distance ahead so as to allow for the movement of the target during the time interval between the shooter's decision to fire and the arrival of the projectile at the target. In other words, the difficulty consists of making the correct forward allowance.

Now it was explained in Volume II and in Chapter VIII of this Volume that the time interval which governs the forward allowance is really composed of three different and distinct periods, namely:

(1) The time taken from the brain's decision to fire, to the actual pressing of the trigger, which may be called the " Sportsman's Time."

(2) The Time up the Barrel.

(3) The Time of Flight.

The Time up the Barrel and Time of Flight have been dealt with fully, and can be regarded as comparatively definite periods. If forward allowance depended solely on these shooting would be much more easy—and incidentally much less interesting—because practice and experience would enable one to gauge the correct amount of allowance required in varying conditions with fair accuracy.

But the existence of the Sportsman's Time brings in a big complication. I remember, many years ago, seeing a photograph of the start of a 100-yards race. This particular race was won in quite good time, but the interesting thing about the photograph was that it showed the smoke of the starting pistol quite clearly while the runners were all in their original positions on the line ready for starting. This proved that the actual signal for the start had been given and yet not one of the runners had been able to act on that signal. It was a striking example of the well known fact that the human brain requires an appreciable time to react to any signal.

Numerous scientific experiments have been carried out in order to ascertain the extent and scope of this reaction. Instruments have been devised in which some signal is given by external means, either a flash, sound or touch. This signal is called the Stimulus. The movement made by the person under observation as the result of the Stimulus is called the Reaction, and the time between the Stimulus and Reaction is measured.

It has been found that not only does this time vary very considerably with individuals, but that it also varies on different days with the same individual. Further, that it is affected differently in different persons by such influences as food, alcohol, tobacco and fatigue, both mental and physical. This explains why some men can shoot better after lunch and others worse ; and also why some are unable to shoot if they smoke, and others unable to shoot if they do not.

But the main fact emerges that the Sportsman's Time can be a constantly varying factor, and it is this variation which adds so greatly to the difficulty of shooting.

In general terms there are two methods of shooting at a moving target, by " Intercepting " or by " Swinging."

Intercepting consists of deliberately firing at some point in front of the moving target, the whole of the forward allowance being allowed for in the distance of this point ahead of the target.

There are some men who can shoot in this way successfully, but I am sure that they are very rare. And I am equally sure that no beginner will be wise even to attempt it—except perhaps in two particular types of shot which will be mentioned shortly—because the difficulty of overcoming the constantly varying time element made up of the Sportsman's Time is so great as to be overwhelming in the case of at least 99 per cent. of shooters, if not more. On occasions all of us have probably brought off successful shots by intercepting ; but these occasions are usually very rare, and I am inclined to think that success has been due to chance more often than to skill.

The method of shooting which is almost universal is to " swing " with the gun as the shot is taken. The broad principle underlying this method is as follows.

Let us assume that a flat, vertical sheet-iron target is moving across the shooter's front at such a pace and range that the correct forward allowance caused by the Time up the Barrel and the Time of Flight is 10 feet. Let us also assume that a bull's-eye is painted on the target exactly 10 feet to the left of the right-hand edge, and that the target is moving from left to right. Then if aim is taken at the right-hand edge of the target the forward allowance will be correct and the bull will be hit *provided the uncertain and variable time element of the Sportsman's Time can be eliminated.*

This can be done by aiming at the right-hand edge of the moving target without altering the aim until after the trigger is pressed. *In other words, if the gun is kept swinging so as to be pointing the correct distance in front of the moving object which it is desired to hit, and this movement is maintained until after the trigger has been pressed, the Sportsman's Time is eliminated altogether because the forward allowance has been kept the same throughout the period occupied by the brain's decision to fire.*

The whole secret of "Swing" is to shoot with a moving gun. This movement need not necessarily be rapid, but it is essential that it should be maintained until after the trigger has been pressed ; as if it is checked before this pressure takes place no allowance will have been made for the Sportsman's Time, and a miss behind will be the result.

When once the beginner has realised this fundamental fact he, or she, will have made a big advance.

So far I have only considered swing in theory, and I will try to suggest how theory can be translated into practice. I am convinced that in all ordinary shooting it is useless for the average person to try to give any definite number of inches, feet or yards, as a forward allowance. But it may be useful to know what the allowance should really be in certain cases, and to realise that at long ranges it should be more than double what it is at short. Such knowledge helps to impress the necessity of forward allowance upon one's subconscious mind and to make one shoot automatically.

For to be successful shooting must be automatic : and it is impossible to be automatic if one is thinking whether the allowance should be 10 feet or 13. All that can be done is to realise that forward allowance is necessary, and to learn by experience how to make it correctly without checking the swing.

In the most general terms the best way to do this is, I believe, to bring the gun up pointing *behind* the tail of a bird and then to swing the muzzle past the bird in the direction of its flight ; and when the muzzle has completely passed the head of the bird to press the trigger *without checking the movement of the gun in any way.*

It is almost impossible to estimate with any degree of accuracy how far ahead of the bird the muzzle will be pointing when the trigger is pressed. And I am sure that it is a mistake to try. In the parlance of the shooting school instructor, one should " blot the bird out " with the muzzle of the gun before pressing the trigger. That is, for instance, in the case of a bird flying from left to right, the muzzle must be swung sufficiently ahead of the bird to hide it with the barrels. If this is done successfully in the case of a straightforward shot at normal sporting range a kill will probably result. For it must be realised that this method of shooting makes an automatic increase in forward allowance as the range is increased because the method is dependent on the angular distance which the gun points in front of the bird. This angle becomes more or less constant, but if the range is increased the actual forward allowance is increased in proportion.

If the bird is missed, or hit in the tail, the angle which the gun is pointed ahead of the bird must be increased by carrying the swing through a little further before pressing the trigger. The extent of this " follow through " or " blotting the bird out" can only be ascertained by practice ; and it will naturally vary with the range, angle of flight, and variety of bird. The principle, however, is always the same whether the bird is flying towards one overhead or crossing from one side to the other.

It may help the beginner to imagine that his gun is long enough to reach the bird and that he must try to ruffle its feathers up the wrong way by stroking it with the muzzle from tail to head. In fact one of the best hints I have ever heard for dealing with high pheasants was that one should try to " stroke them down." I have always thought that this phrase described exactly what swing should be. Nothing in the nature of a jerk or hurried movement: but merely a steady follow through until after the trigger has been pressed.

And the same principle applies to birds flying towards one. In their case the gun cannot be pointed behind the bird's tail: but it can be pointed just below the bird, when all that it is necessary to do is to give the gun a "lift" with the left arm (assuming the shooter to be firing from his right shoulder) which will "blot the bird out" as before. If the trigger is pressed without any check in this "lifting" movement the bird will probably be killed.

Different people derive different impressions from a particular word or phrase. But personally I have found that word "lift" the greatest help in tackling approaching birds such as driven partridges. To me it describes exactly the movement I should impart to my gun barrels with my left arm, and so I hope that it may prove of equal help to some of my readers.

The going-away bird is often rising, and then it needs almost exactly the same treatment. That is, the gun should be "lifted" with the left arm and the bird "blotted out."

When a going-away bird is not rising but flying quite level, or else when it is dropping, it offers, I think, one of those two types of shot which should be intercepted.

The second of these types is the bird flying almost straight overhead and away from one.

In both these cases it is almost impossible to swing in any way and interception seems to be the only solution. But it is not an easy solution, and some men find it more difficult than others. Practice is the best, in fact the only, means of obtaining proficiency.

Ground game, too, can be dealt with similarly. In the case of a crossing hare or rabbit the beginner should pretend to ruffle its fur the wrong way, or stroke its ears forward over its face, with the muzzle of his gun. If he does not follow through sufficiently the splash of the shot charge on the ground is almost always seen and will tell him where he has missed.

Anything in the nature of hurry is fatal. A good shot is never hurried, although he is invariably quick. But there is a great difference between being hurried and being quick. A hurried shot is nearly always jerky, and jerkiness tends to a check in the swing before the trigger is pressed, which means a miss behind.

The ideal method of shooting is to bring the gun up to the shoulder and swing through with the left arm in one single movement. If one can cultivate this habit one will be far more likely to follow through without any check in the swing than if one shoots " by numbers," as a drill book would put it. In fact, so quick is this whole movement, including the actual pressure of the trigger, that it is frequently believed to be "intercepting." But it is not because the gun muzzle was still moving when the trigger was pressed, and in " intercepting" the gun muzzle is stationary at the moment of discharge. Some men bring the gun up to the shoulder in one movement, and then pause. They then aim behind the bird and swing through. That is they make two deliberate and separate movements. Frequently they shoot quite well. But I am sure that they are far more prone to check their swing on days when they may be a bit off colour than they would did they never make a check between the movement of putting the gun to the shoulder and that of swinging on the bird. For a check is always liable to beget a check. Nothing can be more infectious.

And if anyone acquires the habit of this shooting " by numbers " he will be very liable to " poke " at going-away birds. That is, he will press the trigger while the gun is stationary. Many men who shoot well at driven birds tend to " poke " when walking up. As a rule this is because they bring the gun up to the shoulder in one distinct movement and then try to " lift " with their left arms. The very fact that they check the rhythm of the whole movement by stopping when the gun is at the shoulder means that the *right* arm controls the pointing of the gun instead of the *left*. And this will almost always mean a check in the swing or lift. In such circumstances a man will usually miss a going-away bird below with his first barrel because he has allowed the right arm to take charge. He will then try to rectify his mistake by giving a desperate lift with his left arm and will probably miss high because he has overdone the lift. If he brought the gun to his shoulder, lifted with his left arm and pressed the trigger, in one continuous movement the left arm alone would have control of the barrels and a kill would be almost a certainty.

Another very common example of cause and effect in the checking of swing is given by an overhead approaching bird which can be seen from a long way off. The shooter watches the bird coming nearer and puts his gun to his shoulder in readiness, but naturally does not begin to swing until the time for taking the shot has arrived. But the fact that he has already checked the rhythm of movement once when he waited for the bird with his gun at his shoulder makes him check again and he stops his swing and misses behind.

In such a case the shooter should wait until the bird has come within shot before he begins to bring his gun up.

The whole question of swing is really dependent on style, and good style is just as important in shooting as in casting a fly or spinning bait or in any game. And this brings us to another, and very important, point, namely Footwork.

It is impossible to bring one's gun up to one's shoulder and swing in correct style unless one's arms are free to move across the body. This means that the body must be placed relatively to the arms in such a way as to allow them the maximum of freedom for swinging the gun. And the only way of placing the body is by placing the feet correctly. In other words, footwork. So important is the correct placing of the feet that I am inclined to think that it amounts to 70 per cent. of the total importance in shooting. For unless the stance is right it is impossible to bring the gun up and swing through in good style.

Footwork and swing can be practised with great advantage at home indoors. The gun should be brought up to the shoulder and swung past some point on the wall or ceiling and the trigger pressed without the swing being checked. This can be done again and again, different "targets" being taken so as to vary the angle as much as possible and thus render footwork necessary.

There is one point in connection with swing which is not infrequently discussed, and that is its possible effect on the flight of the shot charge. Some shooters believe that the swing one gives the gun affects the flight of the shot charge and imparts a corresponding "swing" to the shot, like water out of a hose.

But there is no truth in this theory, as was explained on page 67.

Nor is there any truth in the theory that swing throws the shot forward to any practical extent. It is true that the actual velocity of the shot charge is the resultant of the two velocities which act at right angles to one another; namely, the velocity due to the combustion of the powder which is imparted in the direction of the bore, and the velocity imparted by the swing which acts in a direction at right angles to the bore of the gun. The former velocity, however, is so much the greater that the latter has no practical effect whatever.

In all the general types of shots which I have considered so far the assumption has been made that the bird is flying straight. As a matter of fact birds as often as not fly with a slight curl in the flight, and the greater the curl the more difficult the bird is to hit. The amount of forward allowance may be correct; the swing may be perfect; but allowance will not have been made for the fact that the bird is not flying in a straight line; and a miss is then almost inevitable. Nothing can be more baffling than a curling bird and it is difficult to offer any useful advice. But the best tip I have ever been given myself was a hint from a first-class shot who told me to try to shoot just in front of the "inside wing."

Then there is a very general belief that birds are

never missed in front. I suppose this idea gained ground because the majority of birds are undoubtedly missed behind. Feeling doubtful as to the impossibility of missing in front, a good many years ago I questioned one of the best shooting school instructors I have ever known, and who has now been dead for many years. His reply was to the following effect:

"If anyone can really shoot at all he will be able to know fairly well where he is missing. That is, he will know if he is behind; or under a crossing bird; or too much to one side; and so on. But if you ever get a run of misses which completely mystify you, when you know you are not checking your swing, then you can bet your last shilling that you are missing in front."

Some years later I was a guest at a covert shoot when our host had a shooting school coach down for the day. With great kindness he asked me whether I would like this man to load for me during one stand, and naturally I jumped at the offer. There were plenty of birds and I had quite a good stand, but the coach assured me that I had missed quite a number in front.

Two seasons later I was fortunate enough to have a first-class shooting school coach loading for me throughout the day at what was probably one of the most remarkable pheasant shoots in the south of England. There were four stands in the day and at two of them it was exceptional to see a bird nearer the floor of the valley in which we stood than 90 feet—and normally 60 feet up makes a good high bird. Both the coach and myself were astonished at the number of misses I had in front—not so many as behind, but still quite a lot—and thanks to his help I was able to correct these in a way which I would never have done otherwise.

And since then I have ample confirmation of my own tendency in this direction by the use of Rocket cartridges. So I am quite convinced in my own mind of the fallacy of the "impossible to miss in front" theory. In fact, I do not see how anyone who has seriously thought about the subject can hold it; and I can but pass on that old shooting school instructor's advice that if you are ever completely mystified as to where your shots are going, assume you are missing in front and reduce your lead slightly.

This brings me to another matter, that of "Calling one's shots," or being able to say with fair accuracy where the majority of one's misses have gone. No man can be regarded as even a moderately good rifle shot unless he can say whereabouts his shot has struck the target immediately after he has let it off. That is, he should know whether the shot is high, low, to the right, or to the left, according to how his sights were aligned at the exact moment of the release of the trigger.

When shooting at flying game with a shotgun, it is admittedly much more difficult to call one's shots than it is when shooting at a fixed target with a rifle. Nevertheless, just as the rifle shot can say what his fault, if any, was, so should the game shot generally be able to tell what he has done wrong in the case of a miss. To be able to detect one's own faults is not difficult, although it is, of course, impossible to say whether one has missed a bird behind by one yard or two. All that one *should* be able to say is: "I checked my swing that time and was behind"; or "I saw that crossing bird over the top of my muzzle and so I was underneath." It is never possible to do more than generalise, but every shooter should be able to do that.

And in this connection I am sure that rifle shooting can be of the greatest help. I am aware that there is a common belief that rifle shooting completely spoils one for shooting with a shotgun. But like many other common beliefs I think it to be false. In fact I hold, as I have stated, exactly the opposite view. I do not suggest for a moment that a long course of target shooting with a rifle is the proper immediate preliminary training for a week at driven grouse or partridges. Rifle shooting may, perhaps, tend to make some men "poke" if they use a shotgun directly afterwards. But an hour's practice at clay targets, or even a couple of half-hours in a room swinging at imaginary birds will do much to eradicate the " rifle style " and get one back into " shotgun style."

The real help that rifle shooting—and by that I mean target shooting—gives is that it teaches so much about shooting in general. One makes a certain definite mistake and sees the result on the target. In course of time mistakes become fewer and the percentage of bull's-eyes larger, until one realises that the combination of rifle and ammunition is capable of making bull's-eyes every time if only one will let it have a fair chance.

The combination of shotgun and cartridge similarly needs a fair chance ; and the mistakes which shooters commonly make, and which prevent this fair chance being given, are in some cases identical with the mistakes made by the rifle shot. In rifle shooting, however, these mistakes are more easily detected ; and if a shooter has once learnt to detect them with a rifle he will find that he can detect them with a shotgun. And from detection it should be but a short step to correction.

So it is for this reason that I believe that rifle shooting can help in shotgun work.

By far the most common fault committed equally by those who use rifles and shotguns is faulty trigger pressure. It may have been noticed that throughout these volumes I have invariably used the term " pressure " to denote the pull on the trigger in preference to the more usual term " pull." I have done so purposely because the trigger should always be pressed, and never pulled. Anything in the nature of a pull is almost bound to jerk the gun or rifle in the hands and so change its alignment at the very moment of firing, when the shot will obviously go wide of the mark,

The trigger should be pressed by a quick yet absolutely smooth movement of contraction of the trigger finger, and any other form of release is fatal to good shooting.

Even the best of rifle shots will at times " pull " a bad shot while the beginner will more often than not " pull " nine bad shots out of ten. On a target the results of such bad shots are obvious, and as the marksman becomes more proficient the number of " pulled " shots diminishes, with a corresponding increase in the score.

But in shotgun work there is nothing to indicate where the shots are going, and it is quite possible for a man to go on " pulling " shot after shot and never suspect the reason for his missing. In fact so common is this fault of bad trigger pressure that I am inclined to believe that more birds are missed each year through this cause than through any other single fault, except perhaps checking the swing.

Anyone can find out for himself quite easily whether he has a tendency to " pull " his shots. All that he need do is to get a friend to load for him and hand him the gun ready loaded and then shoot at some fixed mark. Every now and then the friend should load the gun with a dummy cartridge so that the shooter will be taken unawares and snap an empty barrel when he thinks he is going to fire a live round. When this happens both he and his friend will be able to see the whole gun " bob " when the trigger is pulled, and it should be obvious to both that this " bob " will be more than enough to jerk the gun off its proper alignment.

The best cure for bad trigger pressure is constant snapping with an empty gun. At first the gun can be pointed at a stationary mark and snapped, and when the shooter is satisfied that he can press the trigger without moving the gun in the least bit off its alignment he should practise swinging and snapping at the same time.

Incidentally it may be mentioned that the best test of all for anyone's trigger pressure is shooting with a ·22 pistol. These weapons are wonderfully accurate, but owing to their short barrels they are very sensitive to the slightest suspicion of a jerk during the pressure of the trigger. The man who can place *all* his shots within a 3-inch circle at 20 yards with a ·22 pistol can regard his trigger pressure as being satisfactory, but until he can do this he should lay no claim to proficiency.

Another very common fault in both rifle and shotgun shooting is not holding the weapon with the barrels level. If the barrels are tilted over to one side the shot will go wide and low to the side down to which the barrels are tilted. So this is another point which should be noted during swinging practice and the beginner should cultivate the habit of always keeping his barrels dead level no matter at what angle he is shooting.

Flinching at the shot will invariably cause a miss. This can be detected in the same way as faulty trigger pressure, that is by snapping an empty gun which was believed to have been loaded. Probably the best remedy is to shoot for a time with very lightly loaded cartridges, as flinching is the outcome of undue recoil. It is for this reason that it is always a mistake to start a young boy with too heavy a gun. A ·410 is an ideal gun for a boy when he first begins, and when he is fourteen or fifteen he can be promoted to a 28-bore, which should last him until he is old enough to take a full-sized gun. I am quite aware that some boys of sixteen shoot with 20-bores, 16-bores and even 12-bores with success. But I also know for a fact that many others have been put off shooting or have developed the habit of flinching through being over-gunned. Many parents seem to forget that a 20-bore can kick in a most unpleasant way, and there can be no more certain method of putting a boy off shooting than to give him a gun which punishes him. It is impossible to lay down any absolutely hard and fast rule for all boys as to this question of size of gun ; but if there is any question of doubt it is always better to err on the side of too small a gun than one too big.

Two faults which belong rather to shooting with a shotgun than a rifle are failure to bring the gun up properly to the shoulder and what is known as "rainbowing."

If the gun fits correctly, and the shooter nevertheless fails to bed the stock properly into the shoulder, the reason is that he is too hurried. Unless the butt fits in exactly the right place it is impossible to get the head down to the stock and so control the alignment of the gun. So it should be clear that incorrect mounting of the gun will almost always cause a miss. The shooter should examine his bare shoulder at the end of a day's shooting, and if he sees any marks of recoil on his arm he will know that he was not bringing his gun up properly all the time, and that many of his misses were the result of this fault.

The cure is practice, and yet more practice, with an empty gun.

"Rainbowing" is a shooting school word and means dropping the muzzle of one's gun when swinging on a crossing bird and so describing an arc of a circle with the muzzle instead of a straight line. Of course when one does this a miss below is inevitable. The root cause of this fault is almost certainly an incorrect stance which makes it difficult to carry the swing right through. As a rule, one is only inclined to make a "rainbow" with one's gun muzzle when trying to swing on a bird right round to the extreme right or left, and the better way to take such a bird would generally be to move the feet and so turn the body slightly before bringing the gun up.

Practice in swinging with an empty gun, however, can be the greatest help, and it is really best to conduct this practice in a room. For one can then swing along the line made by the junction of one of the walls and the ceiling, when one can see at once if the gun muzzle is dropped.

So it will be seen that practice in swinging and snapping with an empty gun indoors can help one to correct almost all the common faults in shooting. This will not come as a surprise to anyone who has had experience of rifle shooting, as snapping and aiming drill are *the* best forms of practice of any apart from the real thing, which is naturally the best practice of all. But few people can obtain unlimited practice at the real thing, and so it should be remembered that even ten minutes a day in one's bedroom before turning in for the night can be of the greatest use, while it also helps to develop the muscles which one needs when shooting.

But convinced though I am of the great possibilities which can be derived from such practice I would sound one note of warning. I have already referred to the importance of good style, and it is quite possible for a beginner to cultivate a really bad style so thoroughly by solitary practice that he will find it very difficult to eradicate later. So whenever possible I think that the beginner should take a series of lessons at a shooting school first of all. This will start him off in the right way, and once started he can practise on his own to his heart's content : for it is really just as easy to cultivate a good style as a bad, provided only one begins in the right way. Hawker, in his *Instructions to Young Sportsmen,* writes that he would rather see a man miss a bird in good style than kill it in bad, and the reason is plain. All that a man with good style needs is more practice and confidence, while for a man with bad style there can be little hope of his ever becoming a really good shot. If he is satisfied with success obtained in the wrong way, he can never improve.

The advent of the shooting school has really made the biggest change in shooting for forty years. Not only can the beginner get started in the right way, but the experienced shot can benefit. An afternoon's practice at a shooting school just before the season opens is invaluable. Not only can one have one's pet faults checked, but it is possible to practise again and again at some particular bird which seems to be peculiarly difficult. Most of us have our favourite birds and our abominations. It is satisfying, perhaps, to have a few shots at our favourite birds ; but it is far more useful to go on practising at our abominations. A good coach, who sees the shot in the air, can tell exactly what one is doing wrong besides telling exactly where one's shot is going. This last is admittedly important, but the why and wherefore is more so. And once some pet fault, perhaps only a temporary lapse, has been detected and put right, snapping practice at home with an empty gun will help one to continue in the path of virtue.

I have sometimes heard sportsmen express doubt as to the possibility of a coach seeing the shot in the air, and suggest that those who profess to do so are gifted with exceptional imagination. Such a suggestion is quite incorrect, for there is really nothing wonderful about seeing the shot in the air, nor is it particularly difficult to do so. Like many other things it is really a knack which can be acquired by practice.

Probably the best way to begin to learn the knack is to watch someone else shooting with a revolver at 50 yards. Stand behind him and as nearly as possible in line with him and the target and watch the target through a pair of field-glasses. The revolver bullet will then be seen to hit the target almost as if some great bee had settled on it. Once the bullet has been seen through glasses it will not be difficult to see it with the naked eye provided one keeps the eye focused on the target. The mistake people make when trying to see revolver bullets or charges of shot is to focus the eye on the air just in front of the muzzle and then try to catch the projectile up. This is useless. One must allow the projectile to flash into one's field of focus and it is for this reason that field-glasses can be of help at first, as they compel one to focus on the target.

With glasses one should be able to see a revolver bullet at 20 yards every time, but as the bullet is travelling considerably faster at 20 yards than at 50 yards it needs a bit more practice, and it is on this account that I suggest that a start should be made at 50 yards.

A charge of shot is certainly more difficult to catch than a revolver bullet, but almost anyone should be able to acquire the knack in time. Stand close behind the shooter in direct line with him and the target, which should be a clay target thrown straight away at first. Keep your eyes focused on the clay target and pay no attention to anything else. The shot charge will then suddenly appear as a little dim cloud above, below, to the right, or to the left of the target. If the target is actually hit you probably will not see the cloud, but if the shooter misses it is unmistakable. Once you have seen it you will see it again and again ; and you can then try to catch it on crossing targets. After a time you will find that you need not stand in absolute prolongation with the line of fire, but the nearer you are to this line the easier it will be to see the shot charge.

No one can ever see his own shot charge, as he cannot have his eyes concentrated and focused correctly both for shooting and seeing the shot.

Crossing shots at very long ranges present a difficulty in addition to that of forward allowance which is not always realised. This is the question of the allowance necessary to counteract the drop of the shot due to gravity below the line of aim. In ordinary shooting this problem scarcely arises, because the larger effective killing circle at long range makes a sort of automatic compensation for the drop, at any rate up to ranges at which shots can normally be expected to kill. At 40 yards, for instance, with an ordinary game gun no allowance for elevation is really necessary, although at 50 yards it is certainly an advantage to make such allowance. Usually, it will be sufficient to swing just over a crossing bird, instead of just in line with it ; and even at 40 yards there is no harm in keeping well up on the bird during the swing.

It must be remembered, however, that the great majority of shots are fired at an appreciable angle up into the air, and that in such cases the actual divergence of the shot from the line of aim must always be less than in the case of a shot taken in a perfectly horizontal direction.

So I think it can be assumed without material error that in ordinary game shooting the drop of the shot can be disregarded apart from swinging a little over a very wide crossing bird.[1]

[1] Wildfowlers are frequently faced with a very different problem, for they may have to take shots even up to 100 yards at fowl on the water, which means a horizontal line of aim, and therefore the necessity for the maximum allowance for the drop due to gravity. Accordingly this point of view deserves consideration.

The first thing to remember is that only large shot is likely to

Another question which sometimes crops up is that of the effect of wind on shot pellets. Does a strong crossing wind, for example, deflect the shot charge to any appreciable extent ? Does a strong head-wind reduce the velocity of the shot sufficiently to effect penetration ? And are different sizes of shot affected to varying degrees ?

Such are very reasonable questions which need answers.

It can, then, be assumed that for all practical purposes of sport wind has no appreciable effect on shot pellets. It is true that a strong wind blowing across the line of fire must give the pellets a slight deflection. But this deflection rarely amounts to as much as 10 per cent. of the total forward allowance required on a crossing bird.

be used in such circumstances, and so the effects of gravity on small shot need not be considered. This is not an unimportant point because a somewhat rough and ready method of calculation will give results which are close enough for all practical purposes for large shot, although the same method would not be equally applicable to small shot.

This method is merely to assume that the drop of the shot below the line of aim is the same as that due to gravity in the time available (that is the time of flight) without taking into account the reduction due to the resistance of the air. In the case of small shot (No. 6) this reduction will be appreciable : but in the case of large shot, such as BB, it will be almost negligible for the short periods of time under consideration.

The drop due to gravity is $\frac{1}{2}gt^2$ feet, where g is the acceleration of gravity (32·2 ft. per sec. per sec.) and t is the time of flight in seconds. This result is given in feet. The time of flight for any given range and any given observed velocity will be found in Tables XIV and XV in Volume II.

As an example it will be seen from Table XV in Volume II that for an observed velocity of 900 f.s. and a range of 90 yards the time of flight of a charge of No. 1 shot is 0·5 of a second. This gives the drop at this range to be approximately 4 feet. Similarly, from Table XIV in Volume II we find that the time of flight of a charge of BB shot for an observed velocity of 850 f.s. and a range of 100 yards is 0·5980 of a second, which gives a drop at this range of about 11½ feet.

Drops such as these are quite enough to make an appreciable difference in shooting, and so wildfowlers should remember to make adequate allowance by aiming well above the birds when taking horizontal shots at extreme ranges.

The effect of a contrary wind is even less. For when shooting into the teeth of a strong wind the velocity of No. 6 shot would be the same at 39 yards as it would normally be at 40 yards in still air.

Nor does the size of pellet in ordinary use make any difference. It is true that a strong cross-wind will deflect small shot, such as No. 7, more than large, such as No. 4. But the difference in the degree of deflection is so slight as to be negligible.

The proper use of the safety slide is a common source of disagreement. When walking up, should the gun be kept at " safe " or should it be " at full cock " ? This last, but so common, expression is, of course, quite incorrect. If a hammerless gun has been loaded and not fired the locks must always be at full cock ; the safety slide merely bolts the triggers.

Personally I think that the best use of the safety slide is entirely a matter of early tuition and practice. I am sure that the best method is to keep the slide at " safe " until the actual moment of mounting the gun to fire. The safety should be pushed forward with the thumb as the gun is brought to the shoulder and this movement of the thumb should be incorporated automatically into the whole movement of bringing the gun up. But I also think that this system should be taught when the beginner first starts to handle a gun, and the more youthful the beginner is the better. Once the habit has been acquired it becomes quite automatic and quite apart from any questions of safety it confers one great blessing on the shooter who has acquired it : he is never caught " at safe " when confronted with a sudden chance and so fails to get a shot off. For the shooter who has been trained, or has trained himself, to push forward the safety slide as he mounts the gun is always " at safe " when the gun is not at his shoulder, and so when some sudden and unexpected chance occurs he brings his gun up and fires exactly as he is always accustomed to bring his gun up and fire.

I do not wish to appear even to suggest that those

AN UNUSUAL METHOD OF LOADING

The photograph on the left shows the cartridges being inserted, the right arm being brought under the butt. In order to close the gun it is only necessary to raise the right elbow

who normally keep their guns at the ready are not safe shots. But I do believe that the "always at safe" system is the better, partly because those who have learnt it are never taken by surprise and partly because there can be no denying the fact that a gun with the triggers bolted is less liable to be discharged by a fall than one in which the triggers are free.

The truth really is that there are only two classes of people who handle firearms: those who are safe and those who are not. I would feel more comfortable with a neighbour who belonged to the first class but who carried his gun "at the ready" than with one who belonged to the second class even though he did always keep his gun at "safe." Incidentally members of the first class always open a gun to see if it is loaded whenever they pick one up or put one down; members of the second class do not.

And now for my last point of all. For reasons of safety it should be a habit when loading always to "bring the stock up to the barrels and not the barrels up to the stock." That is, the barrels should be kept pointing towards the ground throughout the process of loading. One day when out partridge driving I learnt what struck me then, as it still does, as being a most interesting tip for loaders. I noticed that my neighbour's loader reloaded with his right arm *underneath* the stock instead of over it as usual; and so when an opportunity occurred I asked for enlightenment. This I received; and I was so impressed by the advantages of this, to me, unusual method that I think that some of my readers may be equally interested.

The two photographs in Plate XXIII convey better than any words how this manner of loading is achieved. In the left-hand photograph the gun is broken and held by the left hand in the usual way. The right arm, however, is placed underneath the stock and the cartridges are inserted as shown. In order to close the gun all that it is necessary to do is to raise the right elbow in the manner shown in the right-hand photograph.

The advantages of this method lie in the fact that the stock is always brought up to the barrels, and so the gun is kept pointing downwards ; while guns which are at all stiff to close can be snapped to with the greatest ease owing to the leverage obtained by the right elbow.

My mentor told me that his various loaders had found that this method had required a little getting into, but that once they had acquired the knack they preferred it to the more usual method and found it both quicker and easier.

APPENDIX

TYPICAL PATTERNS AT DIFFERENT RANGES

THE following patterns have all been reproduced from photographs of actual results obtained on plates and card targets; and they can be regarded as being typical good patterns. It is possible to obtain so many variations that I have purposely only taken the patterns given by ordinary 12-bore 2½-inch game guns bored True Cylinder, Improved Cylinder, Half Choke and Full Choke. Borings of Quarter and Three-Quarter Choke will naturally give results intermediate to those shown.

In order to enable the reader to compare the total spreads of the shot charges and the densities of the patterns given by smaller bores with those yielded by an ordinary 12-bore, I have included some patterns of 16- and 20-bores and a ·410.

In every single instance the load is the standard for the bore and length of cartridge, and the shot is No. 6 except in the case of the ·410, when No. 7 was used, as No. 6 would have given results which would have been so open that they would have been difficult to assess properly.

One typical Cartwheel and one typical " scattered " pattern have also been included in order to emphasise the difference between good patterns and bad.

The patterns are all reproduced to the same scale except the first four, in which the shot marks would have been too close together to distinguish them individually unless the scale had been increased. But the actual diameter of the circle is 30 inches in each case.

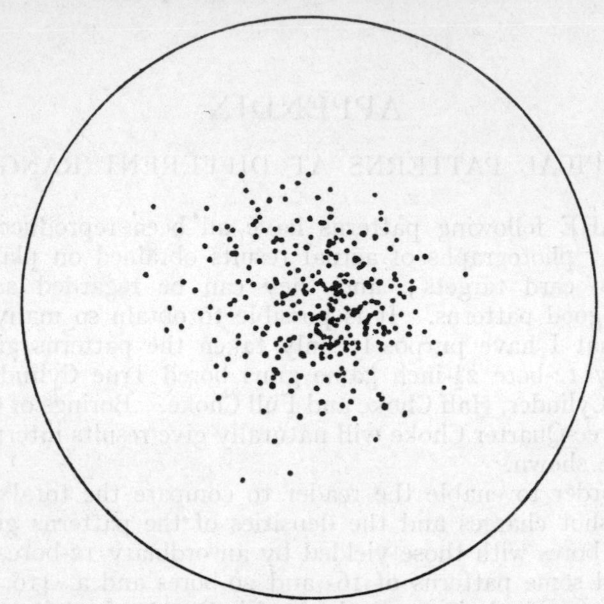

12-BORE $2\frac{1}{2}$-INCH TRUE CYLINDER AT 10 YARDS
Load: 33 grains Smokeless Diamond and $1\frac{1}{16}$ ounce of No. 6

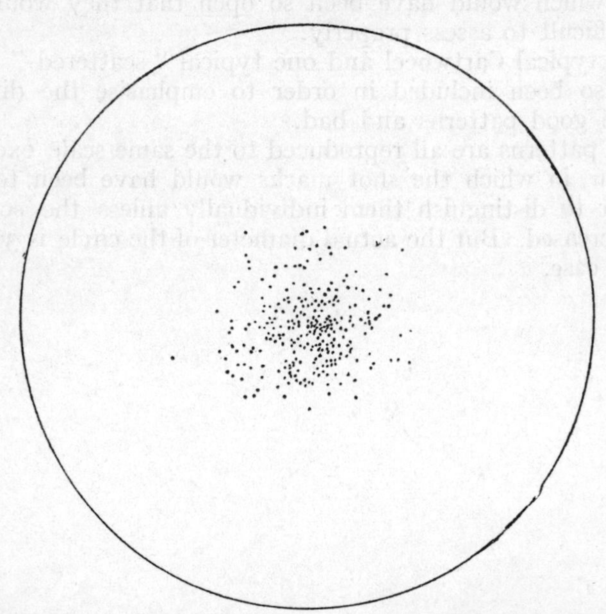

12-BORE $2\frac{1}{2}$-INCH IMPROVED CYLINDER AT 10 YARDS
Load: 33 grains Smokeless Diamond and $1\frac{1}{16}$ ounce of No. 6

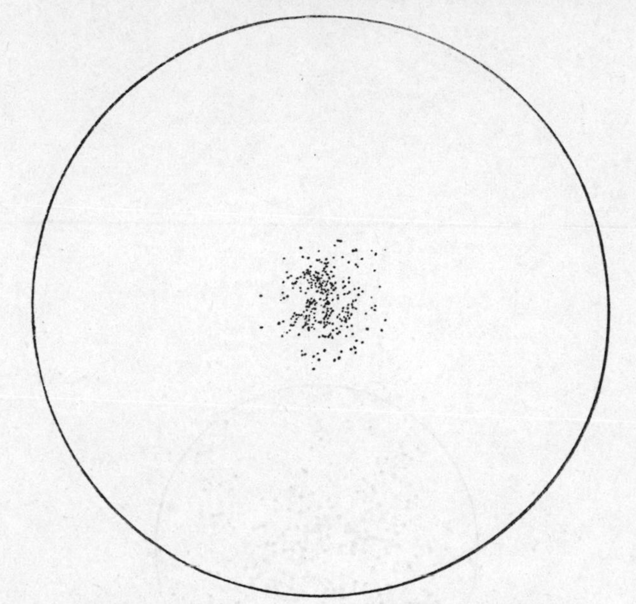

12-BORE $2\frac{1}{2}$-INCH HALF CHOKE AT 10 YARDS
Load: 33 grains Smokeless Diamond and $1\frac{1}{16}$ ounce of No. 6

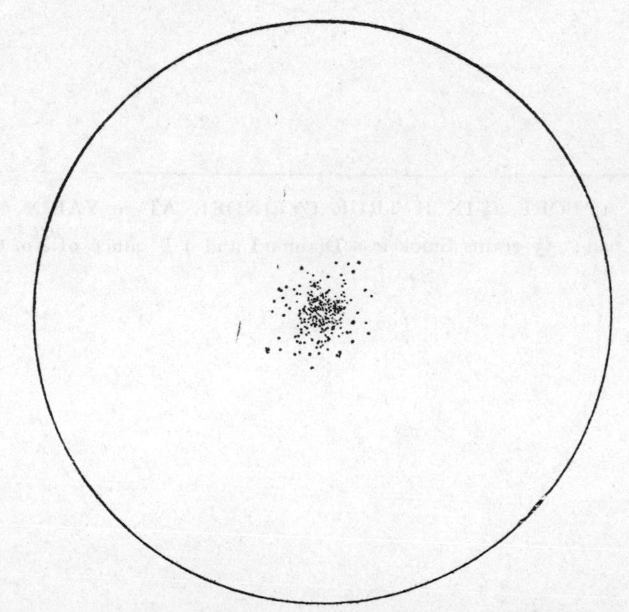

12-BORE $2\frac{1}{2}$-INCH FULL CHOKE AT 10 YARDS
Load: 33 grains Smokeless Diamond and $1\frac{1}{16}$ ounce of No. 6

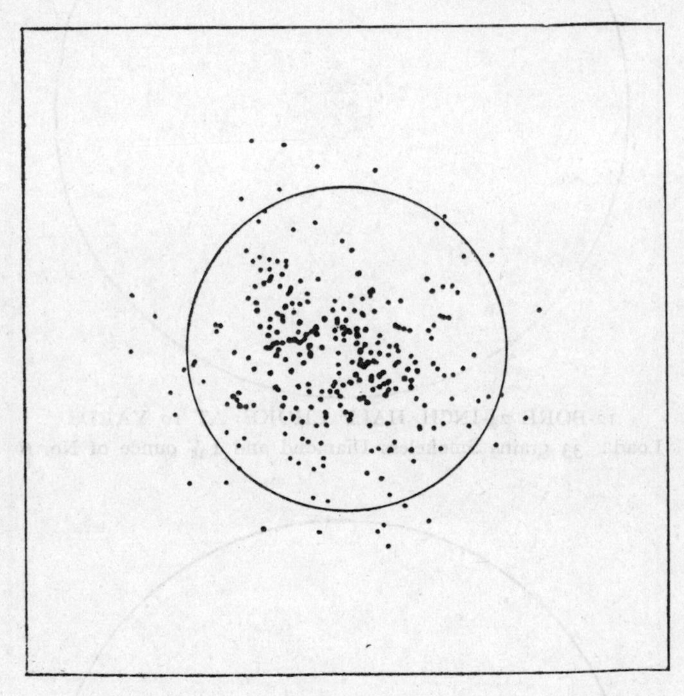

12-BORE $2\frac{1}{2}$-INCH TRUE CYLINDER AT 20 YARDS

Load: 33 grains Smokeless Diamond and $1\frac{1}{16}$ ounce of No. 6

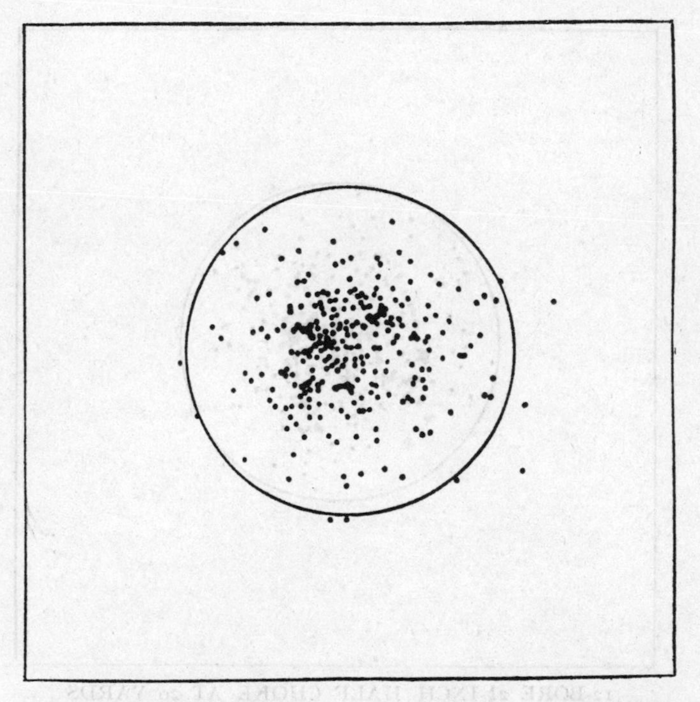

12-BORE $2\frac{1}{2}$-INCH IMPROVED CYLINDER AT 20 YARDS

Load: 33 grains Smokeless Diamond and $1\frac{1}{16}$ ounce of No. 6

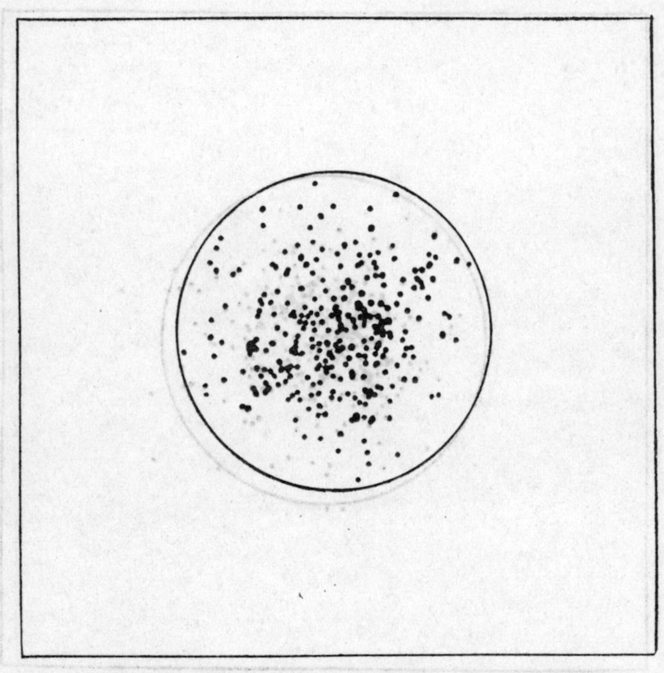

12-BORE $2\frac{1}{2}$-INCH HALF CHOKE AT 20 YARDS
Load: 33 grains Smokeless Diamond and $1\frac{1}{16}$ ounce of No. 6

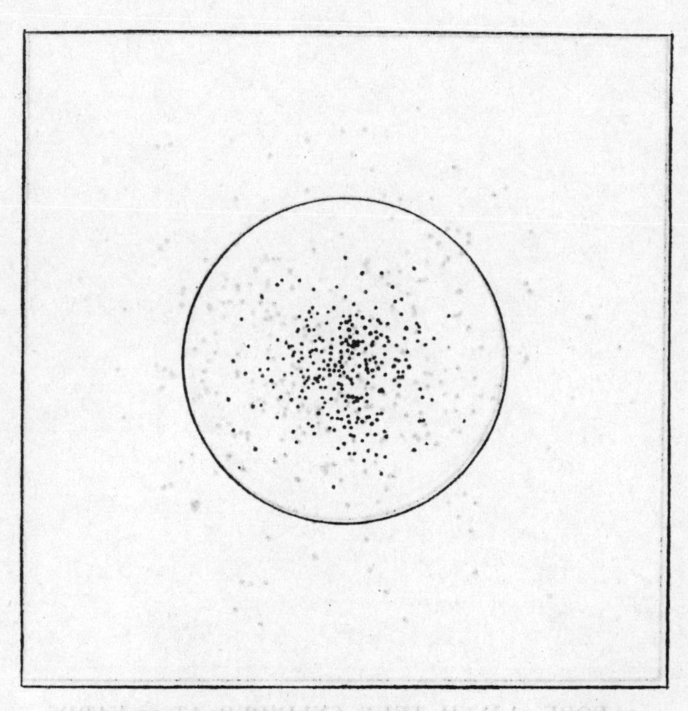

12-BORE 2½-INCH FULL CHOKE AT 20 YARDS

Load: 33 grains Smokeless Diamond and 1 $\frac{1}{16}$ ounce of No. 6

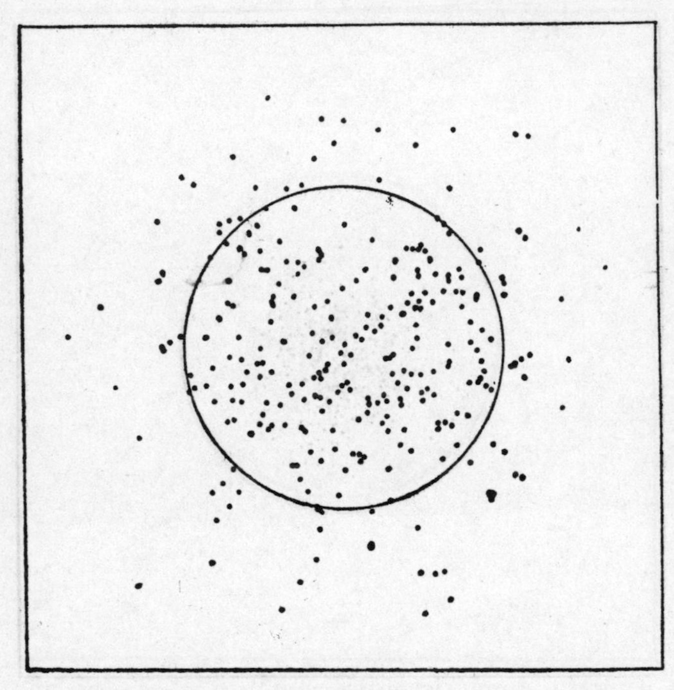

12-BORE 2½-INCH TRUE CYLINDER AT 30 YARDS

Load: 33 grains Smokeless Diamond and 1 $\frac{1}{16}$ ounce of No. 6

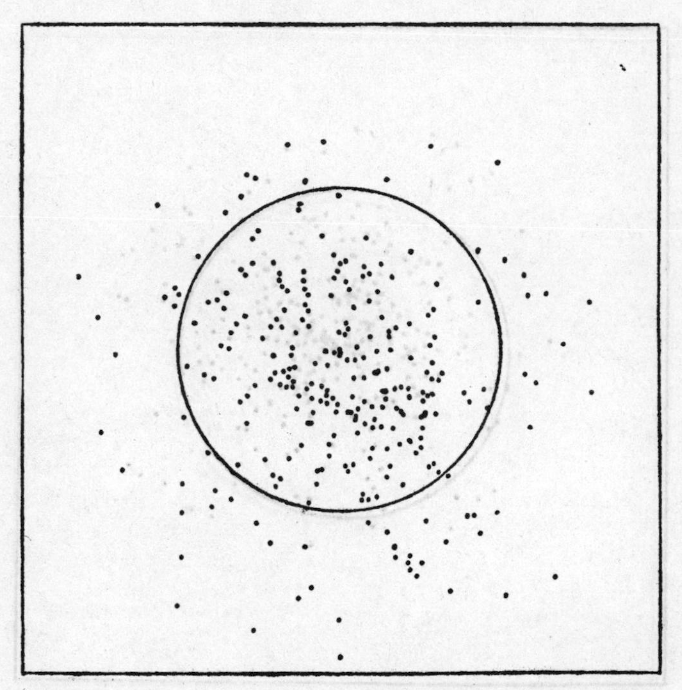

12-BORE 2½-INCH IMPROVED CYLINDER AT 30 YARDS

Load: 33 grains Smokeless Diamond and 1 $\frac{1}{16}$ ounce of No. 6

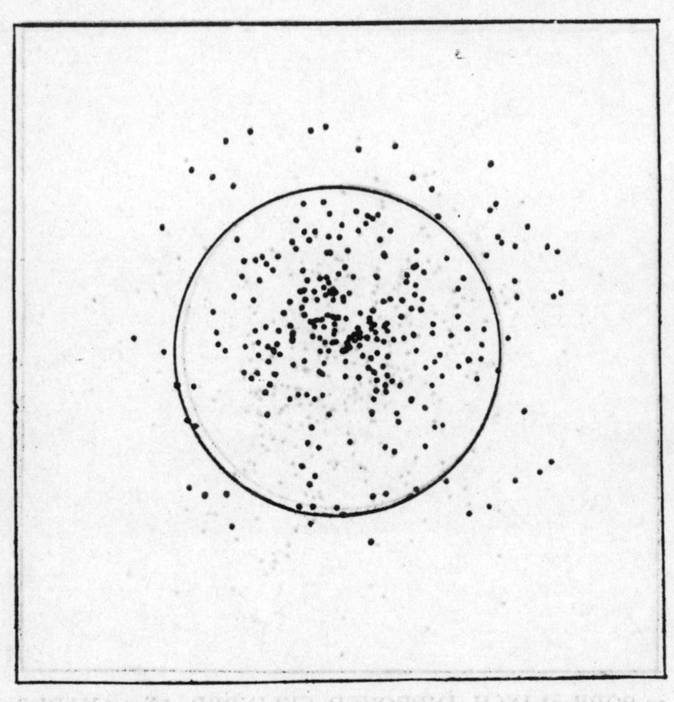

12-BORE $2\frac{1}{2}$-INCH HALF CHOKE AT 30 YARDS

Load: 33 grains Smokeless Diamond and $1\frac{1}{16}$ ounce of No. 6

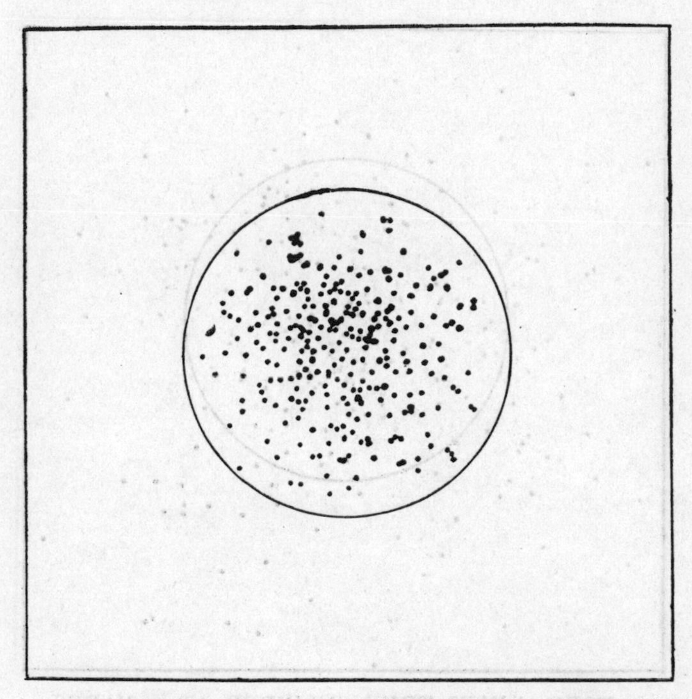

12-BORE $2\frac{1}{2}$-INCH FULL CHOKE AT 30 YARDS

Load: 33 grains Smokeless Diamond and $1\frac{1}{16}$ ounce of No. 6

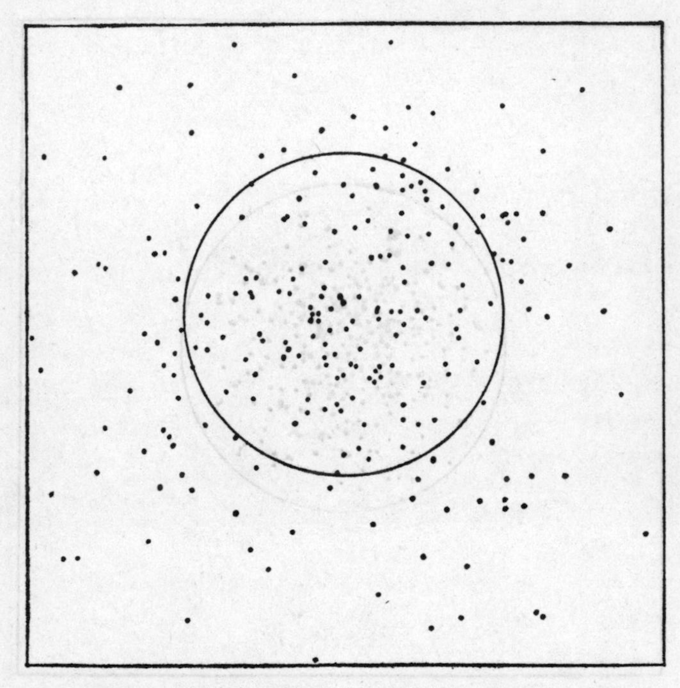

12-BORE 2½-INCH TRUE CYLINDER AT 40 YARDS

Load: 33 grains Smokeless Diamond and 1 $\frac{1}{16}$ ounce of No. 6
127 Pellets in 30-inch circle

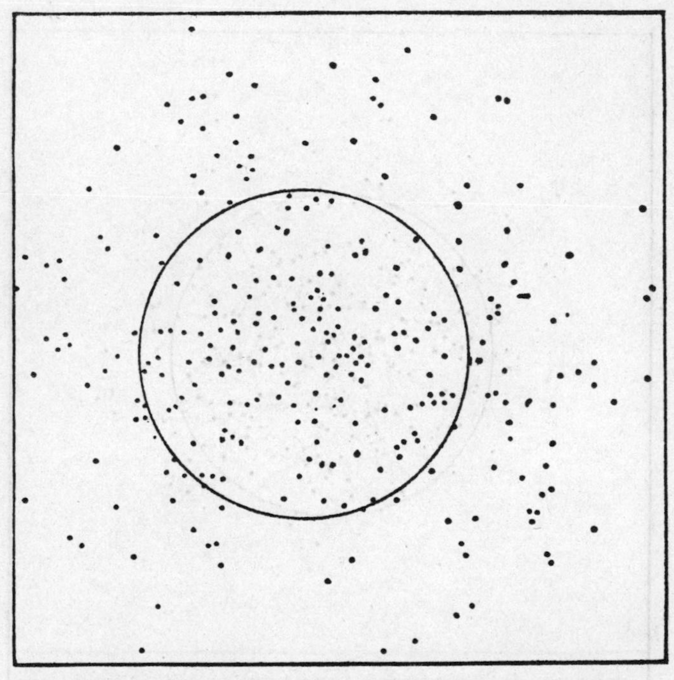

12-BORE $2\frac{1}{2}$-INCH IMPROVED CYLINDER AT 40 YARDS
Load: 33 grains Smokeless Diamond and $1\frac{1}{16}$ ounce of No. 6
142 Pellets in 30-inch circle

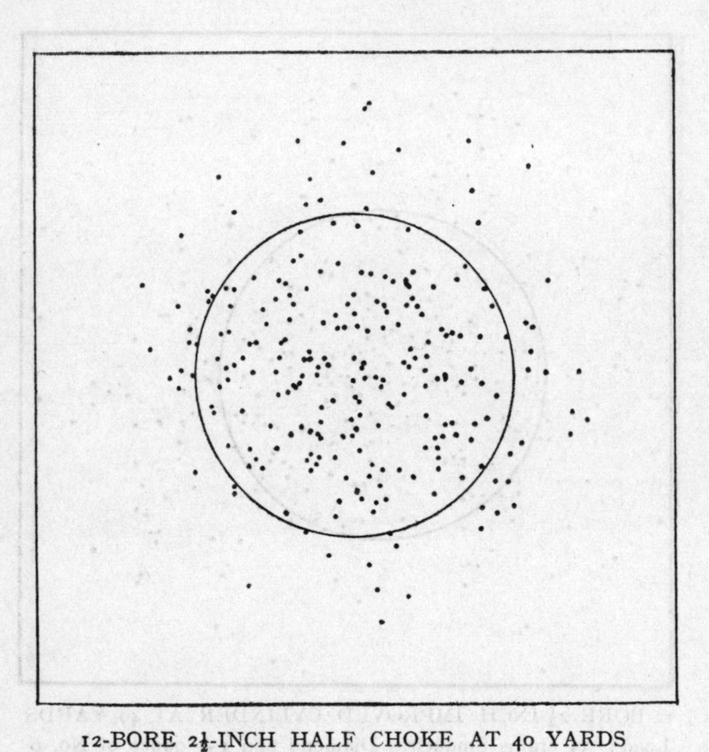

12-BORE $2\frac{1}{2}$-INCH HALF CHOKE AT 40 YARDS

Load: 33 grains Smokeless Diamond and $1\frac{1}{16}$ ounce of No. 6
175 Pellets in 30-inch circle

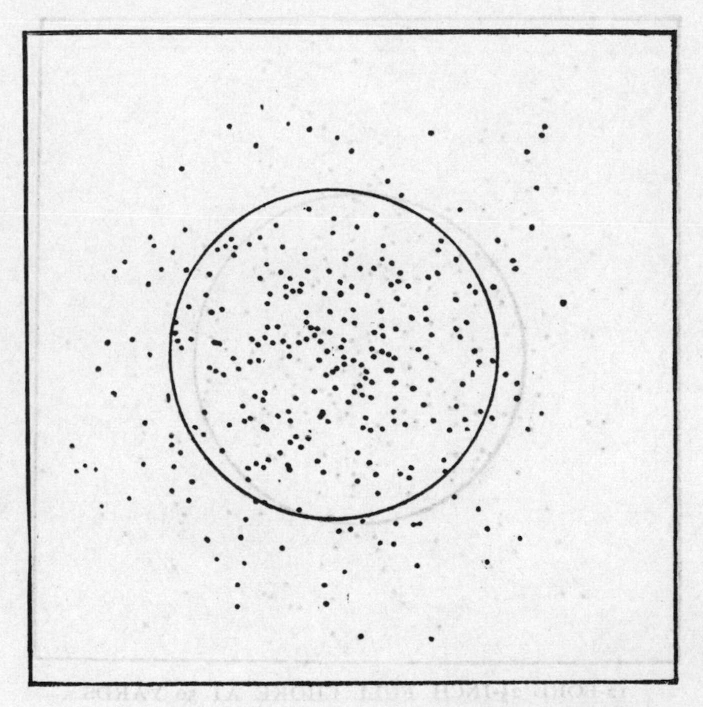

12-BORE 2½-INCH FULL CHOKE AT 40 YARDS

Load: 33 grains Smokeless Diamond and 1 $\frac{1}{16}$ ounce of No. 6
207 Pellets in 30-inch circle

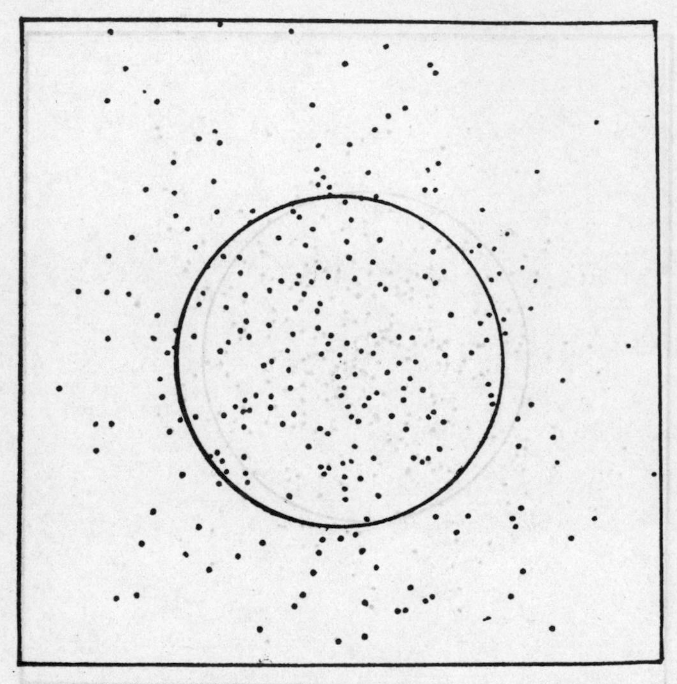

12-BORE 2½-INCH FULL CHOKE AT 50 YARDS

Load: 33 grains Smokeless Diamond and 1 $\frac{1}{16}$ ounce of No. 6
133 Pellets in 30-inch circle

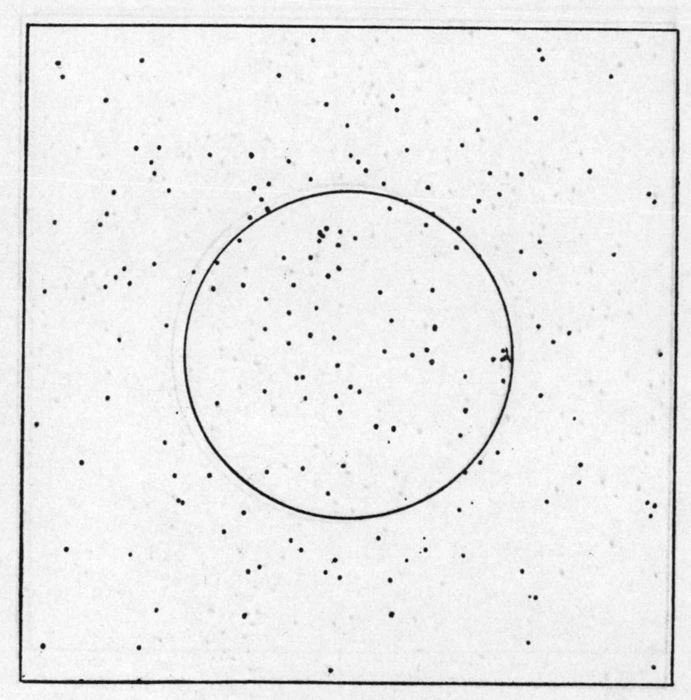

A TYPICAL "SCATTERED" OR "BLOWN" PATTERN AT 40 YARDS

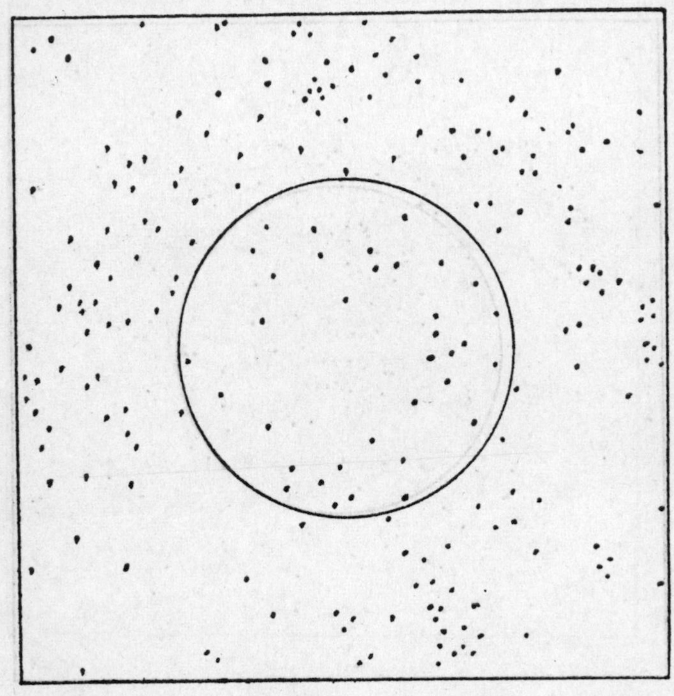

A TYPICAL "CARTWHEEL" PATTERN AT 40 YARDS

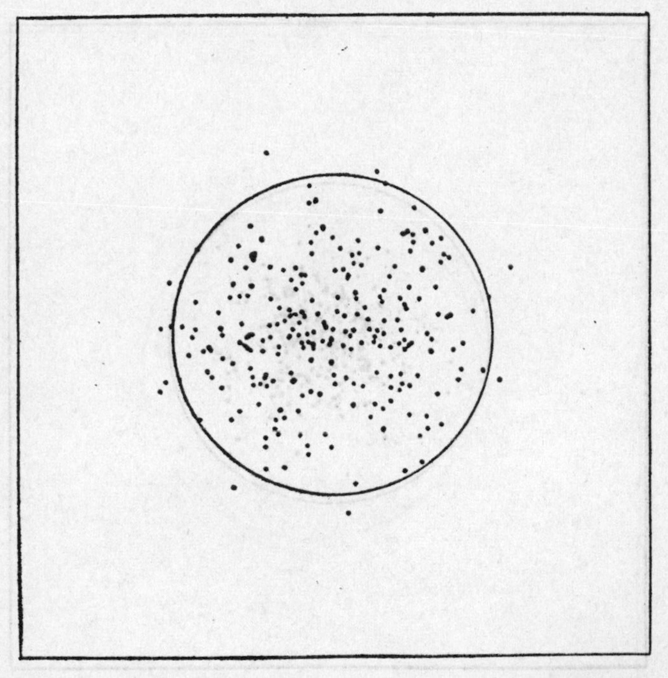

16-BORE 2½-INCH IMPROVED CYLINDER AT 20 YARDS

Load: 28 grains Smokeless Diamond and ⅞ ounce of No. 6

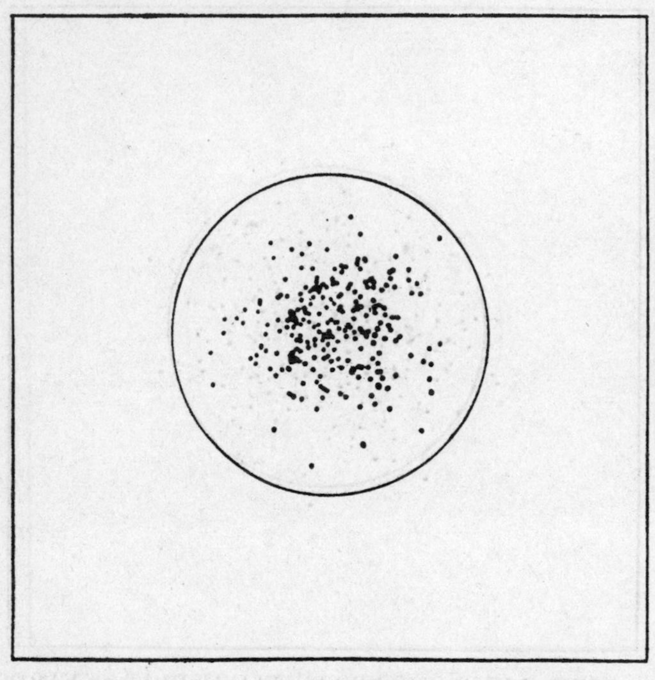

16-BORE 2½-INCH FULL CHOKE AT 20 YARDS

Load: 28 grains Smokeless Diamond and ⅞ ounce of No. 6

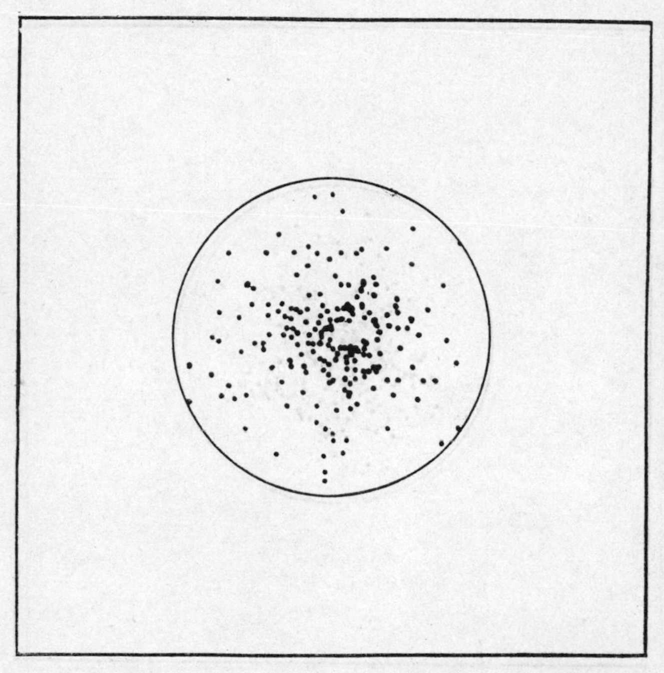

20-BORE $2\frac{1}{2}$-INCH HALF CHOKE AT 20 YARDS

Load: 24 grains Smokeless Diamond and $\frac{3}{4}$ ounce of No. 6

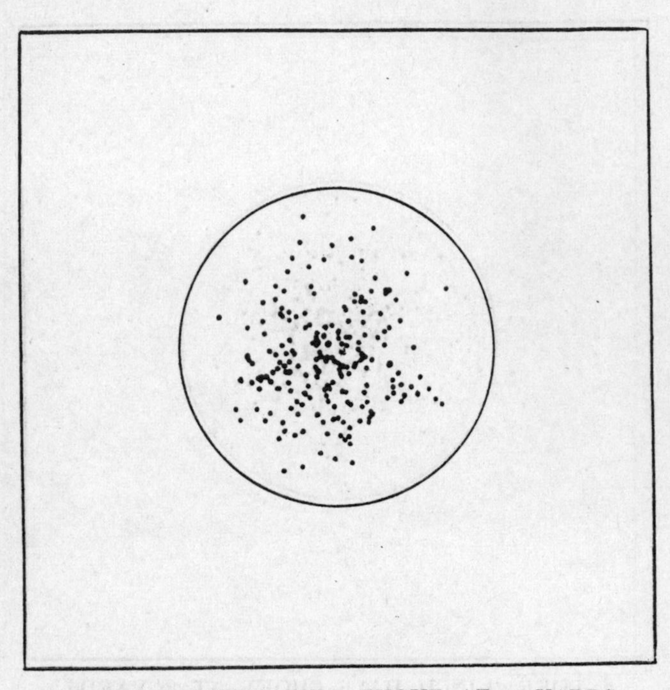

20-BORE $2\frac{1}{2}$-INCH FULL CHOKE AT 20 YARDS

Load: 24 grains Smokeless Diamond and $\frac{3}{4}$ ounce of No. 6

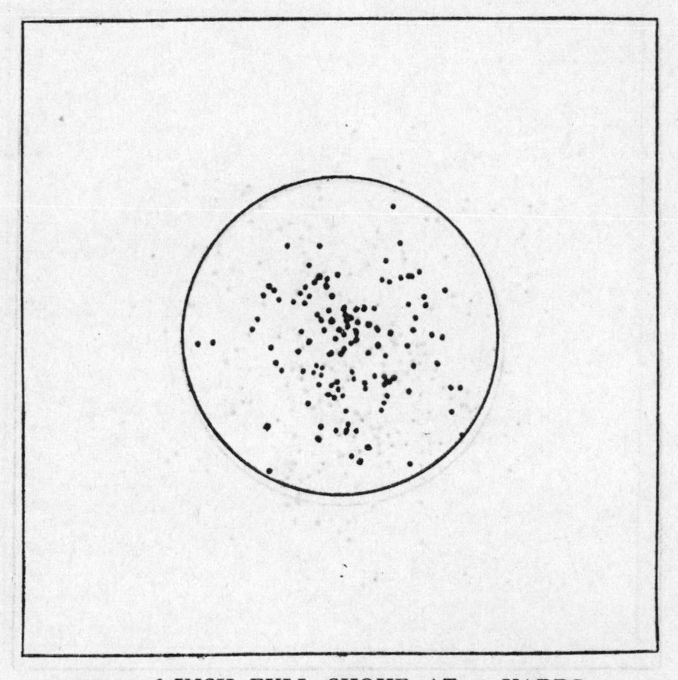

·410 2½-INCH FULL CHOKE AT 20 YARDS

Load: 10½ grains Smokeless Diamond and ⅜ ounce of No. 7

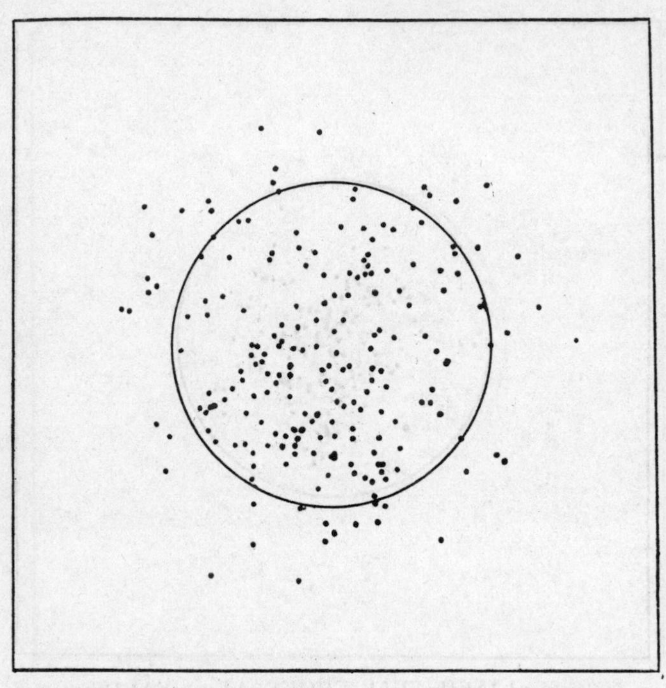

16-BORE 2½-INCH IMPROVED CYLINDER AT 30 YARDS

Load: 28 grains Smokeless Diamond and ⅞ ounce of No. 6

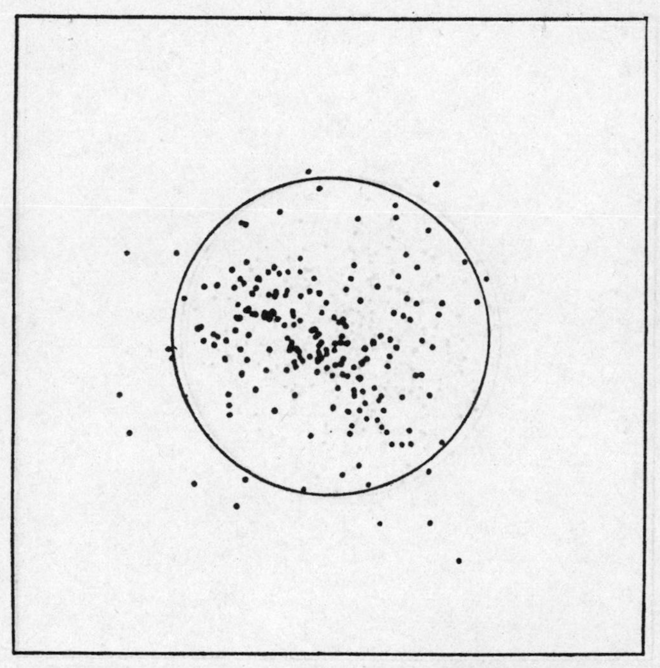

20-BORE $2\frac{1}{2}$-INCH HALF CHOKE AT 30 YARDS

Load: 24 grains Smokeless Diamond and $\frac{3}{4}$ ounce of No. 6

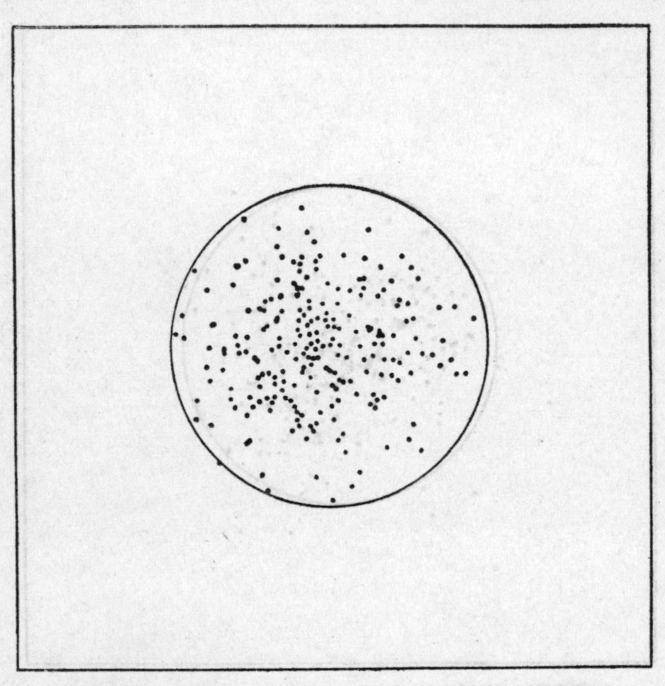

16-BORE 2½-INCH FULL CHOKE AT 30 YARDS

Load: 28 grains Smokeless Diamond and ⅞ ounce of No. 6

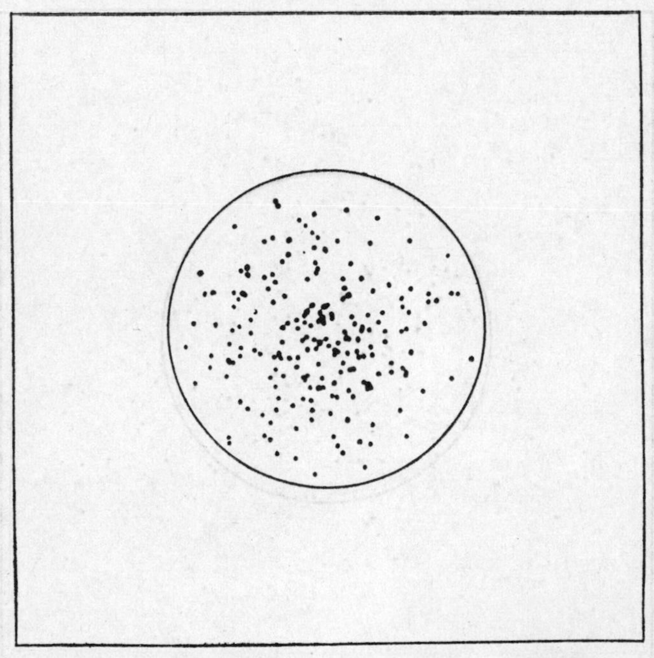

20-BORE $2\frac{1}{2}$-INCH FULL CHOKE AT 30 YARDS

Load: 24 grains Smokeless Diamond and $\frac{3}{4}$ ounce of No. 6

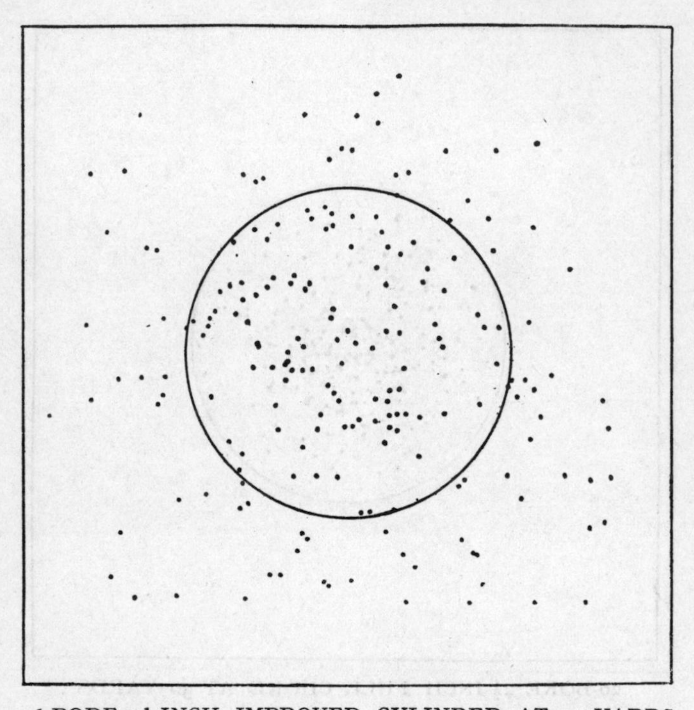

16-BORE $2\frac{1}{2}$-INCH IMPROVED CYLINDER AT 40 YARDS

Load: 28 grains Smokeless Diamond and $\frac{7}{8}$ ounce of No. 6
107 Pellets in 30-inch circle

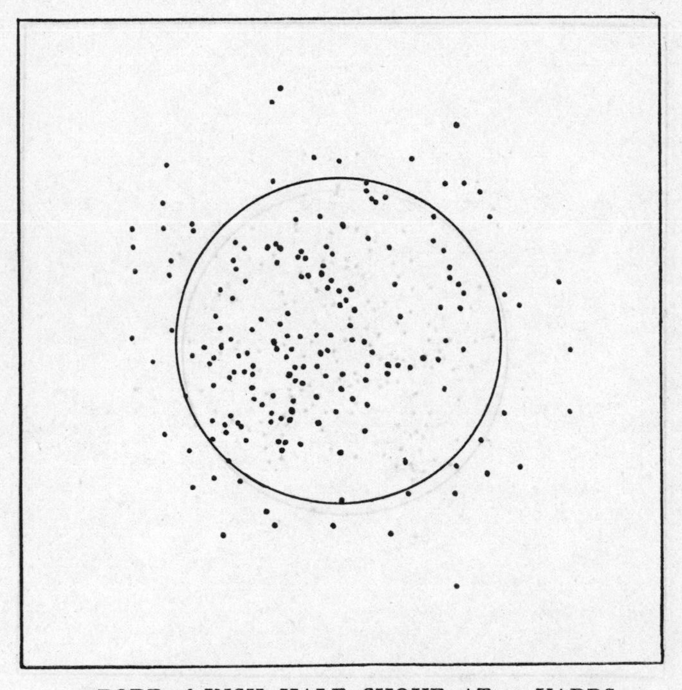

20-BORE $2\frac{1}{2}$-INCH HALF CHOKE AT 40 YARDS

Load: 24 grains Smokeless Diamond and $\frac{3}{4}$ ounce of No. 6
134 Pellets in 30-inch circle

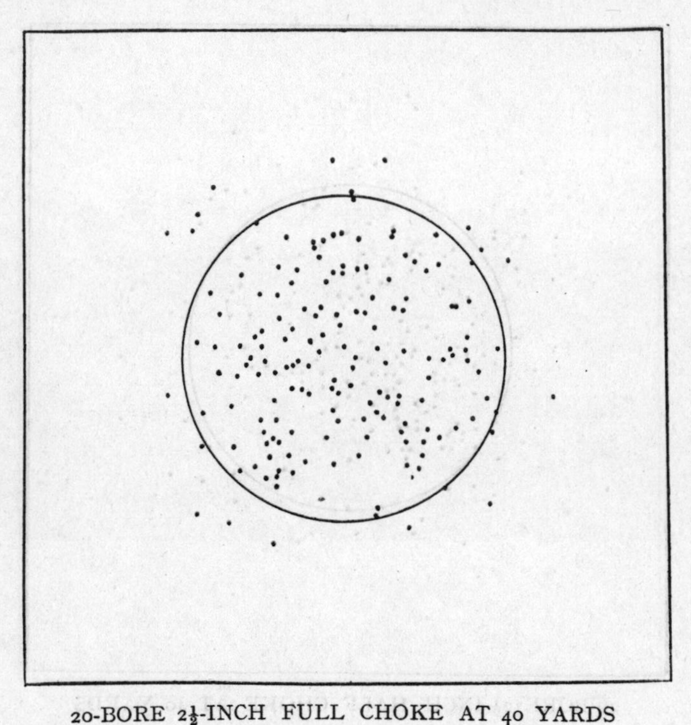

20-BORE 2½-INCH FULL CHOKE AT 40 YARDS

Load: 24 grains Smokeless Diamond and ¾ ounce of No. 6
145 Pellets in 30-inch circle

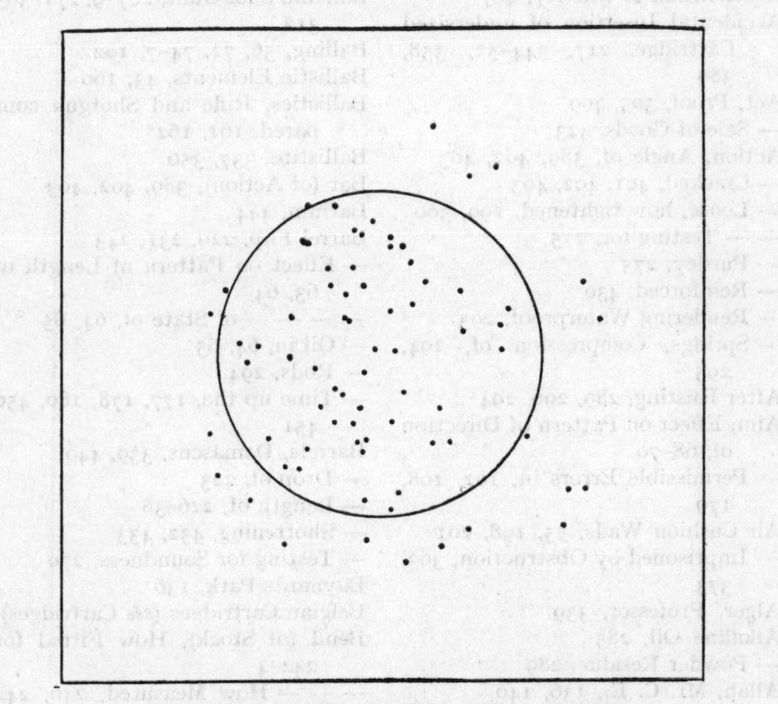

·410 2½-INCH FULL CHOKE AT 40 YARDS

Load: 10½ grains Smokeless Diamond and ⅜ ounce of No. 7
50 Pellets in 30-inch circle

INDEX

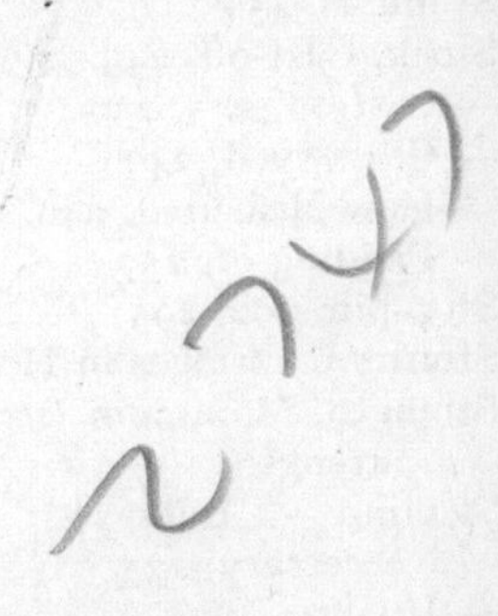